ALSO BY

J. TUZO WILSON

ONE CHINESE MOON
(1959)

With J. A. Jacobs and R. D. Russell:
PHYSICS AND GEOLOGY
(1959)

I·G·Y

THE YEAR OF
THE NEW MOONS

I·G·Y

THE YEAR OF
THE NEW MOONS

J. TUZO WILSON

FOREWORD BY LLOYD V. BERKNER

19   61

ALFRED·A·KNOPF

NEW YORK

L. C. catalog card number: 61–14195

THIS IS A BORZOI BOOK,

PUBLISHED BY ALFRED A. KNOPF, INC.

FIRST EDITION

TO

Pat and Sue

FOREWORD

The International Geophysical Year (IGY) was perhaps the most ambitious and at the same time the most successful co-operative enterprise ever undertaken by man. The IGY was a scientific year. It was a year when men of sixty-seven nations agreed to observe the earth over its whole surface, simultaneously, and with precise instruments designed to the same standards so that the changing phenomena enveloping the earth could be caught and described in their full global sense.

In IGY: *The Year of the New Moons*, Professor J. Tuzo Wilson describes the characteristics of the earth that were observed during the IGY—the elements of our surroundings that give us our ever-changing environment. But more than that, he tells at first hand of the people in distant and varied lands who worked together to make the IGY the great scientific success that it was. Sitting together with me nearly two years ago on an antarctic plane jammed with men and gear, Professor Wilson outlined his plans to fuse the scientific and the human aspects of the IGY in the present volume.

Professor Wilson was president of the International Union of Geodesy and Geophysics (IUGG) during the IGY. This important union of scientists carried a major responsibility for the adequate functioning of the complex system of observations of the "year." The IUGG had joined with l'Union Radio Scientifique Internationale (URSI), the International Astronomical Union (IAU), and the International Geographical Union (IGU) to organize the IGY through the Comité Spécial de l'Année Géophysique Internationale (CSAGI) under the parent body of all international unions, the International Council of Scientific Unions (ICSU). Acting outside the usual political and diplomatic framework of nations, the IGY was planned and executed by scientists working in close collaboration, with immense assistance from their countries. The job took eight years to accomplish, and our comprehension of our environment is still undergoing major changes as a consequence.

During the planning and execution of the IGY, Jock Wilson travelled to every corner of the earth. With great wisdom, the Government of Canada and the University of Toronto provided the time and support that enabled him to oversee the IGY on behalf of the IUGG. As a leading world scientist, Jock Wilson brings the perspective of the impartial, keen observer of events around him, acting without reference to his personal comfort or safety when there is a job to be done or a significant observation to be made. As a Canadian, he is naturally an authority on the polar regions. And as a geophysicist, he counts the whole world as his realm. Those who have read One Chinese Moon, in which he tells of his travels in the People's Republic of China, will have seen the penetrating insight, broad perspective, and dry humour with which he deals with one of the world's most troubled areas.

In 1958 during scientific meetings at the National Academy of Sciences I conferred briefly with Wilson and invited him to join an IGY party of scientists going to the Antarctic for several weeks late that year. Obviously, Wilson could make a definite contribution to the assessment of the difficult scientific work being carried on in that remote "seventh continent." His response was unhesitating; at the expense of other plans, he joined us in our studies, crisscrossing the continent for many thousands of miles between isolated bases and field parties. When an observer was needed for a hazardous reconnaissance with a single-engined plane into little-explored areas, Jock was in the party. When a heated scientific discussion went on in some antarctic hut during a blizzard, he was in the thick of it, tapping a deep store of scientific knowledge. Jock Wilson was always present on a steep climb or a long hike that might continue right through the night; and always he was a delightful companion, with an apt anecdote for any situation. Wilson's cold scientific judgment is agreeably tempered by a spontaneous and exciting love of adventure.

It has been said that rule of law among nations will not be achieved until men are bound together by common threads of cultural understanding. Certainly science is one of those threads—perhaps a major line that permits men to speak to one another with comprehension, confidence, and common purpose. Coming in times of international tension, the IGY was a clear demonstration of the power of such cultural bonds. In this book Professor Wilson has captured the sense of desire of all peoples, within the universal scientific culture, to labor for the benefit of all.

LLOYD V. BERKNER

Retiring President,
International Council
of Scientific Unions

PREFACE

To most people the IGY was little more than a set of initials vaguely associated with a branch of scientific activity that finally was made manifest in the Sputnik. Although it absorbed the imagination and energies of thousands of the world's scientists for eighteen months, to the general public the purpose of the International Geophysical Year was not nearly as clear as the delighted realization that scientists either could not count or did not know how many months there are in a year.

In these days when advances in scientific knowledge affect every facet of our lives, it is important that we all know as much about science as we can. It was my good fortune, during the IGY, to have unrivalled opportunities to travel the world and to meet the men working on IGY projects. This book combines a record of these journeys with an account of the scientific programs. This strange mixture is deliberate. I hope that the parts devoted to travel will bring home to the reader how truly international is science, and show that scientists are as much interested in other aspects of human affairs as anyone else. I also hope that my observations as a scientist

abroad will provide a series of park benches on which the
reader may rest and draw breath before resuming his way
along the unfamiliar paths of science. Such alternations of
work and interruptions are the normal pattern of life of scientists.

For providing opportunities to undertake these travels and
for making them possible, I am particularly indebted to the
University of Colorado; The Romanian Institute of Cultural
Relations with Foreign Countries; the Association of Cana-
dian Clubs; the International Union of Geodesy and Geo-
physics; the Society of Sigma Xi; the Defense Research Board
of Canada; the National Research Council of Canada; the
Academy of Sciences and the Ministry of Geology of the
USSR; the Academia Sinica, Peking; the Academia Sinica,
Taipeh; the University of Tokyo; the Japanese Broadcasting
Corporation; the National Academy of Sciences of the United
States; the New Zealand Department of Scientific and Industrial Research; and the University of Toronto. I should
like to thank the many people who received me so hospitably
during these trips and who answered so many of my questions.

To Dr. Lloyd V. Berkner I am doubly indebted both for
being my host and mentor on a trip to Antarctica, which he
has studied for thirty years, and for his generous Foreword.

For supplementary information I wrote to the secretaries of
national committees for the IGY and many other individuals
in the sixty-seven participating countries, and received valuable replies and photographs. I only regret that I have not been
able to use all the material so liberally provided. The files of
popular and scientific journals also made available important
information. I should like to express my thanks to all these
generous collaborators. I am particularly grateful to Mr. Hugh
Odishaw and Mr. Pembroke J. Hart of World Data Centre
A, to Professor V. V. Beloussov and Mme V. A. Troitskaya
of World Data Centre B, and to members of the Canadian

committee on the IGY for help in assembling information and photographs. I should also like to pay tribute to Ing. Gen. Georges Laclavère of Paris, secretary of the IUGG, for the enormous load of work he has carried (in addition to his normal job) and for the sound advice, inspiration, and assistance he has so often given me.

When a draft of the book had been completed, I sent one or more chapters to specialists for criticism and comments. For their help I am grateful to Doctors G. Hattersley-Smith J. F. Heard, C. O. Hines, P. M. Millman, D. A. MacRae, J. A. O'Keefe, F. Press, D. C. Rose, A. H. Shapley, P. H. Serson, J. P. Tully, and H. Wexler. Needless to say, they are not to be held responsible for what is here said.

I am particularly indebted to Miss Helen O'Reilly and Mr. Henry Robbins for editorial comment, and to Professor W. H. Watson, Doctors M. G. Rochester and T. O. Jones, and Mr. R. Roden for technical comments on drafts of the whole book.

Mrs. Sylvia Derenyi, Miss Sylvia Lummis, and Mrs. Nancy Thoman typed the manuscript, and Mrs. Thoman also prepared the index. Mr. Alex Aiken is the artist responsible for all the drawings.

To all these people I extend my most grateful thanks. Without their help the book would not have covered as large a range or been as accurate.

Above all, I am indebted to my wife, Isabel, for editing the text and for ameliorating much that was difficult or dull.

J. T. W.

CONTENTS

1 · The International Geophysical Year   3

2 · Colorado, July 1957   14

3 · The Sun   19

4 · Geophysical Jamboree, August–September 1957   34

5 · Romania, October 1957   40

6 · The New Moons   54

7 · What the Satellites Revealed   77

8 · Cosmic Rays   88

9 · The North Magnetic Pole, June 1958   103

10 · The Earth's Magnetic Field   110

11 · The Upper Atmosphere   119

12 · Aurora   131

13 · Landfalls in a Frozen Sea, June 1958   145

14 · Greenland and the World's Ice, June 1958   154

15 · Brussels to Moscow, July 1958   170

16 · Gravity and the Earth's Wobble   179

17 · The Soviet Union, August 1958   191

18 · Earthquakes   214

19 · China, Taiwan, and Japan, September 1958   227

20 · The Oceans   244

21 · Hawaii and New Zealand, November 1958   265

22 · Fall-out   276

23 · Antarctica, November 1958   288

24 · The Weather   310

25 · The Year's Harvest   320

TABLES   333

REFERENCES FOR FURTHER READING   347

INDEX   *follows page*   350

ILLUSTRATIONS

The world of the International Geophysical Year   11

Spectrum of sound waves   22

Electro-magnetic spectrum   24

Major solar activity   28

Temperature variation and sun-spot activity   30

The far side of the moon   74

The earth and the inner and outer Van Allen belts   78

High-speed electrons in the Van Allen and Argus belts   79

Fundamental particles and simple atoms   90

Collision of cosmic-ray particle with a nucleus   93

Shower of secondary cosmic rays   95

The earth's magnetic field   98

Cross-section of our galaxy   99

Map of part of the Canadian Arctic   106

Cross-section of the earth's interior   111

The sun's toroidal fields   115

Variation in the earth's magnetic field   117

Phenomena in nearby space   120

The ionospheric sounder   122

Reflection of radio signals by layers of the atmosphere   124

Distribution of aurora borealis   132

Distribution of aurora australis   134
A corpuscular stream   136
A corpuscular stream passing the earth   138
Distribution and frequency of auroral displays   141
Map of Arctic Sea   148
The ice surface of Greenland   156
The ice surface of Antarctica   163
Bedrock of Antarctica below the ice sheet   165
Variations in the strength of gravity in the Baltic Sea   182
The continental fracture system   221
Cross-section of the earth's crust and the upper part of
    the mantle   223
Profile across the mid-ocean ridge   247
Vertical section through the Atlantic Ocean from pole
    to pole   256
Diagram of deep circulation in the ocean basins   259
Position of the Antarctic Convergence   262
Cross-section of part of the Pacific Ocean   269
Changes in carbon-14 in New Zealand   279
Strontium-90 in the atmosphere   282
Strontium-90 activity in rainfall   284
Structure of upper atmosphere as revealed by fall-out   285
IGY stations in Antarctica   294
Storms on the Antarctic continent in 1958   308
Atmospheric circulation   315
Jet-streams in the northern hemisphere   316
Cross-section through a front and a jet-stream   317

PLATES

FOLLOWING PAGE

Sun-spots (Mount Wilson and Mount Palomar Observatories)   40

Sun-spots (detail) (Princeton University Observatory)   40

Solar telescope in Moscow (U.S.S.R.—IGY)   40

Coronagraph and spectrograph (National Academy of Sciences—IGY)   40

Solar flare   40

Balloon, parachute, and mounted instrument package (U. S. Navy)   40

Rocket firing during eclipse (U. S. Navy)   40

Test firing of Vanguard II (U. S. Navy)   40

Vanguard satellite being installed (U. S. Navy)   40

Explorer VII before launching (U. S. Army)   40

Lunar Probe III (U. S. Air Force)   40

Soviet research rocket (U.S.S.R.—IGY)   40

Sputnik III (U.S.S.R.—IGY)   40

Aerobee rocket (U. S. Army)   40

Far side of the moon (U.S.S.R. Information Service)   136

Crab nebula (Mount Wilson and Mount Palomar Observatories)   136

Greek Moonwatch (Greek—IGY)   136

*Indiana Moonwatch team (Smithsonian Astrophysical
    Observatory)*   136

*Solar radio telescope, Australia (W. N. Christiansen,
    Radiophysics Laboratory C.S.R.I.O., Sidney,
    Australia)*   136

*Baker-Nunn-Schmidt Camera, Australia (Australian
    Weapons Research Establishment)*   136

*Jodrell Bank telescope (United Kingdom Information
    Service)*   136

*The all-sky camera (National Research Council of
    Canada)*   136

*Aurora photo with all-sky camera (National Research
    Council of Canada)*   136
Auroral forms in Alaska (J. W. Wright)   136
Ionization counter for cosmic rays (U.S.S.R.—IGY)   136

*Cosmic-ray star caused by collision with nucleus (Na-
    tional Research Council of Canada)*   136
Weather balloon (U. S.—IGY)   136
Spectrophotometer measuring ozone (U. S.—IGY)   136
Czech earth-tides equipment (Csav Geofysikalniustav)   232
Royal Thai observer in field (Thai—IGY)   232
Soviet seismograph (U.S.S.R.—IGY)   232

*Mount Vesuvius (American Museum of Natural His-
    tory)*   232
Lloyd V. Berkner   232
Young Soviet scientist (U.S.S.R.—IGY)   232
Chapman and Bardin (U.S.S.R.—IGY)   232

*Author and Soviet scientists (Photograph by Chief
    Engineer Nicolas Fonfaev)*   232
Soviet drifting station (University of Washington)   232

*Ice-coring on Blue Glacier, Olympic Mountains (Uni-
    versity of Washington)*   232
Henrietta glacier (Royal Canadian Air Force)   232

*Valley glaciers on Ellesmere Island (Royal Canadian
    Air Force)*   232

Ship in spring ice (Canadian Department of Transport)   232

Under-ice living quarters (U. S. Army)   232

Stratigraphy of crevasse walls (U. S. National Academy
    of Science)   232

Drilling in Antarctic ice (U. S. Navy)   328

Ice cave in Antarctic (U. S. Navy)   328

Hummocky sea ice (U. S. National Academy of Sciences
    —IGY)   328

Little America V (U. S. Navy)   328

Snow-covered facilities at Little America (U. S. Navy)   328

Annual layers in ice cliffs (Australian National Antarc-
    tic Research Expedition)   328

Sno-Cats at Ellsworth Station (U. S. National Acad-
    emy of Sciences—IGY)   328

Soviet tractor train (U.S.S.R.—IGY)   328

Lowering coring apparatus from the Vema (Lamont
    Geological Observatory, Columbia University)   328

Lowering Nansen bottle to collect water samples (U. S.
    —IGY)   328

Recovering Soviet double coring tube (U.S.S.R.—
    IGY)   328

Soviet oceanographic research ship, Vityaz (U.S.S.R.—
    IGY)   328

TABLES

1 · *Countries which participated in the IGY*   333
2 · *Bureau of the Comité Spécial de l'Année Géophysique Internationale*   334
3 · *IGY subjects and their reporters*   334
4 · *Members of CSAGI*   335
5 · *Record of artificial satellites and space probes launched in 1957–1958*   335
6 · *Record of artificial satellites and planets launched in 1959*   336
7 · *Record of artificial satellites placed in orbit January 1, 1960, to April 12, 1961*   337
8 · *Features of Sputnik satellites*   338
9 · *Features of Vanguard satellites*   339
10 · *Features of Explorer and Score satellites*   340
11 · *Features of Pioneer space probes and planet*   341
12 · *Features of Discoverer satellites*   342
13 · *Features of Lunik space probes and satellites*   343
14 · *Times and places of Argus experiments*   343
15 · *Radioactive isotopes created by cosmic-ray bombardment of the atmosphere*   344
16 · *True direction of magnetic compass at London*   344
17 · *Changes in the strength of the earth's magnetic field*   345
18 · *IGY stations in the Antarctic*   345
19 · *Some of the world's record cold temperatures*   346

I·G·Y

THE YEAR OF
THE NEW MOONS

CHAPTER 1

THE INTERNATIONAL GEOPHYSICAL YEAR

JUNE 1957

On the evening of June 30, 1957, I sat on the darkening veranda of our summer cottage on the Georgian Bay of Lake Huron, waiting for midnight and the opening of the International Geophysical Year. There in the wilds I had no measurements to make, and I knew that nothing would mark the event; but it was exciting to contemplate what the next eighteen months would bring.

A night breeze stirred through the pines; ripples lapped against the bare rock shore and bumped a boat against the dock. Mosquitoes shrilled on the screening. From far on the other side of the bay came the drone of an outboard motor and from the rocks behind the kitchen the clang and scrape of a metal plate as the children's pet racoon deliberated over her dinner.

Above the low rocky coast, the Milky Way foamed down the seas of heaven like scud marking the set moon's wake, and a thousand stars twinkled as buoys to chart its passage. Their brilliance against the blackness of the night is a light to comfort us in darkness, and marks the shores of man's vision of paradise. In all religions and mythologies the seat of the Almighty and the homes of the blessed have been placed in the unfathomed depths of space.

The mysteries of the heavens were enough to achieve this veneration when the firmament was considered to be just an illuminated back-drop to the solar system; by how much should our wonder and awe have grown now that we appreciate how vastly more immense and grand the universe is! Until the time of Kepler, man believed that the sun rose and set for him; he regarded the heavens as a spectacle mounted for his delectation; and he considered any startling event a miracle. Today we see ourselves as dust in a galaxy of greater size and intricacy than anyone could have dared imagine had it not been revealed by careful observation and precise logic. No longer is our admiration for the beauty of night limited to the few thousand stars that the best eye can see. In our imagination we can now visualize the Milky Way as a hundred billion suns, each like our own, and all of them forming but a single galaxy, just one spiral nebula, among uncounted and uncountable clusters of other similar galaxies stretching in ordered myriads beyond the farthest reach of telescopes.

By any material measure, we are of far less consequence than a speck of dust in a house. From a small room with an earth and a sun and a thousand stars painted on the walls, our universe has expanded into a city of indescribable elegance, vastness, and regularity in which our galaxy, our sun, our earth, and ourselves occupy a humble place.

Our progress in science has not succeeded in giving us a complete understanding of this universe, nor is it likely ever to do so, but by disclosing to us so much more than was at first obvious it has served to put our ignorance and insignificance into perspective. If our discoveries have shown us how small is our understanding and how limited our comprehension, they have also, by revealing the regularity and pattern of the universe, made us aware that through systematic study we can follow most closely the path of creation and see the steps by which the unseen Creator trod.

Just as study has demonstrated that in addition to being larger the universe is also more regular than had been thought, so do other investigations uncover hidden meaning in the nature of all matter, energy, and life. Everywhere in science modern tools and ideas bring to light the elegant and orderly skeins by which nature builds the glory that we see about us, knit in regular patterns from simple stitches. Her apparently infinite materials are made of only a few million chemicals. These are not unrelated substances, but the compounds of one hundred and three elements. Even the elements are not distinct; each consists of electrons, protons, neutrons, and energy arranged in a special pattern. The colours that we see in such a myriad of shades are but electro-magnetic vibrations of varying wave-lengths. Indeed, we may think of all nature in terms of music, as infinitely ingenious and elaborate variations on a few simple themes.

It is plain that creation was not haphazard, but orderly. The way to understand creation better is, therefore, to follow the pattern it has set, which clearly is the road of intellect. It might seem presumptuous to suggest that in science man has found the way to map the path of the Creator, and conceited to claim that man by mathematical logic has solved a few riddles of the universe, thereby achieving a modicum of control over its functions. The scientist, however, is saved from the sin of Lucifer by an ever-increasing awe which holds his self-conceit in check. If science has given unexpected power to man, it has to an even greater extent revealed the unimagined glory of God.

Man was endowed with intellect as well as feeling, and it behoves him to use his intellect to govern himself and his environment. The International Geophysical Year was conceived as the greatest attempt men have yet made to band together to examine, without passion or undue rivalry, their environment, their home and ultimate resource, the earth.

Men, it is true, have studied the earth for thousands of years and have discovered much more about it than about the unseen universe around us, but these studies have been local efforts, each limited to a particular ocean, mountain peak, or storm, or to a single aspect of the earth—its rocks, its magnetism, or its atmosphere. The International Geophysical Year was to be different, not because it would be bigger, though it had to be, but because it would be an attempt to be all-embracing, to fit the earth into the pattern of the universe, to relate its parts together, to discover hidden order, and to interpret the whole in relation to space, and especially, to that greatest influence in nearby space, the sun.

This far-flung and happy enterprise had not sprung into being unannounced; it was the child of two sets of parents. On the one hand it was a direct descendant of the First and Second International Polar Years of 1882–3 and 1932–3; and on the other hand it was an offspring of the international scientific unions, the dozen bodies through which world scientists have been meeting regularly since 1919. So great and successful an operation could not have been conceived, let alone smoothly executed, without the experience thus bequeathed to it.

The First International Polar Year (IPY 1) was proposed by Lieutenant Carl Weyprecht of Austria and organized in 1879 at a meeting of the International Meteorological Congress. A committee under the chairmanship of G. Newmayer of Hamburg and later H. Wild of St. Petersburg laid plans, established rules for taking observations, fixed the duration of IPY 1 to be from August 1, 1882, to September 1, 1883, and later published the results. Eleven nations sent expeditions to twelve bases around the Arctic and to two others in the Southern Ocean.

The conditions prevailing then were less than ideal. So little was known of the polar regions that not all the bases were well sited; for instance, the two antarctic stations in South Georgia and Cape Horn were far removed from the south magnetic pole, which they had been particularly established to investigate. Arrangements for pairs of stations to photograph the aurora were made under the supposition that it appears at a height of 5 miles, but the results were poor because the aurora was discovered always to form above a height of 60 miles. Some parties were ill-equipped for the rigors they had to face. There was no radio by which to communicate or provide time signals. Only the French party used cameras to photograph automatically the readings on their instruments.

In spite of these handicaps, the achievements were great. The first clear ideas of the distribution of the aurora borealis and of polar weather were obtained. Fortunately, the considerable sun-spot activity during this period was accompanied by the two greatest magnetic storms ever recorded in high latitudes. The observations of these storms proved their value forty years later in 1926 when Sydney Chapman, in developing his hypothesis that currents flow in the upper atmosphere, used these records to calculate the strength and location of the currents. In 1882 the southern stations observed a transit of Venus across the face of the sun, and many stations recorded the effects of the volcanic eruption of Krakatoa in 1883—large tidal waves and atmospheric disturbances that travelled twice around the earth. The results were published in a shelf-full of quarto volumes.

Interest in international co-operation in polar exploration then subsided for forty-five years, but revived in time for scientists to plan a Second Polar Year (IPY 2) to celebrate the golden jubilee of the first. The International Union of Geodesy and Geophysics, which had been formed in 1919, played a major role in organizing and financing IPY 2. In particular, it arranged for the publication of a *Photographic Atlas of Auroral Forms* to guide observers, provided many instruments, and financed to a large extent the publication of results.

The IPY 2 was conducted in the same way as the IPY 1. Again the greatest efforts were devoted to the study of meteorology, magnetism, and aurora in the Arctic, but more countries and more branches of science were included. The original resolutions were distributed in eight languages, and eventually forty-four countries agreed to participate, although only half of them organized expeditions.

The IPY 2 was handicapped by being held during a period of minimum sun-spot activity and in the midst of a great economic depression. It is doubtful whether it could have been successful without the great efforts of its president, D. la Cour of Denmark, and the financial support which he persuaded the Rockefeller Foundation to provide.

Unlike its predecessor, however, the IPY 2 generated an interest that continued over the years, and many of the younger men who took part in it played important roles in the IGY. One of them, J. Bartels, has said: "IPY 2 was like chamber music compared to the symphony of the present IGY." To extend the metaphor, IPY 1 might be likened to several soloists, each playing the same tune independently. Nevertheless, each attempt provided both tangible results and the experience upon which the next effort could be built.

The second parents of the IGY were the dozen scientific unions which had been formally organized in 1919. Each union deals with one branch of science and enables scientists from all over the world to meet together regularly. The unions particularly concerned with the IGY were the International Union of Geodesy and Geophysics (IUGG); the International Astronomical Union (IAU); l'Union Radio Scientifique Internationale (URSI); the International Geographical Union (IGU); and the International Union of Pure and Applied Physics (IUPAP).

These unions provided the forums at which the initial plans were discussed, and the International Council of Scientific Unions (an administrative body comprising the chief officers of the unions) co-ordinated their efforts and established the Comité Spécial de l'Année Géophysique Internationale (CSAGI) to run the project.

The infant protégé was conceived at a dinner party on the evening of April 5, 1950. J. A. Van Allen, after whom the Van Allen belts in space have since been named, had invited half a dozen friends to his home in a suburb of Washington to meet Sydney Chapman, the well-known English geophysicist, who was in the process of moving the chief scene of his activities from the University of Oxford to the United States. This remarkable man, who was to become the president of the CSAGI, is an indefatigable traveller and a firm believer in strenuous physical exercise. His hosts have often been hard put to find a convenient swimming pool for his accustomed swim at 7 o'clock each morning. A typical story told of him concerns two consecutive meetings held in 1939. He had attended the first in Chicago, and when he did not immediately turn up at the second in Washington, someone inquired: "Where's Sydney Chapman?" Those who knew him replied: "Just give him time, and he'll be along; you know, it takes three or four days to bicycle from Chicago to Washington!"

All the men who met that evening to do him honour had taken part in the IPY 2 and were destined to be leaders of the IGY. During the evening Lloyd V. Berkner proposed that instead of waiting for the traditional fifty years, they hold the third Polar Year on the silver anniversary of the second. He pointed out that the exigencies of war had developed over-snow vehicles and air-support techniques which would enable scientists to study the Antarctic, that electronic instruments had been infinitely improved during the past twenty-five years, that 1957–8 would be a year of sun-spot maximum, and—the most persuasive argument of all—that if they were to wait a full fifty years for the International Polar Year 3, very few of those present would be in fit shape to enjoy it.

By October 1951, CSAGI had been established and the planning for this momentous scientific endeavour begun. Because its scope was to be so much greater than that of its predecessors, it was christened the International Geophysical Year rather than the International Polar Year 3.

Altogether no less than sixty-seven countries had agreed to participate, and their national committees were represented on CSAGI, but the main burden was carried by a small bureau and by the reporters who were appointed to co-ordinate the efforts of each of the fourteen scientific programs. Their names and those of the participating countries are given at the end of this book.

In a series of meetings, both of CSAGI as a whole and of smaller groups, suggestions were thrashed out. The reporters for the programs indicated what observations they felt were required; representatives of the various countries tried to obtain support for these programs and in many cases made counter-proposals. After a number of exchanges, unified plans were formulated to make the best use of available resources.

It was soon realized that even with the considerable support which was forthcoming the whole world could not be covered with equal intensity. Efforts were concentrated, therefore, in the polar regions, in the equatorial zone, and along several belts joining pole to pole, one through Europe and Africa, another through the Americas, and a third through east Asia and Australia. To concentrate activities further, certain days were appointed for special efforts that could not be carried on all the time. On such days rockets would be fired simultaneously and

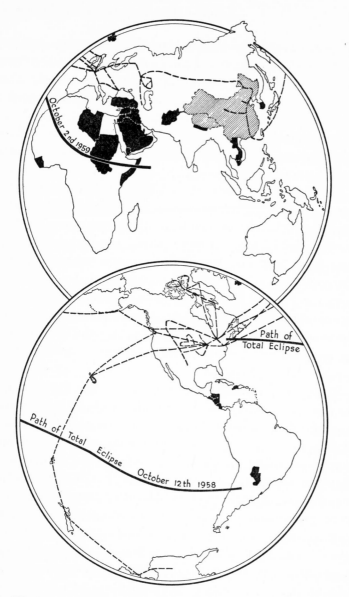

The World of the International Geophysical Year. Countries in black
did *not* participate in the IGY. Heavy lines show the paths of totality
of solar eclipses during the IGY (1957–8) and IGC (1959). Broken
lines show the author's travels during that time.

additional upper-air balloons would be sent aloft. Some of these "world days" were fixed in advance, but plans were sufficiently flexible so that all resources could be focused at short notice on the study of an unexpected scientific event— for instance, a large outburst on the sun.

To facilitate the reduction of results, uniform instructions were prepared, and a whole series of annals published to pro- mulgate them.

Finally, it was agreed that all data obtained in the program were to be freely circulated. Three World Data Centres were established: A in Washington, B in Moscow, and C divided among several European cities. Every country sent observa- tions to at least one World Data Centre, which then was charged with distributing them to the others.

The first year of the planned eighteen-month period was so successful that the Soviet Union proposed in August 1958 that the work be continued through 1959. A reduced effort was agreed upon and called the International Geophysical Co- operation (IGC, 1959).

When the projects were ended, CSAGI was dissolved and the members thanked for their invaluable efforts on behalf of science and of mankind. Those activities which could be han- dled by the unions were once more entrusted to them. The Comité Internationale Géophysique (CIG) was formed, with the same indefatigable secretary as the IUGG, Georges La- clavère, to wind up the IGY and get its results published, and to continue reduced programs of international co-operation. In three regions—nearby space, the oceans, and Antarctica— research had been initiated on so broad a scale that special committees were organized to continue administrative ar- rangements.

It is my hope that in this book the reader may learn some- thing of the important discoveries made during the IGY and

IGC and that he will be able to share the excitement of the scientists who were fortunate enough to have engaged in this exploration of the earth. Perhaps with them he will feel momentarily lifted above the earth and see the whole world in perspective. By launching satellites into outer space, the IGY has disclosed the immensity of the vast and hostile space that surrounds our world; perhaps in the face of this immensity he may discover the essential unity of all mankind.

CHAPTER 2

COLORADO

JULY 1957

On July 1 I had to leave the tranquillity of Georgian Bay to fly to the University of Colorado to hold a series of seminars in physics and geology for summer-school students, and give a public lecture. In July 1957 public lectures on the International Geophysical Year were very fashionable.

I flew over the great American plains to Denver. The immensity and fertility of that checkerboard of fields which constitutes the North American prairies always amazes me. Flying west, whether to Edmonton or to Texas, one passes for hours over plains laid out in one-mile squares that seem to stretch endlessly in every direction.

Watching, I soon grew tired of the monotony and turned to read or eat or doze; when I looked again, subtle changes had interposed. The green had faded to yellow, brown, even orange. A great river twisted its brown flood across the map. Occasionally, a speckled town broke the pattern with a finer mesh of streets. Roads and railways converged and parted, each as fine and as smoothly curved as a fishing-line across the floor.

It was at once a familiar and unknown land to me: familiar from frequent flights across it, and four trips by automobile as a student; yet strange because I had never stayed there, but like a migrant goose had chiefly seen it from above.

Over Nebraska I saw again the flowing dust I remembered so well. At first it was no more than a haze, a shimmer, an almost imperceptible mist over the land. I thought it was but a trick that the vibration of the plane was playing on my eyes. Slowly it grew clearer and more dense until it formed into soft, grey-yellow clouds flowing in gentle puffs across the fields. In 1934 and 1935 I had choked in clouds such as these, seen the dried leaves of the unripened corn blown across the highway, and the dust piled in the lee of sheds and fenceposts.

From 18,000 feet above, one is not part of the land, but one can see how the sun beats down and how its vagaries distribute drought or flood, life or disaster, wealth or ruin, prosperity or despair to the world below. Here, on the border-zone between the green fields of the east and the buff deserts of the west, the power and intransigence of the sun are very real.

In Denver, Professor Charles Norris met me, and we drove to the red-brick campus at Boulder, at the foot of the brick-red mountain slabs which fence the main Rockies.

A few days of lecturing quickly passed, and after them came my reward. Two of the professors of geology drove me back into the mountains to meet their graduate students and to see their field work. Behind Boulder we plunged into the wall of mountains, up a canyon cut by a bucking, white-crested stream, and drove smoothly up along it in a manner that would have amazed the hardy fur-traders and prospectors who first entered these fastnesses. Where once a mule-trail skirted the torrent's wall there is now a four-lane highway; where men ached and sweated under packs and headstraps towards the peaks diesel trucks now pant over Loveland's 12,000-foot pass; where once were gold mines there are now $10 uranium cures for bursitis. In the bar of the Leadville Hotel where miners once toasted Baby Doe Tabor one can airmail a picture post-card home, or order fresh sea-food specials. Even the Indians, hunted no longer, sell moccasins and foot-long hot dogs. At gasoline stations tame bears drink pop by the bottleful.

We left the highway and by dusty back roads entered the heart of the mountains where the hillsides are still lush green and the gentians bottle-blue in the clear, cool mountain air. We passed the ghosts of the old mining camps—Aspen, Ely, Park City, Leadville, Tintic—but saw only one active mine. It is strange that so great a mining state as Colorado should so quickly have yielded up its riches, treasure which went to build Denver and New York. This presages the day when the world's stock of easily accessible minerals will be exhausted, and its remaining store will be more difficult and more ex-pensive to acquire.

My companions, Professors Larry Walker and Warren Longley, showed me the magnificent Colorado scenery and to its beauty added interest by pointing out great folds in the rocks, necks of former volcanoes, and scars of ancient earth-quakes. Weathering had laid bare the bones and tissue of the earth, and erosion had exposed sections of the crust to view. The core of one range of mountains was a great block of granite and gneiss uplifted to 14,000 feet and denuded of its cover. On the lower slopes multicoloured shales and sand-stones lay in twisted layers where they had slipped off this great protrusion. These sights fascinated me, for the study of the causes of mountain-building and the nature of continental structure is my own particular scientific specialty.

Because the solid part of the earth changes so slowly, its study was only marginally included in the program of the IGY, which dealt particularly with the mobile aspects of the earth that would show significant changes within an eighteen-month period. Therefore, I was not as preoccupied during the IGY with my own special research programs, as many geophysicists were, and when the chance came I was free to travel widely. At the same time, because I knew that the key to the physics of mountain-building lies in a consideration of the earth as a whole and in a comparison of the features of all mountains, I welcomed the opportunity to further my own work by going to see as many mountains as possible.

We drove on to the high-altitude solar observatory which the National Bureau of Standards and the University of Colorado maintain on one of the highest ridges of the Rocky Mountains near Climax. The place, with its clear skies and its elevation of 13,000 feet, high above much of the atmosphere, provides particularly good conditions for observing the sun. This solar observatory is a fine example of the 120 throughout the world which maintained a continuous watch upon the sun during the IGY.

The instruments that we saw were of three types. There were radio telescopes equipped with a great dish of wire netting to catch the radio noise emitted by the sun. There was an ordinary telescope fitted with a dark-red filter specially designed to reduce the glare and to make visible the great outbursts of hydrogen gas, called solar flares, which occur irregularly on the sun. The flames of erupting hydrogen are red and can best be seen through these filters, which eliminate almost all other light. Every minute a camera took a photograph of the sun through this telescope. Since much of the equipment was automatic, most of the scientists were not at the observatory but in their offices in Boulder, seeking to interpret the results. A young Austrian astronomer was on duty, and he led us along a foot-path through the mountain glade to see the third and most interesting telescope of all. This telescope was of the type invented by the great French astronomer, Lyot, for studying solar prominences. At one time these jets of incandescent gas which constantly play about the surface of the sun could only be seen at its edges during total solar eclipses, but Lyot devised a means of placing a metal disc far up the tube of telescopes in such a manner that an artificial eclipse would be created.

Our guide allowed us to look at these prominences. The black shadow of the disc exactly covered the bright face of the sun. In the sun's atmosphere we could see great bursts of flame darting out and curving in graceful paths before falling back again. Seeing the motion of these vast flames and knowing that many were larger than the whole earth, we realized vividly with what colossal speed and energy they were travelling— and how violent is the activity of the sun.

Afterwards, as we turned to walk the mountain paths in sunshine, the beauty of the morning was enhanced by our awareness, dim though it might be, of the wonders of the universe which the efforts of generations of scientists have revealed. I have endeavoured, in recounting my travels during the IGY, to communicate to the reader the sense of fascination that accompanied me. To this end, I have interwoven the accounts of my stop-overs with chapters explaining the main programs of the IGY. We can do no better than start by considering the sun itself.

CHAPTER 3

THE SUN

The sun is master of our material life. From its light and heat we derive all our vital powers; without it there would be neither daylight nor seasons, wind nor weather. All would be dark and still and unimaginably cold, for the earth is but the sun's tiny child and creature. Because the sun's influence upon the surface of the earth is so great, a careful study of the sun played an essential and indeed dominant part in the International Geophysical Year.

Our first impression that the sun is a huge furnace is correct enough. True, its fires are not burning in air; their immense heat is generated by hydrogen atoms combining with one another to form helium atoms, with the resultant emission of the vast energy of nuclear fusion. The sun is, in fact, an enormous nuclear reactor, not fissioning uranium as man-made reactors do, but fusing hydrogen as men hope the reactors of the future will. The temperature at the centre of the sun has been estimated to be thirty million degrees Fahrenheit and the pressure three hundred billion pounds per square inch.

The sun, like other furnaces, emits radiation and jets of gas. Some radiation, in the form of light, heat, and weak ultra-violet rays, reaches us every day. It was suspected, however, that other rays of the sun are prevented from reaching us by the earth's atmosphere acting as a shield, for the aurora gives us evidence that the top of the atmosphere is at times violently agitated by blasts of gases or radiation which cannot break through to the earth. The light, heat, and radio waves which we receive from the sun penetrate the shield of the earth's atmosphere through two so-called "windows," and these rays are the only ones directly observable from the earth's surface. This shielding effect of the atmosphere has made it difficult for us to observe the sun, for even on a cloudless day the atmosphere distorts our view and makes the details in photographs fuzzy. Like a gardener in a greenhouse in winter, we look out through misty windows, not knowing how cold it is outside nor from which direction the wind is blowing.

As Sir Isaac Newton said, "the only remedy is a most serene and quiet air such as may perhaps be found on the tops of the highest mountains above the grosser clouds." This ideal was attained just before the IGY when astronomers from the Paris Observatory and Princeton University sent balloons carrying 12-inch telescopes into the stratosphere, the rarefied outermost layer of the earth's atmosphere. This is the limit that a balloon can reach, since it must be lighter than the air surrounding it and so can never rise above the whole atmosphere. One of the most important achievements of the IGY was to send artificial satellites and rockets above the atmosphere to heights from which a clear, unfiltered view of the sun could be obtained. The gardener had at last been able to put his head right out of the window.

Rocket astronomy involves immense problems and great expense. A rocket is near the top of its trajectory only for a very few minutes, and travels rapidly, rotating and tumbling as it goes. If, in spite of these unstable conditions, the instruments are able to obtain records, there is the further problem of recovering the records intact. The instruments themselves are generally destroyed. The V2's that were first used after the war could carry a load of up to a ton, but most of the other rockets available for research can take useful loads of less than 200 pounds each. Satellites were even more severely limited when the IGY began, but within three and a half years of the first launching, sophisticated instruments and the comments of the first cosmonaut have enabled mankind at last to encompass the true appearance of the naked universe. The records transmitted back to earth, combined with those made continuously at many ground observatories (like the one at Climax), have given us a new and clearer understanding of the sun.

It now appears that space, at any rate around the earth and sun, has a "climate" as changeable as that on the earth's surface. It is not, as was formerly supposed, an inert near-vacuum, still and cold. In their thin but violent way, the regions of nearer space are continually shaken and buffeted by a bombardment from the sun of electro-magnetic waves of many frequencies, called radiation, and of high-speed atoms and fragments of atoms which strike the earth's atmosphere in tenuous blasts of "solar wind." To understand electro-magnetic radiation better, we shall compare it to another kind of radiation, sound waves, with which we are more familiar.

Everyone knows that the beating of a drumhead, the bowing of a violin, or the blowing of a horn create vibrations that travel outwards in all directions through the air to strike our ears. Each note has a characteristic number of vibrations per second, called frequency. Thus middle C has a frequency of 512 vibrations each second, and high C 1,024. Notes that we recognize as musical have frequencies ranging between 20,000 vibrations a second for high notes and 20 a second for the lowest. Above these frequencies are ultra-sonic vibrations, inaudible to us but just as real. Below these frequencies we

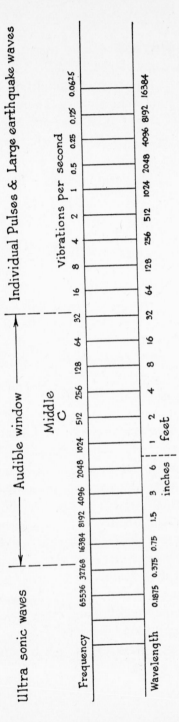

Spectrum of sound waves showing the audible window.

distinguish individual beats and cease to regard the effect as music. This is an idiosyncrasy of ours, for the ticking of a clock or the beating of a heart is just as regular, although less frequent, than the vibration of musical notes. There is, in effect, a great spectrum of mechanical vibrations, and our ears only hear or recognize as music the part within what we may call the "audible window."

A flash of lightning and the accompanying clap of thunder enable us to time the speed of sound. If a flash occurs 1,000 feet away and we hear the clap a second later, we know that the sound has travelled at the rate of 1,000 feet a second. All sounds travel in air at the same speed. When middle C is played, the instrument vibrates 512 times a second, and each vibration will have travelled about 2 feet before the next starts out. This distance is called the wave-length, and wave-length multiplied by frequency gives velocity. Thus, the higher the frequency of a note, the shorter its wave-length. Either of these numbers, frequency or wave-length, defines one particular note and tells us two things about it: which note on the scale is being played, and its pitch, whether high or low, treble or bass.

Just as mechanical vibrations include heart beats, earthquake waves, sound waves, music and inaudible ultra-sonic vibrations which seem so diverse to us but which only differ in frequency and wave-length, so are radio waves, heat, light, ultra-violet, and X-rays all related. They are all electromagnetic waves of different frequencies, distinguished from one another as the music of a piccolo is distinguished from that of a double bass. These electro-magnetic waves travel at the astonishing velocity of 186,000 miles, or 300,000,000 metres, each second. As in the case of sound waves, frequency multiplied by wave-length gives velocity. Thus, radio waves broadcast at a frequency of 1,000,000 vibrations a second (called one megacycle) each have a wave-length of 300 metres. The

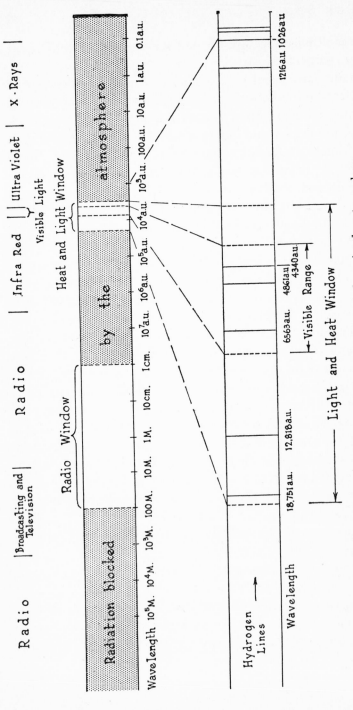

Electro-magnetic spectrum showing two windows in the atmosphere which allow visible waves and some radio waves to reach the surface.

two multiplied together give the velocity. Either number defines a particular wave.

Radio wave-lengths in the broadcast range are measured in metres, short radio waves in inches, heat waves in hundredths of an inch, and visible light in hundred thousandths of an inch; ultra-violet and X-rays have shorter wave-lengths still. All vibrate an enormous number of times a second. Radio waves are defined in terms either of wave-length or of frequency, but short waves are usually specified in terms of wave-length measured in Ångström units, each of which is one hundred millionth of a centimetre.

We enjoy light and colour in our lives, just as we enjoy symphonic music, without thinking what constitutes either; but physicists and composers find it useful to analyse what they see or hear. Sunlight, like a symphony, is a great mélange, but it can be broken into its parts by a prism. We see examples of this in the coloured flashes of pure light from diamonds, dewdrops, and rainbows. Each individual colour in a rainbow represents light of a particular frequency and wave-length and may be likened to a note on the piano. When a musician hears a note, whether it is played alone or as part of a symphony, he can tell two things about it: what note it is, and whether it is treble or bass. A physicist, too, can tell two things about an individual colour or "line" of light. He can say what element was excited to create it and how hot that element was at the time. The lines due to a single element may be compared, for example, to all the "C's" or all the "D's" on the scale; and the temperature of the element is comparable to the pitch of sound.

C notes have characteristic frequencies, such as 32, 64, 128, 256, 512, 1024 vibrations a second; similarly the element hydrogen, if suitably excited, gives rise to lines of light of characteristic wave-lengths, including those of 1216, 4340, 4861, and 6563 Ångström units. It was the strong red line of

6563 Ångström units, created by fast-moving hydrogen gas on the sun, which astronomers saw through the telescope at Climax as they watched for solar flares. Other light could not penetrate the filters in the telescope.

By analysing light, spectroscopists can determine the elements present in the source. The gas helium, indeed, takes its name from the Greek word for sun because its spectral lines were discovered in sunlight before anyone had found the element on earth. The temperature of the source can be estimated by noting which are the dominant lines among those peculiar to each element. If the source is only warm, it emits heat but no light. We all know this, for we recognize that a red-hot poker is not as hot as a poker at white heat. As an object is heated, the dominant radiation changes to shorter and shorter wave-lengths with higher and higher frequencies until at a temperature of about 100,000 degrees, the object emits ultra-violet light, and at about 1,000,000 degrees it emits X-rays. Below the opposite end of the spectrum lie waves of increasingly longer wave-length and lower frequency called infra-red and radio waves.

Careful examination and analysis of the light of the sun to determine which lines are represented enable the spectroscopist to identify not only the elements but also the temperature of different parts. Until rockets and satellites broke through the roof of the atmosphere, much of the evidence for this was indirect, for humans do not notice any but light and heat waves and are cut off from most of the other waves by the benign umbrella of the earth's atmosphere. Even the waves that can penetrate the atmosphere are often partly absorbed, as the disgruntled sun-bather can attest when clouds come between him and the sun.

It is well that the earth's atmosphere protects us from the electro-magnetic energy that floods the universe, for X-rays and ultra-violet light would produce severe burns which might kill us now and which would certainly have prohibited the development of living creatures by preventing the formation of the necessary large molecules.

Through spectroscopy and the satellites and rockets, we have gained a better idea of the shape and nature of the sun. It looks a little like the end of a jelly roll. In the middle is the round yellow photosphere, the part we see every day. This is separated by the red rim of the chromosphere from the paler yellow-green corona. And all three are linked by a variety of eruptions and imperfections, such as sun-spots, solar flares, and prominences which burst through the outer layers from the hot interior.

The photosphere has a temperature of about 10,000 degrees Fahrenheit and radiates most strongly the heat and light waves and those ultra-violet rays which conveniently enough penetrate the atmosphere and reach us through the visible window.

The layer immediately above the photosphere was first seen in total eclipses as a red rim and was called the chromosphere. Because the chromosphere is much hotter than the sun's surface, it radiates light of higher frequency. But this ultra-violet light does not penetrate our atmosphere and so could not be photographed until rockets carried cameras above the atmosphere.

One of the brightest "colours" in the chromosphere is the invisible ultra-violet light of precisely 1216 Ångström units. This wave-length, called the Lyman alpha line, is radiated by hydrogen at a temperature of tens of thousands of degrees and so tells astronomers both the composition and the temperature of the chromosphere.

Above the chromosphere lies the faint but vast corona seen only during total eclipses. Its strange and awesome brilliance casts a faint greenish light of unforgettable beauty which terrified early man. The corona was suspected to be even hotter than the chromosphere and to emit X-rays of short

wave-lengths. To prove this supposition, measurements of the
X-ray flux had to be taken above the atmosphere during a
total eclipse, when the rest of the sun would be hidden. On
October 12, 1958, in the only total eclipse during the IGY, the
necessary data were obtained. The U.S.S. *Point Defiance* had
been sent to the Danger Islands, in the mid-Pacific, which lay
in the path of totality. As the moon passed in front of the face

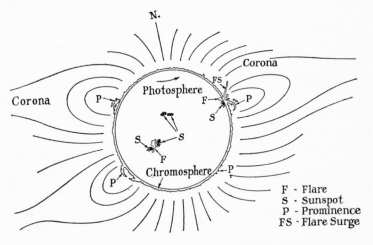

Diagrammatic representation of major solar activity.

of the sun, six instrumented rockets were fired in sequence
from the deck of the ship. The information which they telemetered back showed that at totality (when both the photosphere and the chromosphere were hidden) the visible and
ultra-violet radiation dropped to a low value, but the X-rays
coming from the still-visible corona continued strong. The
thin corona, more tenuous than most laboratory vacuums,
emits X-rays of wave-lengths of 10 to 100 Ångström units,
indicating a normal temperature of about 1,000,000 degrees
Centigrade.

The path of totality of an eclipse is usually so narrow that it

rarely lies over important places, but interestingly enough the
same 1958 eclipse at sunset was total over the large telescopes
of the observatory at Santiago, Chile.

Thus far we have been considering the sun in a quiet state.
It is evident to us all that the total heat radiated by the sun
does not vary greatly from year to year. This average state,
however, is interrupted by cyclical and irregular disturbances;
for superimposed on the tremendous background radiation are
many small and irregular variations which, although they do
not greatly influence the sun's heat, produce other terrestrial
effects quite out of proportion to their energy. Among the
varying features are small rising and falling jets of hot gases
called spicules and prominences; much larger, brief outbursts
called solar flares; longer-lived complexes of sun-spots; and
bright patches accompanying them known as faculae and
plages. These erupt from the photosphere through the outer
layers of the sun, knitting them together, and presenting fascinating problems for observation and interpretation. Chief of
these variations are sun-spots, which were first recorded two
thousand years ago by the Chinese. When the sun's brilliance
was partially filtered by mist, they noticed some particularly
large spots and called them "flying birds." Others were observed through the first telescopes, between 1608 and 1615;
Galileo's insistence that they were blemishes on the most perfect of heavenly bodies placed him in disfavour with the
Church.

The nature of sun-spots has long intrigued astronomers, and
one of the objectives of the Polar Years and of the IGY was to
try to discover what causes them. The problem has not yet
been fully resolved, but much is now known. Sun-spots grow
and disperse intermittently; they rotate with the sun once every
twenty-seven days and may last for several revolutions. Although they look small on the face of the sun, they are really
vast, a minor one being larger than the earth. Associated with

sun-spots are strong magnetic fields; the spots always occur in pairs, one of north and the other of south magnetic polarity. They are known to be giant vortices, or funnels, which appear dark because the gas in them is cooler than the rest of the surface. It has been recently suggested that these vortices are parts of belts of rotating gas within the sun which protrude from its surface to form sun-spots.

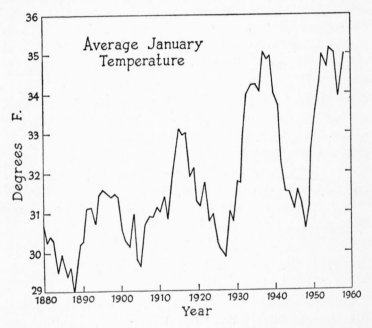

Chart shows temperature in New York varying with cycles of greatest sun-spot activity.

The number and the position of sun-spots is not constant. In 1843, after sun-spots had been under observation for more than two centuries, Heinrich Schwabe reported that they fluctuate in number and size by periodic cycles averaging a little more than eleven years. Associated with the sun-spot cycle are many other interesting effects, such as solar flares, which tend to increase in number and intensity at sun-spot maxima. By good fortune the IGY coincided with the most intense maximum yet recorded. These effects were pronounced, and numerous large solar flares were observed.

A solar flare had first been spotted on September 1, 1859, by Richard Carrington. He had projected an image of the sun on a screen so that he could sketch a group of giant sun-spots, when, as he says, he noticed that "within the area of the great north group, two patches of intensely bright white light broke out. Seeing the outburst to be very rapidly on the increase and being somewhat flurried by the surprise, I hastily ran to call someone to witness the exhibition with me and, on returning within sixty seconds, was mortified to find that it was already much changed and enfeebled." This astonishing event, which was noticed by at least one other observer, was exceptional. No solar flare of equal brilliance has been noted in the century since, and indeed no more were seen until 1892 when G. E. Hale invented a spectrograph capable of photographing the sun in the light of a single line.

Flares were found to be great outbursts of hot hydrogen. Because in temperature and composition they are different from the rest of the sun's surface, they can be seen, as at Climax, through a filter which only transmits the particular wavelength by which they shine most brightly.

Thirty hours after the solar flare, Carrington noticed a sizeable magnetic storm and brilliant displays of aurora, which, he suggested, had been caused by the flare. There is no doubt now that he was correct, that solar flares do cause striking effects in the earth's magnetic field, in aurora, and in radio transmission. The violence of these outbursts was demonstrated in an experiment performed in California in August 1957. Within a few minutes of the first observation of a large solar flare, rockets carrying instruments were fired above the atmosphere. They recorded X-rays of wave-lengths as short as 1 or 2 Ångström units. Such unusually short wave-lengths indicate that above the solar flare temperatures as high as 10,000,000 degrees Centigrade were being generated in the sun's corona.

Flares vary widely in size and frequency. With few sunspots, only one or two small flares, each lasting only a few minutes, may occur in a month, but during years of peak solar activity there may be several each day, some of enormous power, often visible for over an hour. The cause of flares and their exact nature is not known, but their size, their catastrophic nature, and the powerful effects that they have upon the earth are unmistakable. They are violent explosions which in a few minutes may grow as large as vast sun-spots and cover ten billion square miles. By means of these flares the sun ejects jets of tenuous gas which, moving at hundreds of miles a second through space, slam into the earth's atmosphere as gigantic shock waves. The most powerful of them squash the earth's magnetic field, play havoc with communications, and induce auroral displays that light up half the earth. These violent bursts of radiation and atomic particles have been called solar shock waves, or magnetic typhoons. They constitute one of the major factors disturbing the "climate" of nearby space and may well prove hazardous for space travel.

Below are listed the effects which flares can produce, but because the jets of gas are directional and often miss the earth, not all these phenomena are observed every time.

1. A burst of reddish light, visible through filters, which reaches the earth in eight minutes. These waves travel 186,000 miles a second.

2. A flash of ultra-violet light which reaches the earth in eight minutes and produces sudden ionospheric and magnetic disturbances.

3. A burst of short-wave radio "noise," which also takes eight minutes to reach the earth.

4. A flux of low-energy cosmic rays, high-speed atoms, and electrons, which takes half an hour to reach the earth and

which has been observed on less than a dozen occasions, most strongly on February 23, 1956. These particles travel about 50,000 miles a second.

5. A stream of slower atoms and electrons which takes about twenty-four hours to reach the earth and gives rise to auroral displays and magnetic and ionospheric effects. These travel about 1,000 miles a second.

Better understood than solar flares are solar prominences such as I saw at Climax. These are great clouds and jets of gas, forever playing over the surface of the sun, rising to heights of 50,000 miles and more, but lacking the strong terrestrial effects of flares. Presumably this is because they are less violent and do not escape to bombard the earth's upper atmosphere.

Another interesting point about the sun which was clarified during the IGY was the nature of the green flash often seen at sunset and less frequently at sunrise. It had been maintained by some that this was a momentary optical illusion, but the observers of the autumn sunset at the south pole station disproved it. There, over the level snow fields, the sun sank so slowly for the winter night that the green flash was visible for half an hour. In addition, both Father D. J. K. O'Connell, director of the Vatican City Observatory, and Professor M. Minnaert of Holland took photographs and published papers proving that the green flash is due to diffraction of the sun's light by the atmosphere. The green flash is as real as the flash of colour in a diamond or a rainbow.

CHAPTER 4

※

GEOPHYSICAL
JAMBOREE

AUGUST–SEPTEMBER 1957

Later in July I returned from Colorado to Toronto to plunge again into the preparations for the XIth General Assembly of the International Union of Geodesy and Geophysics, which was to open in Toronto at the end of August. Whereas the International Geophysical Year was a great but brief world-wide project in geophysics, the IUGG had long been the less-publicized but permanent forum for international geophysics. The IUGG holds a general meeting every three years, and it tries to distribute these and its smaller meetings fairly among the sixty member nations.

International science is organized chiefly in two forms, both with useful but different functions. On the one hand are the operational agencies, such as in the United Nations, the World Health Organization and the World Meteorological Organization, which were established with the definite objectives of improving health and forecasting weather. These bodies have large budgets and permanent staffs; their meetings are attended by civil servants and involve the execution of governmental policies. On the other hand are a dozen unions, some almost a century old, corresponding to the main branches of science. Their function is to enable scientists to meet and discuss science. They have official recognition, and government as well as private scientists attend, but they are not bound by government policies and diplomatic usages. The fees paid by the member countries are small and the unions have no permanent staffs. They do not carry out broad routine tasks, for their function is to promote science, not to utilize it. The International Union of Geodesy and Geophysics is one of these unions.

The unions function in three ways. First of all, they maintain permanent services and commissions, often located at a university, where all the records for a particular subject are sent from all over the world for collation and publication. In the case of the IUGG there are several such centres for different subjects. The headquarters for geodetic data is in Paris, and all observations that might further the task of measuring the size and shape of the earth are collected there. All records of earthquakes obtained by six hundred seismological observatories are sent to Strasbourg and Cambridge; a few selected stations send reports of large earthquakes by cable to Washington, whence preliminary information is immediately made available to the press and to relief organizations. Standards for the analysis of variations in sea water are prepared and maintained at Copenhagen; the wobble of the earth's axis is studied at Naples; geomagnetic data of different kinds are collected at Gottingen, de Bilt, and Tortosa. Anyone wishing information on the world's earthquakes or on geomagnetism may obtain published summaries, instead of having to write to six hundred seismological stations or two hundred geomagnetic observatories.

Because most of this work is done by men and women who

love to do it, by professors in their spare time and by their dedicated assistants, astonishingly little cost is involved. It says a great deal for the devotion and very little for the advertising acumen of scientists that such extensive work should have gone on for years with so little support and no public acknowledgement. The budget for the IUGG for 1958 was $80,000, most of which went for research, publications, and travel expenses. Most of the unions have no paid staff and their headquarters is in the office of whichever scientist has been elected secretary. This frugality may be startling, but it has its rewards. The unions, having no large benefactors, are almost wholly free from interference and can pursue without fear or favour whatever course a majority of the delegates and members decide upon.

The second function of the international unions is to sponsor world-embracing ventures in science, such as the International Geophysical Year. The third function is to hold regular meetings, such as the one in Toronto, which constitute the chief forums for international exchange by leading scientists.

The XIth General Assembly was to have met in one of the American republics. Unfortunately, eighteen months before the meetings were to take place, its government suffered a rather violent upheaval, and the scientists there asked to be relieved of the responsibility. Five or six bales of cablegrams and letters, and three months later, the bemused geophysicists of Toronto awoke to the realization that they would be playing host to the largest meeting of the world's geophysicists to be held during the IGY. They had but a few months in which to transform themselves from scientists into convention managers.

Anyone who has ever taken part in one of these affairs knows the basic requirements for a successful meeting. The first is a town sufficiently large to absorb the influx of 1,500 people without complete dislocation of its civic housekeeping.

Ideally the town should contain a place where the 1,500 people can be housed and fed within easy reach of the lecture halls in which they are to meet, give their papers, and hold their discussions. Unnecessary complications arise when the scientists have to stay in hotels at one side of the city and hold their meetings five miles away, with heavy traffic in between. The lecture rooms themselves must provide certain amenities; nothing is more distressing than to attempt to show slides with a defective lantern in an ill-ventilated room that cannot be darkened. For the peace of mind and well-being of the delegates there must also be good post offices, an adequate number of telephones, maps, signs, and information bureaus staffed by linguists. Facilities must be provided for the press, since scientists have at last realized that the public has an interest in what they are doing. Most important of all is the creation of an easy, friendly atmosphere to dispel the wariness natural among members of diverse groups. The scientific papers given during the day are most thoroughly discussed over drinks or dinner, and the resolutions that must be passed at formal assemblies are often most easily hammered out at lunch.

The University of Toronto, with its residences and lecture halls, was admirably suited to house both delegates and meetings. The committee members could devote themselves, therefore, to overcoming mechanical difficulties and to promoting amity.

Typical of the many mechanical difficulties were the banking arrangements. On the first day of registration we collected $20,000 in cash, in every known currency, I think, except gold bars and wampum.

Ensuring a desirable atmosphere entailed just as much effort. The three general assemblies preceding this one had been held in Oslo, in Brussels, and in Rome. Even Toronto's most ardent admirers would not suggest that as a city it holds the historic interest of these three capitals, but we knew we could rely on the hospitality of its citizens and the beauty of its surrounding countryside. Lacking a Roman forum to display to visitors, we would make do with Niagara Falls. The hospitality, too, was unusual. The opening party was an official reception given by the Province of Ontario, on the face of it a solemn and ceremonious occasion. It was held in the Royal Ontario Museum, just around the corner from the university —an admirable location providing both propinquity and spaciousness. It did not, however, provide the amenities considered by the caterers as essential to the serving of food and drink. But these ingenious men were equal to the task. They took over an ancient Chinese tomb for their kitchen. After the delegates had made their way past the official reception line, the first sight that greeted them was a neat maid efficiently concocting hot hors d'oeuvres in the lee of a stone camel.

To the bewildered eye of the onlooker these large meetings appear to be a cross between a scientific forum and a circus, and for the unfortunate scientist involved in their organization the circus aspect seems to predominate. He may echo the query of the public: "Why hold these troublesome and expensive meetings merely to allow scientists to listen to a lot of papers that they could equally well read in any of a number of scholarly publications in the peace and quiet of their own libraries?" The answer is simple. These gatherings further the internationalism of science since they provide continuing opportunities for scientists to meet each other, to learn of each other's work, and to cross national boundaries and see how others live and work. The question I am most frequently asked in connection with the IGY is whether there was a genuine exchange of information between nations and especially between East and West. There *was* a genuine exchange, and it was possible because the men and women concerned had been accustomed for years to meet in a friendly atmosphere to discuss new information, ideas, and discoveries. The International Geophysical Year was but a vaster, more comprehensive version of these regular sessions, conducted in the same atmosphere of scientific enquiry.

As I write, I have just returned from a small meeting in Paris. My colleagues included a Spanish Jesuit, a Hungarian Jew who had immigrated to the United States as a boy, a Japanese professor, an ardent member of the Soviet Communist party, and a scion of an ancient and aristocratic Italian family of astronomers. All was harmony because, however different our view on other matters might be, we had a common bond in science and geophysics—hence the simplicity and ease of scientific meetings as opposed to political or business ones. This is not due to the sound reason and sweet temper of the scientists involved, which are no greater and no less than in any other group of well-educated, sophisticated men and women, but rather it is due to the nature of the subject discussed. It is a great deal simpler to work out a plan for charting the world's oceans than it is to discuss freedom, wealth, politics, or religion.

CHAPTER 5

ROMANIA

OCTOBER 1957

The Toronto meetings were scarcely over when with a feeling of rising excitement I left my cluttered office, the lecture rooms, the stacks of unused documents, the bills and thank-you letters and set out to visit the Communist half of the world for the first time. I had been invited by the Romanian Government to visit and lecture on geophysics at various universities and institutes.

The invitation had both surprised and intrigued me, for I had no connection with Romania and I knew that very few Westerners went there. But I could see no reason for not accepting. I was not engaged in secret work; no one could object to my lecturing on mountain-building, and I might learn a great deal about the geology and geophysics of eastern Europe. As a rather conservative, retired colonel, I was not greatly disturbed by the thought that I might be accused of being a Communist sympathizer. Romanian scientists had attended the meetings in Toronto, and if the president of an international union could not pay a return visit to discuss geophysics,

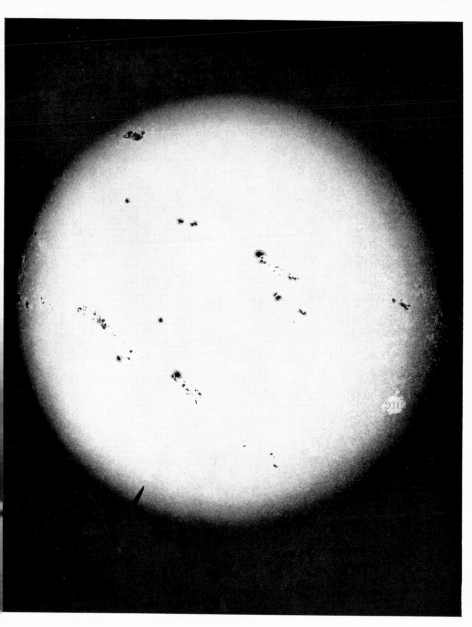

Sun-spots as seen through a telescope.

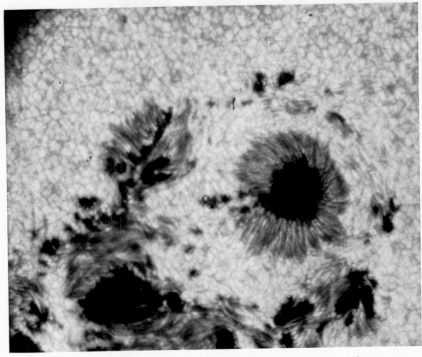

Detail of sun-spots and granulation on the sun's surface as photographed from a high-altitude balloon.

Mirrors of a coelostat are adjusted to reflect the sun's image into a solar telescope at the Shternberg Astronomical Institute, Moscow. Moscow University is seen in the background.

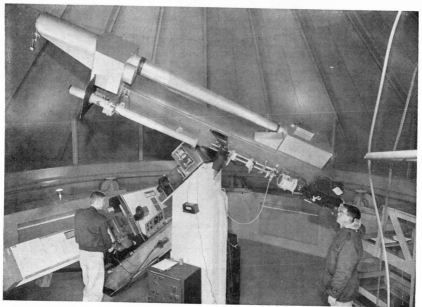

The five-inch coronagraph and spectrograph at the high-altitude observatory at Climax, Colorado. Observer at right is inspecting the solar-flare patrol instrument.

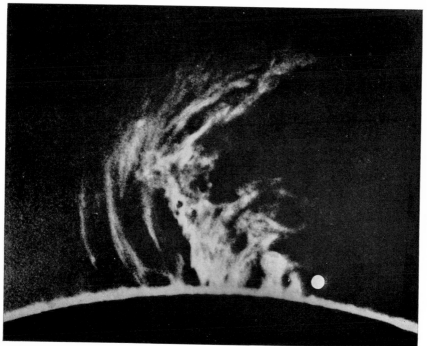

A large solar prominence, 140,000 miles high. The small white disc indicates the relative size of the earth.

Balloon, parachute, and mounted instrument package for high-altitude solar research are readied for launching in Minnesota.

The fourth of six rockets is fired from *U.S.S. Point Defiance* during the total solar eclipse of October 12, 1958, at the Danger Islands, Central Pacific Ocean.

The firing of the first successful Vanguard rocket on March 17, 1958. A small test sphere entered into orbit and became the second U. S.–IGY satellite.

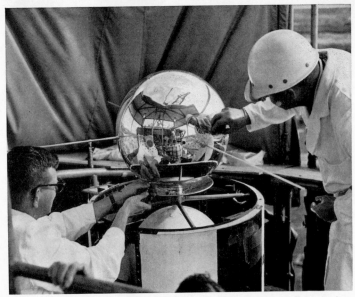

A highly polished twenty-inch Navy Vanguard satellite is installed in a rocket at Cape Canaveral, Florida.

Explorer VII, last and largest of the satellites in the U. S.–IGY program, is inspected before its launching on October 13, 1959.

Launching of the U. S. Air Force's Lunar Probe III on November 8, 1958, which failed to reach the moon when its third stage did not fire.

The instrument container and part of the parachute of a Soviet research rocket recovered after carrying 4,840 pounds of experimental equipment to an altitude of 132 miles in May 1957.

Replica of Sputnik III, which was launched on May 15, 1958. It carried 2,130 pounds of instruments and power-supply source.

The firing of a United States Aerobee rocket at the research launching site at Churchill, Manitoba, Canada. The antennae are used to track the rocket. Instruments on different rockets measure different properties of the upper atmosphere, aurora, and cosmic rays.

then there is neither much use in having international organizations nor much hope for world understanding.

Nevertheless, it was with some misgiving that I left Toronto. It was that gay northern season, gayer than southern springtime, when the maples light the woods like flame—a brilliant presage to the dark, cold poignancy of winter.

The chill and apprehension vanished overnight; I was in Europe again, caught up in its fascination and busy with the problems of my journey. They were not trivial. During one short day in Paris, I twice had to visit the Canadian Embassy, the Hungarian and Romanian Consulates, and the Hungarian Embassy. They seemed to be located in out-of-the-way places. With the greatest rush and difficulty I got all my visas from the uncomprehending and secretive officials in their untidy little offices, and finally I was at the platform to catch the Arlberg-Orient Express. The Romanians had suggested that I fly, but perhaps under the influence of spy movies I chose this famous train. My feeling of triumphant satisfaction as I climbed onto the sleeper marked Paris-Bucuresti turned to disappointment when I saw that the corridor was deserted; the beautiful blonde spy, the two Englishmen discussing cricket, the German agent, and the other *dramatis personae* must have already gone to bed. I did the same.

Next morning the sun glistened on the first autumn snow on the Alps. The big wet flakes had reached the tracks at the Arlberg tunnel, but in Austria the snow had turned to rain. The churches reached up from empty fields to point to heaven with slim spires or with the stubby thumbs of Byzantine domes.

As the train rattled out of the defiles and entered the broad and smiling valleys of Austria, the clouds cleared and the sun shone on the brown forests and the white peaks above. The face of Austria was coloured like that of a weather-beaten old man, and in the evening as we approached Vienna and the border I felt the old world dying.

The Vienna station epitomized the West. It was new, brilliantly lighted, and gay with people; its kiosks were full of good things. As the crowd swarmed off the train, I lingered in the door of my compartment, and an American said to me: "Aren't you getting off? This is the end of the line!" Unwittingly, he had expressed my worst fears; so I got off to take a last look at the West and to buy an emergency supply of chocolate, cheese, and fruit.

When I returned, the modern express had vanished and a porter told me that I would find my car on another track. It was in a dark corner at the farthest end of the station, linked together with one other through-coach and several dishevelled freight cars into a mean little train of some of the oldest rolling stock in Europe. The porter said that the cars came back from the east stripped and filthy but that he, fortunately, would be leaving it at the border.

More ominous even than the train were the people on the platform. Several thick, squat men in long leather trench coats and caps stood and stared at each passenger in turn. Several policemen, and an Austrian soldier in a dark green uniform and a Tyrolean hat, stood watching them, silent and armed. The half-dozen other passengers slipped down the platform, climbed on board, and locked themselves in their compartments. So did I.

I did not go to bed, but waited to see the border. It took us a long time to reach it, and even longer to get across. There were long waits and much shouting. Outside were flood-lights and soldiers with rifles and fixed bayonets. Two sets of officials came to my compartment. One talked for a while, but seeing that I could not understand him, repeated, "Geld?" several times. I said, "Nein!" and he went away. Another scrutinized my passport and took it. The train picked up speed and ran steadily on. It had crossed the border and there was nothing to see outside and nothing to do inside except go to bed.

When I wakened, the train had stopped. I roused myself to look out and saw that we were in a big station. It was Budapest. I quickly got dressed and left my compartment intending to explore. I poked my head out of the window, but the view was not encouraging. The station was nearly empty, and except for several policemen and two or three groups of security guards, the few people looked incredibly poor and dejected. The special police, dressed in peaked caps and long overcoats of light blue cloth, were impressive in their armament: a revolver, a three-foot night-stick hanging from a wide black belt, and a Sten gun carried at the ready. An old woman with a pinched face tried to sell thin newspapers printed in Hungarian, and four youths, balanced on little ladders, scrubbed the car windows as though their lives depended on it. No doubt they were glad to have any kind of job, but their vigorous efforts had little effect. They had no water!

Soon the train pulled out. The city, as we passed through it, appeared to be completely dead. There was no traffic, few people moved, no smoke came from the factory chimneys. On the outskirts we passed a low hill, its sides marked by zig-zag trenches. On the top, a solitary tank with a big gun manoeuvred slowly and aimlessly about. No one was in sight. If the city was a lifeless head, the country resembled the corpse.

I suppose that any countryside is generally empty of people, but that day, a year after the revolt, the Hungarian plain seemed to me oppressively, ominously deserted and still. In general appearance it was much like the Po River valley in Italy, but it lacked any gaiety whatsoever. No children played. No one waved at the train. Scarcely a wagon ever passed on the dirt roads. There were no tractors in the fields, no cars in the towns, and few people on the village streets. I had never been in Hungary before so I could make no comparisons, but the impression I got was of a land poverty-stricken and apathetic to a degree I had never seen elsewhere and did not want ever to see again.

Although I had been warned that there would be no diner, and was fully prepared to breakfast on chocolate and cheese, I ventured down through the train in search of one. It was there, an old car, empty save for two wistfully cheerful Hungarian waiters in faded blue uniforms threadbare and ragged at the cuffs. After some difficulty with language I got them to bring me an egg and a roll and some poor plum jam. I asked for coffee but they brought tea, a miserable approximation to the genuine article which seemed to be an infusion of local herbs doctored with lemon and sugar. They charged me at least ten times too much for this simple meal. When I pointed out that they had put the decimal point in the wrong place in calculating the conversion, they were not abashed as they made the correction, but smiled so sadly that I tipped them twice too much into the bargain.

At lunch I was again their sole support except for a German, who had a bottle of beer. The one main course was an incredibly bad stew or goulash, mostly of potatoes, with a little tomato and a few pieces of very tough meat of some unidentifiable animal. The only dessert was chocolate biscuits wrapped in tinfoil, which I was soon to recognize as the highest luxury available in eastern Europe.

Late in the afternoon we came to the Romanian border, which was just as complicated to cross as that separating eastern and western Europe. Between the two border stations there was much shunting and stopping, and the engine, the diner, and all the crew, including the porter, were changed. Soldiers with fixed bayonets or tommy guns stood about, and the whole train was thoroughly searched.

Just as we reached the foothills of the Carpathians, it got dark. The train puffed up dark valleys, between mountains that I could scarcely see. I was too discouraged even to look to see if there was a Romanian diner on the train. In any case I did not want to waste the food I had bought, so I sat sadly in my compartment and ate it.

Next morning I awoke as we approached Bucharest. I was beginning to think that the countryside and railways of one European plain look much like those of another, when I was surprised to notice a large army camp full of soldiers. A little farther along, a train-load of artillery under canvas was partly hidden behind some cars on a siding.

We entered the city and stopped at a station which was noticeably more active and in better trim than those in Hungary. A dozen Romanian scientists and officials were waiting on the platform to greet me. I was warmly welcomed by Dr. A. Demetrescu, the courtly senior astronomer and geophysicist of Romania, and his colleagues: Drs. Constantinescu, Popovici, Sabba Stanescu, and two interpreters; Domnisoara (Miss) Carin Pavelescu; and Mr. Pamfil Diplan. Drs. Demetrescu and Constantinescu had been the Romanian representatives to the meetings in Toronto, but the other members of the welcoming committee I had not met before. The four doctors comprised the Romanian National Committee on Geodesy and Geophysics.

Russian Pobeda taxis took us all to the Athenée Palace Hotel on one side of the main square in front of the former Royal Palace. My room was large, clean, and comfortable, and it was well looked after by diligent German-speaking Schwabian maids. After some breakfast, the two interpreters proposed a short walk through the centre of the town.

Bucharest was much larger and more attractive than I had expected. It is a city of a million people and its handsome avenues, parks, and buildings justify its nickname of the "Paris of eastern Europe." But the automobiles for which the fine roads were built had vanished. There were very few vehicles but a great number of people walking, among them many Russian soldiers.

We walked on, crossed a market, and climbed a hill to the National Assembly building and the Patriarchie, the principal cathedral of the Romanian Greek Orthodox Church. It was open but not very crowded. I gathered that churches were allowed to remain open if they at least half-heartedly followed the party line, because in this way propaganda could be brought effectively to those who would not otherwise listen. This church was, of course, a show-place, and I was not surprised to find a priest and a few old women praying and lighting candles—which would demonstrate to groups of visitors that there was religious freedom.

My guides next took me to the headquarters of the Office for Cultural and Scientific Relations with Foreign Countries. It was in a fine old mansion that no doubt formerly belonged to some wealthy family. The senior official who received me had a dry, hard manner, and the hollowness of his pleasantries were greatly heightened by his extraordinary glasses. They were large and the outside surface was mirrored. Presumably he could see me, but I could only see two great gold discs in a blank face as expressionless as that of a bullfrog. Over Turkish coffee and Tuica (plum brandy) we discussed my tour. I had long ago decided that the only sensible behaviour for a guest in a Communist country was to be polite and reasonably agreeable. Rudeness would show the West in a poor light and keep me from seeing the scientific work I wanted to see. I had no intention of compromising myself or of pretending that I favoured Communism in the least, but I surmised that they wished to impress me with their scientific work and that, knowing I was not in sympathy with their politics, they would not raise matters which would be embarrassing. My host, for such I suppose he might be called, said nothing to which I had to take exception, and our conversation, like a bat, flittered aimlessly back and forth, chased by the interpreters.

We returned to the hotel and at 3 p.m. were served a lengthy lunch in the marble and plush main dining-room of what had once been a fine hotel. Unlike the upstairs, which was still efficiently run, the dining-rooms and meals were atrocious. Service took a very long time, and weiners, sauerkraut, and corn porridge did not seem suitable fare for such ornate surroundings.

After lunch I dutifully followed my guides through two art galleries, one of them a former royal palace. King Carol's royal cipher was still discernible in the plaster mouldings in some of the rooms. There were two magnificent El Greco's and a group of older paintings vaguely labelled Flemish school or XVII-century Italian, but the place of honour was given to a large display of the works of two Romanians, Grigorescu and Luchian, the latter a rather unimpressive Impressionist, the former an enthusiast for peasants, gypsies, and very large oxen. I noticed with some pleasure that the paintings were titled in English. This, I assumed, perhaps falsely, was for the enlightenment of the large delegations from the underdeveloped countries which travel through all Iron Curtain countries and for whom English is the lingua franca.

At eight o'clock, without pausing to dine, we went, in pursuit of more culture, to the main concert hall to hear the Second State Orchestra (the First was touring Jugoslavia) and a large chorus in Berlioz's "Damnation of Faust." We returned to the hotel, at 11:30 p.m. and, like the other guests, settled down to the main meal of the day. These extraordinary eating hours were the norm in Romania and quickly produced a feeling of dyspepsia and lethargy. As far as I could judge, the regime had exaggerated the normally late hours of southern Europe for the deliberate purpose of stupefying the people. Nothing saps the energy faster than to work from seven to three without a break, to have an excessively late lunch, and to go to bed after midnight full of a large and soggy meal.

The next day work started, and on that and succeeding days I was taken to the laboratories and offices of the Bucharest Observatory, the University of Bucharest, the School of Mines, the Geological Survey, and a newly organized school for petroleum technology. Most of the senior staff and the older technicians had held the same positions under King Carol, under Prince Michael, during the German occupation, and through the shifting regimes of the Russian Communist domination. Some of them probably remember Queen Marie. They were all the scientists the country had and they were indispensable. In the Communist countries I repeatedly noticed that scientists are the most durable of officials. This is not because they are turncoats, but because their work is non-political. They were all enthusiastic Romanians and that sufficed. Their Communist masters, needing scientists and having none to spare, avoided asking questions that might be too embarrassing. So did I. It was enough for me to see the skill and loving care with which they tended their ancient telescopes ("This one is the largest in eastern Europe outside of Russia; that one was newly installed for the IGY solar program"), their pride in the books and maps of their country which they had published, and the devotion of the favoured graduate students allowed to work in the faded laboratories of an ancient professor.

It was not a bright new world. Theirs was a hard struggle amid desperate poverty upon which they put the bravest faces. Only by a chance remark did I gain an inkling of what it must be like to be the intellectuals of a proud people oppressed for seventeen years by an occupying army. One student said to me: "I have spent four years learning Russian, but only so that I can read translations of American text-books since we cannot get the English originals." Another professor in a threadbare suit questioned me about salaries in Canada and the West. "No," he said, "not in dollars, but in something I can understand—how many pounds of beefsteak will your salary buy?" When I had answered him, he turned to his colleagues who hushed him ("The walls have ears") and bitterly said: "You see, they lied."

For the most part we avoided such discussions, which were useless under the circumstances and embarrassing to everyone, and turned our attention to the astronomical and geophysical instruments, the geomagnetic and gravity maps, and the charts showing the location of the major earthquakes of the area. They showed me rock specimens, and I was able to assure them of resemblances, about which they had conjectured from available writings, between some of their peculiar rocks, asbestos and nepheline syenite in particular, and Canadian counterparts.

On another day I was taken to see the Government printing bureau. It was a vast affair in the best wedding-cake style of new Moscow—twelve stories high in the centre and covering seven acres. It had taken six years to build. Since I saw no other new building in Romania, except the cabinet offices facing a park in which still stood a large statue of Stalin, I concluded that its erection must have occupied most of the building industry of the country during that time.

Inside the front door was a large hall decorated with marble panels and carved doors and furnished with plush side chairs. Opening out of it was a concert auditorium. Both were said to be for the benefit of the workers, but since the auditorium had no seats in it and the hall was reserved for one dance a year, their use seemed limited. I was told that great emphasis was placed on the welfare of the workers, but the same official also admitted that the only parts of the building that had not yet been completed were the workers' club and workers' canteen, although a temporary canteen for two thousand was said to be functioning. Perhaps these amenities were not necessary in view of the eight hours of uninterrupted work which was the normal shift. The dishevelled and dispirited workers contrasted strongly with their palatial surroundings. The table setting might be fine, but they would have to wait for the jam until tomorrow.

In any case, the output appeared to be prodigious. The quality did not seem high, but there was immense activity. I was told that each day this vast plant produced 100,000 books, 50,000 magazines, and 50,000 pamphlets, as well as 5 daily and 15 weekly newspapers, the newspapers having a combined circulation of 2,500,000. Some people have expressed amazement at these figures. Although I cannot vouch for their accuracy, I think it possible that they are correct. The Communists are great propagandists; this plant was said to do 80 per cent of all the printing in Romania, so that even this output would provide only one or two books a person a year. Most of the books were school texts or Communist works, and all were cheaply printed and bound on automatic machinery in very large editions.

I had been invited to Romania to give four lectures on geophysics, and these provided my greatest surprise. The first lecture was to be given at the university in the evening. As we approached the hall, we saw that the corridor was full of people trying to get in. The hall was packed with people, who stood up and clapped as we made our way to the front and again applauded tumultuously when I had been introduced. Although I am a fairly experienced speaker, I had never known anything like it. I was astounded. My visit had not been tangibly publicized, and few of them could have heard of me anyway; and my topic, mountain-building, could not possibly generate such enthusiasm. I realized that these people were spontaneously expressing their pleasure at one of their rare contacts with the untrammelled West. I spoke with sentence-by-sentence interpretation for nearly an hour and a half, and received the same enthusiastic ovation when I had finished. It was very moving.

My visits and lectures in the capital concluded, I set out on field trips to see the geology. I had asked to see the Iron Gates where the Danube cuts through the Carpathian Mountains, and my hosts suggested a drive to Sinaia, Brașov-Stalin, and Cluj in Transylvania. In spite of the fact that the British Embassy had told me that the border was closed and that no one had been allowed near the Iron Gates for years, I was taken there by the very capable geologist who had mapped the region before the war. We spent two pleasant days driving and walking amid the grand scenery and fascinating geology of this classic region. We stayed in the spa on the site of Roman baths at Baile Herculane, and examined the ruins of the Roman fort and bridge across the Danube at Turnu-Severin. A Roman road, cut like a ledge alongside the river, passes through the most precipitous canyons on the Jugoslav side. From across the river one can see a great Roman inscription and make out the emperor's name, Trajanus. The Romanians made no bones about their pride in their Latin origin, which they claimed to date from the invasion by Trajan in A.D. 101–105. As they pointed out, the name of their country means "Roman," and they resent the efforts to make them forget it by changing the spelling on new coins to Rominia or Ruminia. Inasmuch as they have fought (and often been defeated by) Slavs and Turks for eighteen hundred years, and still retain a language which closely resembles Latin, it is probable that Romanians will continue to distrust the Russians and furtively hold their own views.

At the head of the rapids on the Danube we joined a party of Jugoslav and Romanian engineers and cruised in a river steamer back through the chasms by which the Danube crosses the Carpathians. It was a beautiful trip, and one that few Westerners have made for at least seventeen years. Cautiously at first, but more affably as the beer circulated, the engineers discussed the building of a Danube system to match the St. Lawrence sea-way. The plan is a century old but has always been held up for political reasons.

Many powerful tugs and barges of great size snorted up the river, flying the flags of all the Communist countries. Some were oil tankers, and one was a new Hungarian pleasure ship that I supposed was being exported to Russia across the Black Sea.

On the other trip three geologists and an interpreter drove me past Ploeşti, only now recovering from war-time bombing, to Sinaia, the mountain resort of kings and princes. The white cliffs of the mountains were glorious in the sun, their sides bright with golden beech trees and their peaks topped with dark green firs. We stopped often to examine the rocks. After crossing the old border into Austria-Hungary at Predeal in the mountains, we dined in Braşov-Stalin (the first is the old name, the other is the new official name, for in keeping with the rather grim situation in Romania, Stalin is still officially respected). Then we took the train to Cluj.

In the capital of Transylvania there are two universities and nearby an observatory where scientists were working on a program for the IGY. I was told that I was the first Western scientist to have visited the observatory in the past seventeen years, but that two Russians had been there. With the aid of interpreters I delivered two technical lectures on mountain-building, to the same wild acclaim as in Bucharest, but I was now used to the idea that it was my scarcity value, not my oratory, that aroused these displays.

It would be gratifying to think that the October of 1957 would forever be associated in the minds of the Romanian geophysicists with my paper on orogenesis, but it is certain that it will not. It will be remembered as the month of the launching of the first Russian Sputnik. It caused a tremendous to-do. Newspapers, radio, and loud-speakers carried no other news. The whole powerful propaganda machine spouted glory to the Soviets and the Communist party. Newspaper men descended upon me in droves demanding a statement. I considered my position rather carefully. Had I been in Toronto I should in all honesty have praised the great achievement loudly, but in Bucharest to do so seemed to me to smack of being a "fellow-traveller." I therefore said only that it was "interesting and what had been expected." Pressed, I said: "Everything has gone according to plan." This last secretly delighted some of the Romanians, who get a little tired of five-year plans, increased production programs, and other Communist plans of which they hear so much. Pressed further, I pointed out that really I knew nothing about the Sputnik, for I could neither read nor understand Romanian and in all the excitement everyone had forgotten to explain. This was just as we were about to begin lunch. Before the meal was over, the reporters were back with reams of teletyped news from abroad in French and English. They demanded that I read them and comment. I read, but I still said: "The Sputnik is interesting!"

Only after fourteen attempts was I left alone. So far as I know, two lines in one paper were all that was devoted to my entire visit to Romania.

CHAPTER 6

❊

THE NEW MOONS

The Sputnik placed in orbit while I was in Romania was the first of two dozen artificial satellites successfully launched by the end of 1959. Many people have seen them hurtling across the sky at twilight, but not everyone has realized that the plan to make them and to exchange the information which they gathered was part of the International Geophysical Year.[1]

Many scientists had talked about the idea, and a proposal made in 1953 by S. P. Singer of the United States at a conference at the University of Oxford led to detailed planning. On July 29, 1955, President Eisenhower announced that the United States Navy had been assigned the task of launching Vanguard satellites as part of the IGY program, and soon afterwards the Soviet Union said that they would do the same. No other nation has yet joined them.

Looking back, one wonders to what extent American scientists felt that through satellites they could open paths by which to investigate nearby space, and to what extent they

[1] The IGY agreements guaranteed the free exchange of scientific observations, including those obtained by artificial satellites. But there was never any plan to exchange information about the prime requisite for putting satellites into orbit: powerful and accurate rocket motors.

wished to jolt their military leaders into taking rocket development as seriously as the Soviets were known to be doing. Certainly great credit is due to the Soviets for the achievements which enabled them to launch the first satellites, and led the world to revise its estimate of Russian technical ability.

In scientific results the Americans and the Soviets are closely matched. The advantage of the better launching vehicles and larger satellites of the Soviets has been compensated for by the greater number of satellites launched by the Americans, their superior instrumentation, and their more efficient methods of tracking and of recovering data. By skillful design and use of miniature electronic components, the Americans have packed as many instruments into their smaller satellites as have the Soviets into their larger ones. Up to the end of 1959 the Americans attempted six times as many launchings as the Russians. Although half of them failed, the Americans still were successful in sixteen cases, against six successful Russian attempts. The diversity of orbits thus attained gave the Americans a wider sampling of space from which to draw conclusions. It was because of this that they were the first to recognize the Van Allen belts of intense radiation around the earth. This discovery is perhaps the most surprising yet made by artificial satellites, though the Russian photographs of the far side of the moon are the most sensational.

By April 12, 1961, when Yuri Gagarin, the first cosmonaut, circled the earth, the Russians had launched fourteen artificial planets and satellites, of which four still remained aloft. The Americans had successfully fired thirty-nine objects into space, of which no less than twenty-four were still in orbit around the earth or the sun.

To me, the most exciting fact about the satellite program is that the tremendous initial problems of starting the exploration of space were no more complex or diversified than the problems that continued to present themselves as the projects developed. Scientists were faced by results so surprising and so unexpected that they had to cope with each problem as it presented itself, adapting their instruments and their techniques to the unsuspected intricacies of space.

All satellites have been launched by rockets propelled by the same force that causes recoil in guns. A rocket may be thought of as a gun which uses the firing of its ammunition to propel itself; the gases spouting from its rear are its ammunition. To make the recoil powerful, thereby causing the rocket to travel far and fast, the weight of the ammunition or fuel must be large in relation to the rocket, and the fuel must be ejected with the maximum heat and speed.

Rockets all have the same ancestry. First invented by the Chinese as fireworks, military rockets up to 24 pounds in weight were used by European armies as artillery early in the nineteenth century. Intensive Russian experimentation began with the work of Nescherskii and Tsiolkovskii near the end of the nineteenth century. Early in this century Robert Goddard, an American, greatly improved the design and efficiency of small rockets. In the 1920's Hermann Oberth worked out the theory of rocket flight in greater detail, and during World War II his ideas were used by the Germans to produce the first large rocket—the V2—capable of carrying a ton about 200 miles horizontally, or 100 miles straight up. During the fading days of the war both Americans and Russians captured scientists who had been employed on this program and continued to utilize them and their ideas. Probably all the rockets used to launch satellites during the IGY were developments of the V2.

The principles of launching satellites can be briefly explained. As everyone knows, a ball tossed into the air falls again at the same place or nearby, according to the direction in which it is thrown. This is what simple rockets do. During the IGY many were fired to carry instruments up 100 or 200

miles. If, however, the ball is attached to a string and vigor-
ously twirled, it does not fall but goes round and round on
the end of the string. To start with, it must be given a rotary
motion, which must exceed a minimum speed if the string
is to be kept taut. A satellite revolves about the earth in exactly this fashion, for the attraction due to gravity takes the
place of the string. To place a satellite in orbit, a rocket must
first propel it above the atmosphere and at the same time im-
part to it a large and precise speed in a horizontal direction
so that it neither falls back to earth nor flies away into space.
The spent rocket-cases, of which there may be several for a
single satellite, either fall to earth or go into orbit themselves.
Friction of the air quickly slows a revolving ball unless it is
continually propelled, but if a satellite is placed in orbit
above the atmosphere during its initial firing, it will coast
around the earth on the end of its gravity-string for a long
time. In outer space, because there is little air to slow the satellite down, it has no need of a motor, but if it fails to get above
the atmosphere, or if it gradually loses speed and re-enters the
air, it will be quickly slowed and fall to earth.

To place a satellite 100 miles above the earth and accelerate
it to the required speed of about 18,000 miles an hour horizontally requires immense effort. The only engines which have
so far been successful are rocket engines blowing themselves
along by a blast of white hot gases emitted at tremendous
speed and pressure from the rear. They resemble airplane jet
engines, except that in outer space they cannot get air with
which to burn their fuel and therefore have to carry with them
liquid oxygen and kerosene. Sometimes other combinations,
such as benzene and nitric acid, or secret mixtures are used.

Once the fuel is consumed, the large empty fuel tank and
the engine become useless encumbrances and are jettisoned.
Another rocket with a smaller engine and less fuel takes over.
As many as four of these stages may be fired, each one attached

to the nose of its predecessor. The later stages are often little more than giant sky-rockets, hollow tubes filled with some relatively slow-burning explosive. In the nose of the last stage of all is the capsule carrying instruments. In some instances the capsule is ejected to orbit by itself; in others the last rocket-case retains the payload and is, itself, the satellite. Because of these two different techniques, it is difficult to compare the weights of satellites, but in all instances the weight of the capsule containing the instruments is a very small fraction, sometimes only a thousandth part, of the weight of the whole rocket at launching.

Astronomers, who felt a responsibility for keeping track of the new moons, suggested a numbering scheme similar to that used for comets. It was proposed that each satellite be given a name consisting of the year followed by one of the letters of the Greek alphabet. Thus the first three satellites were called 1957α, 1957β, and 1958α. Of course the satellites were also known by their popular names: Sputnik I, Sputnik II, and Explorer I.

In some cases satellites and protective covers are ejected from the last rocket stage by springs, so that a flock of as many as five pieces may spread out surprisingly quickly. These parts are numbered in order of brightness; for example, 1957 α 1 and 1957 α 2.

The design of the rocket vehicles and their satellites is extremely intricate, for some have over 100,000 parts. The controls of many early vehicles were built to function automatically, but the Explorer and Discoverer series responded to some instructions sent from the ground, and the Soviets are believed to have been able to correct the course of their Luniks. If everything works properly and the launching is successfully completed, the small satellite must be followed visually or by radio and interrogated.

In order to track the more important pieces and obtain information from them, complex and widespread systems had to be established. Of these, undoubtedly the most extensive is the American Moonwatch, a system of amateur astronomer teams operating at about one hundred twenty stations in the United States and another one hundred twenty throughout the rest of the world. At each station, teams watch a segment of the meridian in the sky for the passage of satellites across it. Since many are too faint to be visible with the naked eye, small telescopes are used. Several, pointed at different angles, are required to cover the zone. Because satellites are only visible at twilight, when the earth and the sky are dark and the satellites are lit by the sun, watch need only be kept in the morning and evening. The time and the direction of each passage are carefully recorded, and the information sent to the Astronomical Observatory of the Smithsonian Institution at Cambridge, Massachusetts, which is charged with optical tracking. This observatory also directs the twelve Baker-Nunn camera stations throughout the world, at which huge cameras, especially designed for the difficult task of photographing these faint, fast-moving objects, fix the satellites precisely in time and space.

Besides these optical methods, the Vanguard Computing Centre in Washington is responsible for two other systems which gather information from satellites that are transmitting. The Minitrack stations, of which during the IGY there were four along the Pacific coast of South America and others in the United States, South Africa, Singapore, and Australia, locate the position and height of satellites by radio. More are under construction. Another world-wide series of stations known as Microlock interrogate satellites to obtain the information they have recorded. From all these observations the orbits of satellites are computed and predictions made for future sightings.

The Americans have also recently announced a new scheme,

Tepee, which can record the blast of gases emitted by large rockets. Since the radio waves on which this listening system depends are reflected around the earth, it may be able even to detect launchings on the opposite side of the globe.

Within Russia the Soviets have both optical and radio tracking systems, and the results of their observations on Russian satellites are published regularly in the Bulletin of the Institute of Theoretical Astronomy. Russian predictions of the time of passage of their satellites over foreign observatories are available to those interested. Thus, predictions were received throughout 1959 at the University of Toronto observatory. The distinguished astronomer Mrs. Alla Masevich is in charge of the program and has described it at a meeting of the American Astronomical Society.

Finally, several very large radio telescopes with movable dish-shaped antennae were modified to locate satellites either by radio or by radar devices. The largest of these yet built has a dish 250 feet across and is at Jodrell Bank near Manchester, England.

The recitation of such extensive preparations suggests that tracking should be complete, but this is by no means so, for the problems are immense. In the early days the systems did not work well. The batteries on Sputnik II failed less than a week after it was launched, perhaps due to overheating by sunlight. Because of the distance between ground stations and the lack of experience of the operators, only 3 per cent of the information broadcast by Explorer I in its first month of life was recovered. In contrast, after tape-recorders had been installed to act as memories for satellites, 80 per cent of the data from the later broadcasts of Explorer III was recovered. Again, all traces of the rocket-case of Vanguard I were lost from March 17, 1958, to May 6, 1959. It had been thought that the rocket-case would have less velocity than the satellite, which it pushed ahead with springs, but apparently the case was still firing gently when the satellite was detached and the case had the greater speed. As a result, the trackers looked for the case at the wrong times.

Many people ask: Is there an exchange of data? Do the Russians really tell us what they discover? The answer in most cases is emphatically yes. It is true that there have been cases of delay and obscurity on both sides, but these exceptions are far fewer than people believe. The remarkable thing is not that there is an exchange, but that anyone, in view of the difficulties involved, recovers any data worth exchanging. The problems of keeping track of several objects, at most only a few feet in dimension, which are hurtling through outer space at speeds in excess of 18,000 miles an hour and at heights greater than 100 miles are so complex that it is remarkable how much information has been gathered. The undertaking is further complicated because of the unexpected conditions encountered in space. Experiments designed to measure one supposed property have often found and measured other quite different elements. In spite of rivalry, these common problems have produced something of a bond among the scientists involved; considering the difficulties, results have been reported fairly quickly. The skill and labour necessary to decipher data is illustrated in the American announcement that it would take a year to decode all the messages telemetered from fifteen experiments performed on Explorer VI during the two months its batteries operated.

That both countries have given correct reports is proved by the fact that the partial findings, not fully understood when they were reported, have fitted together to give an improved and revised picture of outer space. Many of the observations do not touch on old theories; but when pieced together they suggest entirely new and unsuspected possibilities.

SPUTNIKS

The first family of satellites, and the one to which the greatest general interest was attached, was the Sputniks. The imminent birth of the Sputnik was first brought home to me in the studios of the Canadian Broadcasting Corporation during the Toronto meeting of the IUGG, as I participated in a television program about satellites with Mme Troitskaya, Professor V. V. Beloussov and Dr. Lloyd Berkner, the chairman of the American Space Science Committee. Mme Troitskaya cautiously confirmed the statement of the U.S.S.R. Academy of Sciences that Russia intended to launch satellites. "Yes," she said, "they will be launched soon, and some will be larger than those planned by the Americans."

A month later, on the evening of October 4, while I was in Bucharest, the Soviet ambassador in Washington was giving a party to conclude the meeting of United States and Soviet scientists who had been discussing the IGY satellite program. In the Embassy, Walter Sullivan, science reporter for *The New York Times*, received word from his paper's monitoring service: "Radio Moscow is broadcasting that a satellite has been successfully placed in orbit." He ran with his news to Dr. Berkner, who got on a chair to announce to the Western world, from within the Soviet Embassy in Washington: "The Soviet Union has placed an artificial satellite in orbit." This news Soviet sources confirmed a few minutes later. Sullivan and Berkner had made the best of a situation which they had expected but which to most Americans came as a profound shock. The events of the succeeding days were without doubt planned by the Russians to increase the impact of their achievement.

Next morning, and daily during the following week, a multitude of radio sets throughout the world could hear the beep-beep-beep emitted by the satellite whenever it passed on its

90-minute orbit around the earth. On the other hand, because this signal was being broadcast on the amateur band frequencies of 20 and 40 megacycles and not on the prearranged frequency of 108 megacycles, the American tracking systems were unable to pick up the signals by Minitrack until the night of October 5 to 6. For several days the satellite did not cross the United States during twilight, and Americans were not able to see it. The consternation was immense; and it was not much relieved when, on October 9, Sputnik I was first observed in North America by a powerful Schmidt camera at the New-brook meteor station in Alberta. The next day, at 10.23 hours universal time, the satellite was seen in the United States by the Moonwatch team at New Haven.

Sputnik I carried a radio transmitter but few instruments. At most, it transmitted information on temperatures within the satellite itself, upon which information the performance of instruments in future satellites would depend. Like Vanguard I, the satellite was spherical and designed to separate from the last stage rocket-case. Both satellite and case could be faintly seen in the sky. Because drag on the rocket-case was greater and because the satellite had been shot ahead by springs, the case travelled more slowly. This caused it to move in an orbit of smaller radius and paradoxically revolve about the earth in less time. The difference was appreciable and the casing gained a revolution and lapped the satellite at 20.24 hours universal time on October 29 when both were passing over the Pacific Ocean. By January 10 Sputnik I had entered the atmosphere and disintegrated.

What precisely were Sputnik's effects? The successful launching showed that the calculations regarding artificial satellites had been correct and opened up vast possibilities for the future exploration of space. On the other hand, the immediate scientific results were not great. The satellite carried few instruments, did not orbit far from the earth, and did not stay up long. The operation of its radio indicated that the temperature within the satellite was suitable for batteries and electronic devices. The distortion of the messages told something of the radio properties of the upper atmosphere, while the rate of slowing by drag indicated the density of the thin air.

The propaganda effect was immense. Since the Americans had proposed launching satellites and had given their intentions widespread publicity, they could hardly complain when the Soviets launched an object which by its visibility and radio signals attracted great attention. But in spite of popular feeling on the subject, the launching of Sputnik I was not a technical defeat for the Americans. They had never intended to launch a satellite as early as October 1957, and in due course they successfully launched many well-instrumented satellites. If it was a defeat at all, it was a political defeat, arising from failure to appreciate the psychological impact of the first satellite and failure to support unconventional technical ideas soon enough.

A month later Sputnik II was launched. The design was similar except that the rocket-case was not intended to separate from the instrumented capsule, which carried a payload six times as great as Sputnik I to twice the height. Sputnik II carried a small dog, many instruments, and extensive telemetering equipment. Again it was a sensation. For the most part it was devoted to the study of space travel. The fact that the dog survived the launching and settled down, when in orbit, to normal living was our first assurance that creatures can survive in a weightless condition and was a preliminary to placing a man in orbit and opening the era of space travel.

Instruments on Sputnik II confirmed that satellites in space are kept warm by the sun's radiation. (Indeed it is possible that Sputnik II's batteries failed from overheating.) It was shown that no micrometeorites punctured Sputnik II as had been feared, but that cosmic radiation was greater than expected. This foreshadowed the later discovery, by the higher-flying American satellites, of the Van Allen belts.

The end of Sputnik II came on April 14, 1958, at 1.55 hours universal time, after it had completed 2,367 revolutions about the earth. Its incipient break-up was observed shortly after dark as it crossed over New England, a glowing body with a faint trail of luminous sparks. The sinking satellite rapidly increased in brilliance as it passed the West Indies until it appeared as bright as the moon at first quarter. It had a glowing tail 70 miles long from which globules like minor comets kept dropping away. A great number of people on islands and ships, including about half the population of Barbados, saw this striking object before it was consumed and faded low in the air over the Atlantic Ocean northeast of British Guiana.

Sputnik III was not launched until May 1958, by which time three American satellites were up at greater heights. The third Soviet satellite was large and impressive. The elongated rocket-case as it tumbled across the evening or morning sky appeared as a flashing meteor often brighter than Venus. The separated satellite was less easily seen but carried a payload of more than a ton, including batteries and instruments for making a dozen experiments, tape recorders for memorizing the observations, and radios for telemetering them back to interrogating stations in the U.S.S.R. A long report on preliminary results was issued in October 1958. The air density at a height of 166 miles was found to be only one ten billionth of that on the surface, but it was, nevertheless, five or ten times what had been expected. At that height the atmosphere was found to consist of atoms separated rather than joined in pairs as in ordinary air. Nitrogen, which forms three quarters of the lower atmosphere, was only present to the extent of 5 per cent. The temperature was high, and the electric state such that the satellite became charged to an electric potential of several volts. Cosmic ray counters analysed the particles coming from outer space and confirmed the radiation in the Van Allen belts which had been found a few weeks earlier by the first Explorer satellites. Other instruments measured the earth's magnetic field and electric currents in the upper atmosphere.

The Soviets launched three Luniks and no Sputniks in 1959, and only three Sputniks in 1960; but in the spring of 1961 five successful launchings paved the way for Yuri Gagarin's first orbit around the earth in 109 minutes on April 12, 1961.

The Soviet program was well designed to achieve two objectives: the placing of a man in orbit and the investigation of the moon. Both were legitimate scientific projects, and both made splendid propaganda. The United States so far has not had such powerful launching rockets, although they are now being developed rapidly. Meanwhile, the Americans have done a much more thorough job in investigating the properties of nearby space and the potentialities of satellites as aids to communication, navigation, and weather forecasting.

VANGUARDS

When the Americans decided to launch artificial satellites for the IGY, the scientists decided to stay clear of existing military rockets and design a program of their own: launching-rockets, tracking facilities, computers, and all. They hoped in this way to remain independent of military security and military requirements and to develop a satellite designed solely for the gathering of scientific information.

The outcome of these fine aspirations was the Vanguard, a most elegant instrument. The United States Navy sponsored it, under the direction of Dr. J. P. Hagen, but many of the ablest scientists in the United States advised on the instrumentation and its scientific program. It was a scientist's dream of a perfect instrument for exploring nearby space.

Unfortunately, the Vanguard program suffered the usual penalty of pioneers and several of the satellites failed to orbit. These failures received much excited publicity, which obscured the many achievements of the men who developed the Vanguards. For instance, the basic tracking facilities have been used by all other satellite programs; the computers evolved for predicting the future orbits of satellites were successful, and the design of the satellites themselves had a wide influence on subsequent satellites. Apart from the major contribution made by very light and compact instrumentation, Vanguard I also proved that solar cells can replace electric batteries as a source of continuous power and that a reflecting paint can successfully control the temperature inside a satellite. The very light, compact instrumentation has meant a lighter load, which in turn has made it possible for Vanguards to be placed in higher and hence longer-lived orbits than any other satellites. All three of the successful Vanguards are still in orbit and are expected to remain aloft for many years. They have demonstrated the satellite's remarkable potential for mapping the earth and predicting the weather. From the observations made on Vanguards earth scientists have been able to establish that the earth is not perfectly spherical, but very slightly pear-shaped, and that the density of the atmosphere at heights of a few hundred miles varies with the seasons and with solar phenomena.

Each of the three Vanguards is different and has made different specific contributions. Vanguard I is a 6-inch test sphere with no room for instruments except a radio transmitter. This set is still operating with power derived from solar batteries charged by sunlight. Careful observations of this satellite have revealed much about the density of the thin upper atmosphere and about the precise shape of the earth.

Vanguard II was the first satellite to attempt to televise the earth. Two photocells provided a crude picture of the extent of cloud cover, but the satellite unfortunately developed an unexpected wobble which made the results almost undecipherable.

Vanguard III consists of a 20-inch spherical instrument package that bears a 26-inch conical nose of fibre glass carrying magnetic instruments, to which the third stage rocket-case was intentionally left attached to reduce tumbling. The instruments included an extremely sensitive proton-type magnetometer, ion chambers to measure X-rays of 1 to 10 Ångström units emitted by the sun, and four methods of detecting meteoritic particles.

EXPLORERS

As soon as Sputnik I was launched and the extent of its success was known, the United States Army was authorized to use modified military rockets to launch satellites. By using the Jupiter C or Redstone ballistic rocket as first stage, and concentric bundles of respectively eleven, five, and one solid-fuel Sergeant rockets for subsequent stages, the Army was able to place three Explorers in orbit during the first half of 1958. It seems probable that this could have been done at least a year earlier had the politicians realized the psychological impact which satellites would have, had the services not been so divided by rivalries, had the scientists not been so keen to do an elaborate job, and had the security agencies not been so opposed to using secret military IRBM's for satellite launchings. No one, in fact, in the United States appreciated the importance of the job in time.

In Explorer I, which was launched in January, the casing of the last empty rocket carried 11 pounds of instruments with which to measure internal and external temperatures, micro-meteorites, and cosmic rays. The rather scanty data gathered confirmed the results obtained by Sputnik II that micro-meteorites were not as dangerous as had been feared, but that cosmic rays were more intense than had been expected. An additional complication of significance was that at heights greater than those reached by Sputnik II the counters appeared to fail. At the time this was attributed to faults arising from hasty construction. Explorer II failed to orbit, but better counters and a tape-recorder to store information were installed in Explorer III. By fortunate mischance this satellite reached 1,741 miles at its highest point instead of the 1,270 intended, and swept within 121 miles of the earth at its lowest. It therefore covered a very wide range and disclosed that up to a height of 1,000 miles the radiation count was normal, but at 1,600 miles the radiation was so high that it was likely to be lethal to humans. It was now apparent that the counters on the previous satellite had failed not because of a mechanical defect but because they were too small to cope with the magnitude of the task and had become choked. On May 1, 1958, when announcement was made in Washington of the discovery of this belt of intense radiation, it was named in honour of Dr. James S. Van Allen, who had designed the equipment that had disclosed its existence. A fortnight later Sputnik III was launched and confirmed the findings of Explorer III. Explorer IV was designed particularly to examine this Van Allen belt.

Early in 1959, Pioneers and Luniks, in flights towards the moon, showed that there were not one but two of these belts. In August 1959, Explorer VI was launched in a large and highly elliptical orbit to explore the belts in more detail and to discover whether they changed with the sun's activity. So that this satellite could monitor the radiation in these belts and transmit this and other information for a long time, its radios were powered by solar batteries supported on four vanes—giving it the name, "the paddle-wheel satellite." One paddle seems not to have opened, and the radio became silent after two months.

Except for its functions, Explorer VI had little in common with the earlier Explorers, for it was launched by a United States Air Force Thor-Able Intermediate Range Ballistic Missile rocket. Instead of being the shell of a Sergeant rocket and weighing a few pounds as did the previous Explorers, it weighed 142 pounds and had 100,000 components in a 2-foot spherical container with four 3-foot vanes around it.

Explorer VII, which was launched October 13, 1959, and weighed 91.5 pounds, was designed to make seven measurements, of which the two most important concerned the radiation balance of the earth. Our weather is profoundly affected by the fact that near the equator the earth receives more heat than it radiates, while near the poles it loses more than it receives. This lack of balance drives the winds. To learn more precisely the nature of the energy received and lost, this satellite carried three sets of sensors to measure radiation of different wave-lengths as the satellite swung from 50° north to 50° south latitudes about the earth. A photocell recorded the direction of the sun. Other devices measured the intensity of ultra-violet light and short X-rays during solar flares, the intensity and nature of cosmic rays, and the prevalence of micro-meteorites.

PIONEERS AND SCORE

When several satellites had been successfully placed in orbit close to the earth, President Eisenhower announced that permission had been given for the Air Force to make three attempts to send a rocket to the moon, and for the Army later to make two attempts. The first attempt ended seventy-seven seconds after lift-off, in a tremendous explosion caused by failure of the first-stage engine. On October 1, 1958, the whole program was taken over by the civilian National Aeronautics and Space Administration. Pioneers I and III were then successfully launched and reached distances of 70,700 and 63,-580 miles before they fell back to earth. They had not been going fast enough to escape the pull of the earth's gravity. Pioneer II failed, but early in 1959 Pioneer IV was placed in orbit around the sun as Artificial Planet II. None of these Pioneers provided much information about the moon, because the scanner provided for that purpose on Pioneer IV failed and the others did not go far enough. But as we have said, they did establish the existence of the second Van Allen belt.

The last satellite of 1958 was an Atlas ICBM (Intercontinental Ballistic Missile) fired into orbit by the Advanced Research Projects Agency and the United States Air Force. It was vastly larger than any previous American satellite; with the attached but empty case of the last stage rocket it weighed 8,750 pounds and was claimed to be the heaviest satellite yet launched. No doubt this was true, and it was the first demonstration of the power of American ICBM's. However, Academician L. I. Sedov quickly pointed out that the real test was the total weight placed in orbit. He claimed that the detached rocket-cases of Soviet Sputniks weighed even more, but he did not say how much more. The Atlas-Score carried no scientific instruments, but it contained a radio transmitter which, when interrogated, broadcast a recorded Christmas message from President Eisenhower.

DISCOVERERS

During 1959 the United States launched a series of six Discoverer satellites which were designed to test the ejection and recovery of capsules and to study environmental conditions. In one of the Discoverers, four live mice were sent into

orbit as part of a biomedical experiment. Though the Discoverers were not part of the IGY program, some geophysical
information was obtained by observing them. During 1960
this series of launchings was continued and extended, and the
first capsules were ejected and recovered from orbit.

LUNIKS

On January 2, 1959, between the launching of Pioneer III
and Pioneer IV space probes, Lunik I, or Mechta, was
launched. Two days later it missed the moon, passing within
3,700 miles of it and continuing on its way to become the first
artificial planet to be placed in orbit around the sun. Its
path is close to that of the earth but outside it and considerably
more elliptical, with a year of 450 days. The new planetoid has
a last stage weighing 3,245 pounds, of which 795 pounds is
payload, so that its launching—an outstanding engineering
feat—probably required an initial rocket-thrust of 500,000
pounds. It is a hopeful sign that this great technical achievement received general acclaim. Congratulations were sent to
the Soviets by the heads of other states as well as by their
fellow scientists.

Lunik I carried nine sets of instruments planned to measure
the earth's and the moon's magnetic fields and the intensity
and nature of the fast-moving atomic particles of outer space.
At an altitude of 75,000 miles two pounds of sodium were
vaporized and ejected from the planetoid in the form of a visible flare, which enabled the satellite's position to be precisely
fixed. This may have been intended as a guide for correcting its
path towards the moon. If so, it was unsuccessful. After transmitting information for a few days, it faded forever from sight
and hearing. It is doubtful whether Lunik I will ever be identified again.

On September 12, 1959, a second similar body was launched

toward the moon. The Soviets provided information and asked the astronomers at Jodrell Bank radio telescope to track the space probe. Fortunately they were able to locate it, receive its radio signals, and track it up to the moment of impact. When the Lunik entered the gravity field of the moon, its velocity was observed to increase as it fell towards the moon. At the moment of impact, the radio signals ceased.

Guided by Soviet information, several other astronomers in Europe, which was at the time on the side of the earth towards the moon, were able to observe the impact. G. Fielder has collected and published the reports of ten observers who were watching on September 13, 1959. The observations made with the seven largest instruments are all in agreement that at 21 hours 02 minutes 23 seconds universal time, Lunik II struck the moon close to the centre of its disc at a point near Mare Tranquilitatis and the crater Schneckenberg. The reports made by observers using the three smallest instruments show discrepancies of a few seconds in time and some uncertainty in location, but these may reasonably be attributed to errors arising from less satisfactory equipment.

Early on the morning of October 4, exactly two years after the launching of Sputnik I, Soviet scientists launched Lunik III, a 614-pound satellite with a 3,424-pound rocket-case, into an immensely elongated orbit around the moon. About six days later, as it swung around between the sun and the moon at a distance of only 4,000 miles from the latter, a radio message from the earth put in motion the most sophisticated display of engineering virtuosity yet attempted in space research. The timing of the signal and the course of the Lunik III, which was at that moment on a line between the sun and the moon, were such that after one light-sensitive device had stabilized the rear end of the Lunik to point at the sun, another took over to point the front end of the Lunik directly at the fainter moon. Two cameras then started to photograph

Diagram of the far side of the moon. Names were sub-
mitted by the U.S.S.R. Academy of Sciences to the International Astronomical Union.

the moon with varying exposures on 35 mm film which had
been shielded from radiation in space.

The film was automatically developed in the satellite. It was
fixed, dried, and stored for a few days until the Lunik again
approached the earth. Television cameras then scanned the
film and transmitted to earth the first pictures ever seen by
humans of the far side of the moon. More than a dozen craters
and dark maria, or seas, were immediately recognized on the
photographs, and other craters have since been made out, but
the moon, like the earth, with its land and water hemispheres,
is not symmetrical in its features. We see the better view, for

the face of the moon is turned to us and Lunik photographed the back of its bald head.

On October 18 Lunik III approached again to within 29,-000 miles of the earth. In accordance with predictions made in November 1959, by L. I. Sedov of the U.S.S.R. at a meeting of the American Rocket Society held in Washington, it followed a highly elliptic orbit about the earth. Perturbations due to the attractive influences of the sun and moon caused the orbit constantly to change in shape until in April 1960 the satellite fell to earth.

ROCKETS

Once satellites, which can stay aloft for weeks or years, had been launched, rockets, whose flight lasts for only a few minutes, might be thought to have lost their value. This is only partly true. Satellites disintegrate below a height of 100 miles; balloons, which need some air for their support, will not go above 20 miles; so rockets remain the only method of exploring the belt between. Rockets also can be fired to be in precise spots at specific times, a valuable attribute demonstrated at the Danger Islands during the eclipse of October 12, 1958. In addition, records can be recovered from rockets. Nothing material was recovered from any satellite until August 1960, but photographs of the earth from great heights and packets of film showing the tracks of cosmic rays were recovered from rockets before and during the IGY.

Rockets have the advantage also of being far cheaper and simpler than satellites, and their size and cost can be further reduced if they are attached to polyethylene balloons and raised through the dense lower atmosphere before firing. Such a combination is called a rockoon. Rockets so boosted may be smaller, carry greater loads, or reach greater heights.

At least seven countries participated in the IGY rocket program. Australia launched rockoons at Woomera. France fired Veronica rockets in the Sahara. Japan carried out an extensive program of firing Kappa and other rockets and rockoons over the northern Sea of Japan. The U.S.S.R. fired over one hundred rockets from a base in the Franz Joseph Islands in the Arctic, from central U.S.S.R., and from Mirny in the Antarctic. The Russian program was a continuation of previous work and involved a wide range of rockets; most were small meteorological rockets, but some carried over two tons of experimental equipment and test animals to heights of over 100 miles, from which they were safely recovered by parachute.

The United Kingdom developed a research rocket, the Skylark, capable of carrying 150 pounds to a height of 90 miles. It is 25 feet long and 1½ feet in diameter. These were fired from a special launching tower at Woomera, Australia. The United States program involved firing over two hundred rockets of various rockoon, Aerobee, and Nike types from ships in many parts of the world and from four bases in the United States and one in Churchill, on Hudson Bay, Canada. Various animals were sent aloft to test their physiological reactions and later were recovered. Canada assisted in the large American program at Churchill, chosen because of its location within the maximum auroral belt.

CHAPTER 7

WHAT
THE SATELLITES
REVEALED

In 1959 Professor James A. Van Allen, head of the physics department at the State University of Iowa, wrote of the radiation belts around the earth which he discovered and which bear his name: "So far, the most interesting and least expected result of man's exploration of the immediate vicinity of the earth is the discovery that our planet is ringed by a region—to be exact, two regions—of high-energy radiation extending many thousands of miles into space. The discovery is of course troubling to astronauts; somehow the human body will have to be shielded from this radiation, even on a rapid transit through the region. But geophysicists, astrophysicists, solar astronomers and cosmic-ray physicists are enthralled by the fresh implications of these findings. The configuration of the region and the radiation it contains bespeak a major physical phenomenon involving cosmic rays and solar corpuscles in the vicinity of the earth. This enormous reservoir of charged particles plays a still-unexplained role as middleman in the interaction of earth and sun which is reflected in magnetic storms, in the air glow, and in the beautiful displays of the aurora."

At the beginning of 1958 it was supposed that above a height of a few tens of miles the tenuous upper atmosphere of the earth was uniform and that most of the time it was approximately similar at all latitudes and only diminished in density at increasing distances from the earth. It is true that the aurora

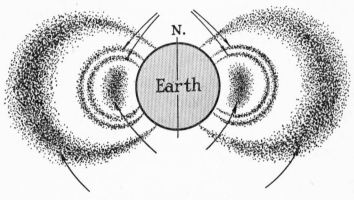

The earth, its inner and outer Van Allen belts of intense radiation, and the artificially created and temporary Argus shells between them.

required special explanation and so did certain other phenomena in radio transmission, but the observed relation of these to solar disturbances had led to the general belief that these effects were all produced during the bombardment of the earth by intermittent blasts of gas from the sun.

Van Allen's discovery indicates that at all times two belts exist in the upper atmosphere. More recent discoveries suggest that a third, weaker and more distant, belt may be present. All act as reservoirs for more numerous, hotter, and more active gas particles than are present elsewhere. It is believed that these gases are held in place because they are trapped by the earth's magnetic field, but it is not yet clear why these belts exist where they do, and why there are not others.

The two main belts lie around the equatorial regions of the earth, one outside the other as though the earth was a man dressed in a rather loose cummerbund with a large barrel around him. The gas particles trapped in these belts are not static. They dash wildly from pole to pole and back every few

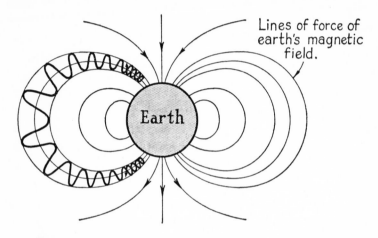

Lines of force of earth's magnetic field.

Earth

Diagram illustrating the corkscrew-line paths pursued by high-speed electrons in the Van Allen and Argus belts.

seconds like caged animals trying to escape. They can do this without much interference, for at these heights the atmosphere is very tenuous, but the energy they carry is great and could be fatal to space travellers unless they took off from a polar region and so went around one end of the Van Allen belts. Each particle follows a corkscrew path within what may be thought of as the stave of a barrel. Particles can drift from stave to stave, but they escape slowly from the barrel-shaped Van Allen belts only at one end or the other.

These reservoirs are fed, at least in part, by solar winds.

When a blast strikes the reservoirs and disturbs them, they overflow at the ends. Some mechanism based upon the excitation of the outer belts by solar activity appears to promise a better means of explaining magnetic storms, aurora, and radio blackouts. Failure to appreciate the existence of these reservoirs in the Van Allen belts made earlier explanations of the aurora unsatisfactory.

These belts were not discovered or even suspected until satellites and rockets reached them. Because they are high and transparent, they could not be detected from the ground. Under the circumstances, they were found by chance rather than design. Our knowledge of the belts is still fragmentary, but indications are that they vary greatly in shape and intensity with fluctuations in solar activity. A more precise picture will emerge when there has been time to interpret fully the results of Explorers VI and VII and of later satellites.

Although the implications were not understood at the time, some evidence for the Van Allen belts had been found earlier in the regions where the aurora is at a maximum and where the horns of the outer Van Allen belt thrust down into the earth's atmosphere until they are only a few score miles above the ground. In 1953 scientists from the State University of Iowa launched rockoons from United States Coast Guard vessels off Newfoundland into the maximum auroral belt and found that the radiation at a height of 30 miles was much more intense than they had encountered elsewhere. Subsequent rocket flights showed that this radiation persisted even when there was no aurora, contrary to theories then held. In 1957 larger United States rockets were launched, and it was found that the temperature of the atmosphere at a height of 150 to 200 miles was about 3,000° F over Churchill but only half that value over White Sands, New Mexico. The rockets at Newfoundland and Churchill had, of course, entered the horns of the outer Van Allen belt. This discrepancy was not understood until the two belts were discovered by Explorer I and Pioneer II.

THE ARGUS EXPERIMENT

Few discoveries in science are wholly new or independent. Many years ago the Scandinavian scientists Carl Störmer and H. Alfvén had suggested that charged particles might become trapped in the earth's magnetic field and would then spiral back and forth from one polar region to the other around magnetic lines of force. They pointed out that if this were true the particles would be reflected at each end, near which the radiation would be most intense. To test the validity of this speculation, N. C. Christofilos, of the University of California, suggested that belts of radiation might be created artificially by the detonation at great heights of small nuclear charges.

The potential geophysical interest and the obvious importance of a knowledge of high-altitude nuclear explosions in anti-missile defence were reasons enough to undertake the experiment. It was christened Argus. Three nuclear devices were fired from the U.S.S. *Norton Sound* at a height of 300 miles over the south Atlantic Ocean in August and September 1958. Explorer IV was aloft at this time to monitor the results. To collect further observations, a number of high-altitude rockets were launched from key locations along the Atlantic coast of North America. The experiment was a great success. The particles generated by each explosion spread out to form zones of radiation like the Van Allen belts, but smaller and weaker than either of the two natural belts and located between them. These artificial zones were called the Argus shells. Immediately after the explosions the shells were recorded, as anticipated, by Explorer IV, which reported sharp peaks of radiation on every subsequent passage through the shells. No such peaks had been recorded before or have been since.

The shells slowly faded in intensity but were recorded until Explorer IV's batteries failed on September 21, and again feebly by Pioneer III on December 6, but none was detected in March 1959 by Pioneer IV. All the electrons created by the explosion had leaked away. Although the charged particles in the Argus shells were trapped by the same magnetic field as those in the Van Allen belts above and below them, they slowly dispersed because they lay in a region where they were not replenished by natural processes.

Just as auroral, magnetic, and radio effects are particularly strong in maximum auroral belts where the horns of the outer Van Allen belt come closest to the earth, so it was anticipated that there would be horns of similar kind in Argus shells. This expectation was admirably fulfilled. When the explosions took place, electrons, guided by the earth's magnetic field, raced along corkscrew paths aligned like barrel staves about the earth. At the northern end they were reflected back. Slowly they spread out sideways to complete a barrel-shaped belt of radiation around the globe. Overhead, immediately after each explosion, a colourful aurora formed in the sky. At the opposite, or conjugate, point in the northern hemisphere near the Azores a brilliant auroral display was observed from aboard the U.S.S. *Albemarle*, which had been sent to keep watch. This artificially created aurora started a few minutes after the distant detonation of Argus III and lasted for several minutes. Similarly, electro-magnetic disturbances and fading of radio waves were observed in both the launching and the conjugate areas.

To make additional measurements of the radiation in Argus shells, a series of nineteen high-altitude rockets carrying counters were fired to heights of up to 300 miles over Florida,

Virginia, and Puerto Rico. As these passed through the shells of Argus radiation, they detected intensities as much as 100,-000 times normal. It was found that each explosion created a separate thin sheet of radiation shaped like a concentric barrel about the earth between the outer and inner Van Allen belts. Each Argus shell was about 13 miles thick, but the second and third Argus shells overlapped each other.

The shells remained constant in position and thickness for a hundred hours, during which time every electron made approximately one million trips between the two polar regions. This provided information about the stability of the earth's magnetic field, while the rate of decay and the fact that the shells did not thicken or diffuse suggest that the electrons are chiefly lost by scattering into the atmosphere near the ends of their paths where they are reflected back and forth in the denser atmosphere near the ground.

MICROMETEORITES

Before any satellites had been launched, great concern was felt lest space be so full of tiny, high-speed micrometeorites that vehicles would be damaged and any future space travellers killed. The particles, which become visible as meteors or shooting stars when they reach the atmosphere, were known to travel at speeds sometimes exceeding 25,000 miles an hour relative to the earth, and the worst was feared of them. To study these effects, many satellites carried microphones or fine wires to record hits. As it turned out, the situation is not serious. One gauge on Explorer I was hit only once during a month and that by a speck of dust less than one thousandth of an inch in diameter. Apparently no satellite has been put out of action by hits. It is radiation, not meteorites, which is likely to prove dangerous to space travellers.

GROUND OBSERVATION OF SATELLITES

The studies which can most surely be made with all satellites, whether instrumented or not, are those depending solely upon ground observation. For example, much can be discovered about the upper atmosphere by accurately timing the satellites. At heights of hundreds of miles the atmosphere is so thin that it would be regarded as a good vacuum in a laboratory, but even thin air slows satellites so that their orbit contracts and their period of revolution decreases.

The orbital period of a satellite can be measured with an accuracy of a small fraction of a second. Thus, the rate at which drag of the thin upper air reduces the speed of a satellite can be precisely determined. Using American and British observations of the orbital period of fifteen satellites and published figures for the size and weight of satellites, D. G. King-Hele has published estimates of the density of the atmosphere at heights of from 100 to 500 miles. The densities, now known accurately for the first time, have turned out to be from five to fifteen times greater than had been previously believed. King-Hele considers that variations due to latitude and season are small, but that the effect of the sun-spot cycle may be greater than expected. This information is important for instruments and essential for the safety of living animal or human passengers.

Luigi Jacchia, of the Smithsonian Astrophysical Observatory, believes that particles shot from the sun during solar flares increase the density of the earth's upper atmosphere and that this increase in density produced noticeable slowing of Vanguard I and Sputnik III one or two days after major flares were observed. He and Robert Jastrow have studied differences in the behaviour of satellites which swing far enough north and south to enter the ends of the outer Van Allen belt and satellites which do not. They conclude that the activity of the solar particles trapped within the belts increases the temperatures in these sections of the upper atmosphere. The activity and heat are most intense in the horns of the belts, at about 65 miles above the earth, where the particles are bounced back to continue their endless, jostling journey. Jastrow suggests that this extra energy may be the cause of the aurora, which is most common at that height and in the latitudes of the horns of the Van Allen belts. He points out that if this conjecture is true the Van Allen belts should contain more particles in the spring and fall, when the aurora is most prevalent. When the data from Explorers VI and VII have been deciphered, this matter should be settled.

IS THE EARTH PEAR-SHAPED?

It has been long known that the earth has the shape of a slightly flattened sphere with an equatorial diameter 13 miles longer than the polar diameter. From observations made on Vanguard I, J. A. O'Keefe concluded that the north pole is about 15 yards farther from the centre of the earth than the south pole. He also suggested a slight neck around the north pole and a bulge a few yards thick in the southern hemisphere; thus, in effect, the earth has a very slightly pear-shaped figure. It has also been suggested that the equator is not perfectly circular but very slightly elliptical.

One may well wonder how O'Keefe discovered these irregularities.

In the hope of simplifying a rather complicated explanation, let us consider the earth as an eccentric matron who has a hat with an elliptical brim. Her eccentricity demands that she keep rotating her hat and swivelling it round and round on her head, always at the nice angle of 35 degrees. Sometimes the wide part of the brim is well down over her nose; sometimes high over her left ear; sometimes low over her right;

sometimes well up on the back of her head; sometimes low on the nape of her neck. The edge of the hat brim corresponds to the orbit of a satellite.

As the satellite swings round and round, irregularities in the earth cause minute changes in the shape of its orbit. At all times the satellite is most affected by the parts of the earth nearest to it. The timing of the orbital period is so precise and the readings of its position are so delicate that minute variations can be detected. By carefully tabulating these small discrepancies, O'Keefe and other scientists have been able to plot the bulges and depressions on the earth's surface.

O'Keefe and his colleagues believe that the earth must be inherently very strong to support its persistent irregularities. Whether the earth has permanent strength or whether it flows slowly to adjust itself to large forces is a question that has been much debated. I am inclined to think that O'Keefe's observation that the earth is slightly pear-shaped is correct, but I do not accept his conclusion that the earth is permanently strong. For the earth to depart from a spheroidal shape it must have been pressed inwards in Antarctica and in a ring through Europe, Siberia, and Canada; these are precisely the places where great loads of glacial ice were placed on the earth during the recent ice age. These loads depressed the earth and caused its present shape. But the earth is now observed to be rising in those places, and I think that it is in the process of slowly flowing back to a spheroid shape. Rather than being permanently strong, the earth is weak and malleable.

OTHER OBSERVATIONS FROM SATELLITES

A great deal more could be written about satellite programs, but most of this would consist of plans and intended programs and partial accounts of results. From what has been said it will be apparent that nearly half the satellites placed in orbit by the end of 1959 had few instruments or else produced few results. Much more sophisticated models have been launched since the end of 1959, but there has not been time for the results to be fully reduced and published. This is not surprising. What is astonishing is how much has already been disclosed.

In future we can expect satellites and space probes to explore the solar system, measuring the magnetic fields and Van Allen belts around other planets and bringing back photographs of them. They can be expected to televise back to earth a complete picture of the whole world's cloud cover. They will supplement our present sparse weather observations over the oceans and polar regions. Other satellites will relay communication and navigation messages all over the world. And of course many men, but not perhaps you and I, are anxious to get into space. Some will probably lose their lives and remain there, riding the solar wind and the cosmic rays to all eternity.

CHAPTER 8

COSMIC RAYS

Rockets and satellites have been essential tools in the study of radiation in outer space. Their value lies in their ability to carry instruments into that radiation before it has been absorbed or altered by the earth's atmosphere. I have already mentioned that the radiation emitted by the sun is of two kinds: electro-magnetic waves, like light and heat, and corpuscular radiation, including blasts of gases from solar flares. These blasts are clouds or swarms of electrons, atoms, and fragments of atoms travelling at speeds of a few hundred miles every second. Cosmic rays are another form of corpuscular radiation in which the fragments of atoms travel alone or in smaller "showers" with even greater energies and higher speeds, reaching as much as tens of thousands of miles a second. It is possible, but not yet certain, that stellar blasts and cosmic rays may form a continuous series. Usually the two types are easily distinguished, however, and most cosmic rays certainly do not come from our sun.

Cosmic rays were first recognized in 1911 by Victor Franz Hess. He noticed the universal presence of a powerful radiation, the intensity of which increased rapidly with height, as shown by instruments sent up in balloons. It seemed to be unaffected by solar or terrestrial changes. Because Hess concluded that this radiation came from outer space, he named it cosmic rays, although he had little idea of its true nature.

Whence come these projectiles? What can their unrivalled energy tell us about the nature of mass and energy? What effect do they have on man? Are they responsible for evolution? Ten years ago these questions had not been answered. Indeed, the nature of cosmic rays was very imperfectly understood. In the intervening time much has been discovered, but so much more needs to be known that these are still leading questions in physics today. Since the occurrence of cosmic rays is a world-wide, natural phenomenon, it was natural that their investigation should have formed one program of the IGY.

Cosmic rays are fragments of atoms which have been battered by their impulsive rush through space. To understand these free-wheeling offspring, we have to recall the basic structure of their atomic parents. Atoms are designed after the fashion of inconceivably small solar systems, with a nucleus for a sun and one or more electrons for planets. Altogether some 90 elements have been discovered in nature, and a dozen more have been made artificially. They differ from one another in a simple and rather elegant manner.

Hydrogen, the lightest and simplest element, has one planetary electron. Succeeding elements—helium, lithium, and so on—have two, three, and successively more electrons up to the ninety-second and heaviest natural element, uranium, which has 92 electrons. Eleven artificially created elements continue the sequence from neptunium, with 93 electrons, through plutonium, with 94, and so on to lawrencium, with 103. All 103 elements are known. None is missing; no others exist. It is all beautifully regular.

The planetary electrons are all identical. They are small,

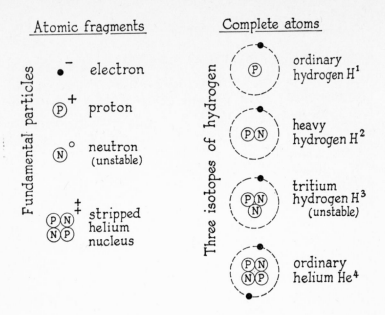

Diagram of the chief fundamental particles and of the simplest atoms made of them. Cosmic rays are very high speed atoms and atomic fragments like those illustrated.

light in weight, mobile, and carry one unit of negative electric charge.

Nuclei are larger and more complex. The simplest is that of the hydrogen atom and is called a proton. The proton weighs as much as 1,836 electrons and is therefore less mobile. It carries a small positive electric charge, exactly equal to the negative electric charge of the electron. A hydrogen atom is made up of one proton and one electron. All other elements have heavier and hence more complex nuclei to hold their larger numbers of planetary electrons in control. Each nucleus has the same number of protons as the element has planetary electrons—one, as I have said, for hydrogen, two for helium, three for lithium, and so on—but the nuclei also have variable numbers of uncharged particles, called neutrons, which cannot exist alone. These three particles—electrons, protons, and neutrons—make up all ordinary matter. Having equal numbers of negative electrons and positive protons, complete atoms have no charge and therefore are not affected by electric and magnetic fields.

If an atom is abused, as by collision with other atoms, it can be damaged. Some or all of the planetary electrons can be knocked off and perhaps later recaptured. This happens easily and the essential nature of the element is unaltered, except that a nucleus stripped of some of its negative electrons acquires a positive charge which makes it sensitive to magnetic and electric fields. Primary cosmic rays are chiefly single stripped nuclei travelling alone at colossal speeds through space.

If, however, a cosmic-ray nucleus travelling at high speed collides with another such nucleus, the impact will disrupt both, changing them to other elements by processes which are not easily reversed. The speed at which cosmic rays travel and the violence of their occasional collisions mean that they are always charged and sensitive to electric and magnetic fields; but since they are travelling very fast, they are not easily deflected from their courses.

Of every hundred cosmic rays about eighty-five are protons (stripped hydrogen nuclei), fourteen are stripped helium nuclei, and the remaining one may be the nucleus of any other element, most likely one of the lighter elements such as lithium, boron, or carbon. Some cosmic rays may be single electrons or even a pulse of X-rays, but this is still under debate. Thus, we see that there are several dozen kinds of primary cosmic-ray particles and that some are much more common than others. They are made of the same material as the ordinary things about us, and only become cosmic rays by virtue of the tremendous speed and energy with which they arrive, one at a time, individual fragments of atoms from outer space.

Most cosmic-ray particles have about the same speed and energy as is given artificially to similar particles by cyclotrons and other high-energy machines in physics laboratories. Such energies are described as being a few billion electron volts (Bev).

Every second or so at the top of the earth's atmosphere a cosmic-ray particle with an energy of a few Bev hits an area as big as one's thumbnail. Faster and more energetic cosmic rays exist, but they are progressively rarer. An area of a square yard is hit about once a minute by a particle with an energy of a thousand Bev, and about once a month by a cosmic ray with an energy of a million Bev. This is about the largest practical size for a counter and the slowest practical rate at which to operate them, but one million Bev is by no means the greatest energy of cosmic rays. At rare intervals one arrives with an energy of over one billion Bev (a billion billion electron volts). Such cosmic rays are so infrequent that one would hit a system of counters as large as a football stadium only once or twice a year. These strong cosmic rays are by far the most energetic things we know. Weight for weight, they completely dwarf atomic explosions. Even more powerful cosmic rays may exist, and a search is being conducted to try to discover whether there is an upper limit to their energy.

So far we have been discussing the nature of cosmic rays winging their solitary way as single nuclei through outer space. Mercurial messengers with speeds rivalling that of light itself, they are the only corporeal bodies to travel from star to star throughout the galaxy.

When these primary cosmic rays reach the atmosphere, they strike other atoms and break them to fragments, giving rise to a variety of effects, depending upon their initial speed. It has only been by means of studies from high-flying balloons near

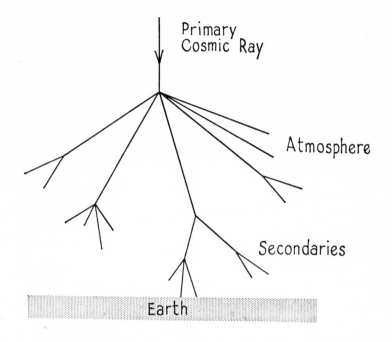

Shower development starting with the collision of a primary cosmic-ray particle with a nucleus and proceeding by further collisions and by decay of short-lived radioactive fragments. Most of the secondary particles reaching the ground are electrons.

the top of the atmosphere and from rockets and satellites above it that we have discovered the nature of primary cosmic rays.

When a primary cosmic-ray particle strikes the atmosphere, its first and commonest effect is to knock planetary electrons off other atoms and so leave a trail of charged electrons and nuclei along its path. Physicists have devised an ingenious method of tracing these paths. The high-flying balloons and rockets carry with them stacks of photographic plates covered with very thick layers of emulsion. When a charged particle passes through a stack of plates, it exposes the successive layers of emulsion in its path and leaves a photographic record of its course. This is exactly the same principle used by the ballistics expert in a murder mystery; he prowls around the library where the body lies, tracing the course of a bullet that has bored its way through a pile of books. By marking the path of the bullet, he can tell the point from which it was fired and the direction in which it was travelling.

High-flying balloons eventually return to earth and the records they carry can be recovered. No capsules were recovered from the satellites until after the IGY, but their counters were designed to transmit a signal to earth each time a satellite was struck by a cosmic ray, thus recording the number of hits.

Eventually a cosmic-ray nucleus may hit the nucleus of another atom, and this is likely to disrupt both. The effects on ordinary cosmic rays of a few Bev are like the interactions on a billiard table. One or both nuclei may be broken, producing a shower of their constituent fragments—electrons, neutrons, smaller nuclei, and X-rays. Similar phenomena can be reproduced in large cyclotrons and other atom-smashing machines in physics laboratories.

Such collisions are most numerous at a height of about 10 miles above the earth. Since low-energy fragments are absorbed before they reach the ground, balloons must be dispatched to that height to study weak cosmic rays.

Balloons are not so necessary for the study of high-energy rays, which produce more exciting results (these cannot be duplicated in the laboratory). Each of these atoms imparts so much energy to the fragments created by the collisions that the fragments surge on, causing billions of secondary collisions. The resulting particles form a cone-shaped spray, or shower, which expands as more and more collisions take place.

When the particles are travelling at nearly the speed of light, collisions may change them into bursts of high-energy waves, which may later reappear as new particles of matter called mesons. These are between electrons and protons in mass and, although short-lived, are highly penetrating and often reach sea level. Such showers of billions of secondary cosmic rays and electrons, though rare, may cover an area of a square mile by the time they reach the surface of the earth.

The deepest interest is attached to the primary cosmic rays which have the greatest energy. They are immensely rare, and if they reached sea level without colliding we would need counters as large as football fields to detect them. But be-

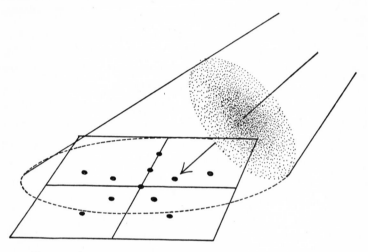

Shower of secondary cosmic rays striking an array of counters on the ground in an oblique direction.

cause they produce showers of atomic fragments, this is not necessary. Instead, several counters of normal size are spread over a large area. A big shower, from a really energetic primary cosmic ray, may simultaneously trigger all the counters scattered over several acres, or even several square miles. The direction of incidence of each ray can be measured electronically by noting the difference in time of arrival at each counter. Weak cosmic rays produce small showers that only trigger one or two counters.

In the spring of 1960 I visited a spread of cosmic-ray counters in Bolivia. A few miles from the highest commercial airport in the world, at La Paz, instrument shelters, like little chicken coops, were scattered over the desolate altiplano at a height of 16,000 feet.

The sun has been observed to affect cosmic rays. The effects are of three kinds. There are small variations associated with the rotation of the sun, small decreases after heavy magnetic storms, and increases of cosmic-ray activity of as much as two hundred and fifty times during some large solar flares. The smaller variations are both probably due to deflections of cosmic rays through changes in the magnetic fields caused by solar wind, and the large variations are almost certainly the result of the emission of bursts of cosmic rays from the sun.

Large cosmic-ray increases due to solar flares have been observed on these occasions:

28 February	1942
7 March	1942
26 February	1946
19 November	1949
23 February	1956
4 May	1960
12 November	1960
15 November	1960
20 November	1960

and it was a matter of great disappointment that none occurred during the IGY. The cosmic rays coming from the sun during these bursts are of low energy and may be but peak occurrences of normal solar emissions. The rarity of these outbursts from the sun and their relatively feeble nature show that the sun is not the normal source of cosmic rays, which arrive continuously and uniformly from every direction. The source of most cosmic rays must be farther out in space.

The rays are indeed cosmic. Two theories have been suggested for their origin in space. One is that they are created during explosions of whole stars, rare and spectacular events, of which the Star of Bethlehem may have been the most famous example. The formation of the Crab nebula was the result of a super-nova burst in A.D. 1054. If super-nova explosions create cosmic rays, more of them should come from the directions in which stars are most numerous, because where there are more stars there will be more chances for super-nova explosions. One such direction is the plane of the Milky Way. The other theory, suggested by the late Enrico Fermi, is that cosmic rays originate with low energies in stellar bursts, like those observed on the sun, and that the cosmic rays are accelerated to greater energies by the action of the galaxy's magnetic field exerted on peripatetic particles during vast aeons of time.

If this problem could be resolved, we would know a little more about the nature of the universe. But before we can understand the attempts being made to determine which of these theories is more likely to be correct, we must consider the effect of magnetic fields on cosmic rays. Being charged particles, cosmic rays tend to be deflected by magnetic fields and to follow them, whether the fields are those of the earth, the sun, or the whole galaxy. Two opposing influences determine the extent of the deflection. The stronger the magnetic field, the greater the deflecting influence; but the faster a particle is moving, the less any particular field will bend it.

Consider first the influence of the earth's magnetic field on cosmic rays. The earth is a large magnet whose lines of force bend inwards to each pole, and above the equator lie parallel with the earth's surface. Cosmic-ray particles can follow the direction of the earth's magnetic field to the poles without being deflected, but cannot reach other latitudes without crossing the field and undergoing at least some deflection. The extent to which a field succeeds in deflecting particles depends on their

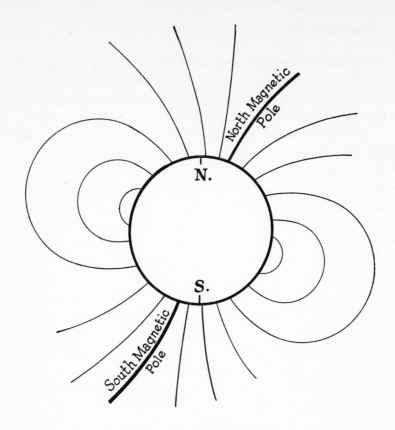

The earth's magnetic field.

speed. Particles, like automobiles being driven around a sharp bend in a highway, cannot make the bend if they are going too fast, but keep straight on and go off the road. Thus, only fast cosmic rays can burst through the magnetic field and reach the equatorial regions, but all cosmic rays can follow the lines of the field and reach the polar regions.

A study of the energy of cosmic rays received at different latitudes makes it possible to plot a diagram of the magnetic field in space around the earth. During the IGY ships and airplanes equipped with counters cruised from the Arctic to the Antarctic to do this. As had been suspected, the picture they obtained showed that the earth's magnetic field is not regular, but distorted. Not only are the magnetic poles in different places from the true poles, but they are not opposite one another, and the field in space over them is crooked.

During the last sun-spot maximum the average value of cosmic-ray intensity decreased all over the world. A long series of observations by S. E. Forbush of the Carnegie Institution of Washington, which has now extended through two complete sun-spot cycles, shows that average cosmic-ray intensity varies in an eleven-year cycle, that the two cycles are out of phase,

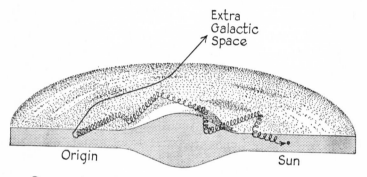

Cross-section of our galaxy, illustrating the extremely crooked path of a normal cosmic ray, which is readily deflected by the magnetic fields of stars, and the nearly straight path of a high-energy cosmic ray.

and that cosmic-ray intensity decreases as solar activity increases. Since cosmic rays are not normally produced by the sun, decreases in intensity must be caused by more effective magnetic shielding. In other words, cosmic rays are a means of studying changes in the sun's magnetic field and determining the effects of increases in solar wind during periods of high solar activity.

Finally, still seeking the origin of cosmic rays, we turn to the galaxy itself. Like other magnetic fields, that of the galaxy tends to deflect cosmic rays; but the more energetic a particle is, the less it will be deflected—the stiffer its path. The galaxy is so big that most cosmic rays wander through it on paths like corkscrews, so that we cannot tell from what direction they started. Fortunately, those rare cosmic rays with energies of over a billion billion electron volts have paths so stiff that they are not appreciably deflected from their course by galactic magnetic fields. Thus, strong cosmic rays should point directly to their source. If cosmic rays are formed in super-novae, the strongest rays should appear to be coming directly from them. But if Fermi's theory is correct, once cosmic rays achieve this stiffness they travel right out of the galaxy in which they originate. Any cosmic rays of greater energy, therefore, are likely to have reached us from galaxies other than our own.

This suggests that a study of the directions from which the most energetic cosmic rays come might provide a means of determining their mode of origin. Bruno Rossi, an Italian who like Fermi fled from Mussolini to the United States, built stations for observing cosmic rays in the United States, India, and Bolivia. In 1960 he announced that a cosmic ray more energetic than any previously recorded had been observed and that he considered it to have come from a source outside our galaxy. It is the only atom of matter so far reported to have reached the earth from a galaxy other than our own Milky Way.

Another way of tackling this problem is to try to determine the average age of cosmic rays. Their age would give us a clue to their probable origin, for cosmic rays coming directly from explosions of super-novae would be far younger than those which had wandered through the universe for a vast time collecting energy. Some idea of age may be obtained by considering the composition of cosmic rays. Old rays can be expected to have suffered many collisions, and collisions tend to break up large nuclei, like iron, into several smaller nuclei, such as lithium. H. S. W. Massey and R. L. Boyd, from measurements of the abundance of light nuclei and the scarcity of heavy nuclei, have suggested ages of a few million years. This would also indicate that many cosmic rays gather energy slowly and are not a result of large stellar explosions. The counters in Sputnik III which separated very heavy nuclei from the rest found that they constituted only 0.03 per cent.

Still another approach to this fascinating problem springs from radioastronomy. The Crab nebula and other super-novae have been found to emit strong radio noise. It seems likely that the radio noise is due to the rapid movement of free electrons in a magnetic field. This makes it probable that super-novae are the sources of some cosmic rays.

Perhaps both theories of origin are correct. If some rays are created by stellar explosions, an interesting corollary follows. Throughout historical time three super-nova explosions have been recorded for certain within a distance of 7,000 light years of the earth. These occurred in A.D. 1054, 1572, and 1604. There is some evidence in the Star of Bethlehem and in Greek records of two earlier explosions. It is thus reasonable to believe that every few hundred million years a star may explode very close to the solar system and envelop it for many years in a cloud of cosmic rays of heightened intensity. Such a bombardment hammering living creatures would certainly have affected the genes by which the characteristics of different forms of life are transmitted. This could have produced a burst of accelerated evolution. The parallels between this possibility and the effects of radiation due to atomic explosions are another reason to warrant their active investigation.

Living processes are affected by cosmic rays in another way. Interactions of cosmic rays with the atmosphere constantly produce several varieties of radioactive nuclei. The best known is carbon-14 (a radioactive isotope or variety of carbon, most of which is non-radioactive). All living creatures constantly absorb this radioactive carbon as carbon dioxide from the atmosphere and water, and its decay creates internal radioactive bombardments within us all—feeble, yet capable of causing evolutionary changes.

The existence of this radioactive carbon in living matter provides a valuable tool for archaeologists. Accurate counting shows that in all living matter the radioactivity is the same as in the atmosphere, but with death breathing stops, and so does exchange with the atmosphere. The radioactivity of the atmosphere is constantly renewed but not the radioactivity in dead creatures. This decreases as the carbon-14 decays, until after 40,000 years it has essentially all disappeared. Thus, a count of the amount of radioactivity in any piece of formerly living matter, be it wood, shell, bone, or mummified flesh, can be used to estimate its age. If it has as much radioactivity as living matter, it is young; if it has no radioactivity, it is 40,000 years old or more; if it has an intermediate amount, its age is less than 40,000 years and can be accurately estimated.

CHAPTER 9

❀

THE NORTH
MAGNETIC POLE

JUNE 1958

In June the Canadian Government invited a party of Canadian and American scientists to fly to the Arctic to inspect geophysical stations and to see the remote and desolate places along the margin of the Arctic Sea which were being intensively surveyed for the first time. After breakfast in Ottawa we took off through warm spring rain and flew in cloud for many hours until we sighted the barren rock hills of Baffin Island. Along the coast, winter drifts were melting to spread pools of light-blue water and muddy stains over fast sea ice.

We landed on the airfield at Frobisher Bay, where every night several airplanes stop to refuel on their flights between Europe and western North America. Frobisher Bay is an undistinguished monument to expediency, a dingy collection of wartime huts and hangars with later out-croppings of temporary buildings thrown up under the sudden necessity of providing radar lines in the Arctic. It mushroomed through the tundra, without benefit of the niceties of town planning, to fill an urgent need.

We had tea in a large waiting room built for the trans-Atlantic passengers and then drove 10 miles in an enclosed jeep to another settlement, new and of very different appearance. It was a village of wooden houses, small and gaily painted, among which a dozen Eskimo children in parkas were playing. They and their parents were all going to school, for the whole community had been uprooted and their life was being transformed. They had always hunted for a living, but their increasing population, the dearth of animals to hunt, and the possibility of earning better livelihoods elsewhere had forced a change. Parents were being trained to use their considerable natural ability to carve soapstone and ivory, while the children went to conventional schools to be equipped to run the airport eventually. Until their lack of knowledge of English (inevitable among nomadic hunters) had been overcome and they had grown accustomed to a settled life, they were being deliberately kept apart from the airbase. I had met one of the Eskimos twelve years before when as a young girl she was living with a missionary family at Coppermine, farther west on the arctic coast of Canada. As a result of good training, she was now the capable and charming nurse of the Eskimo hospital, which she ran in addition to taking care of her own home and family.

From Frobisher we flew across Baffin Island; it looked as barren as the face of Mars, and with high anticipation we saw that the sky over Foxe Basin was clear. The ice was cracking along the low shore, one of the flattest in the world, where the tide runs in and out as much as 15 miles twice a day, but the ice never entirely leaves. Few ships have penetrated this northern extension of Hudson Bay, and it is among the least known parts of North America.

It had been cloudy when I had flown that way ten years before, so that our party had not seen and had failed to discover the last major unknown part of North America. A year later survey planes of the Royal Canadian Air Force noticed and photographed Prince Charles Island. In 1951, when Tom Manning was sent in a small boat to plant the Canadian flag on this last *terra incognita* of North America, he had a detailed aerial map of the whole island (80 by 65 miles) in his hand. The island was now below us.

Our journey over the ice fields of this white and empty *cul-de-sac* of the seas was made the more interesting because we had on board one of its first explorers. The region north of Prince Charles and Air Force Islands had been first visited before the war by a party of adventurous youths under Manning's leadership. One of them, Graham Rowley, was with us. As we crowded over his shoulder by the porthole, he explained: "There ahead, to the right, is Bray Island. On our first trip across it I stopped, when I reached the highest point, to rest the dogs and looked across the strait you see below. There was a new island, the one that is right underneath us now." Some years later, when he was overseas, the Board of Geographical Names had called this Rowley Island and named others after his companions.

We were talking of the last explorations of North America, for the whole of Canada has now been photographed and the Arctic Sea has been searched by radar. There are no more unknown lands; the new frontiers for adventure are the ocean floors and limitless space.

We flew over Hecla and Fury Strait, its name commemorating, as do many polar features (Dolphin and Union, Erebus and Terror), the pairs of ships that first explored them. It only seems regrettable that another incongruous pair, the Racehorse and Carcase, were not so commemorated, too.

It was clear to the horizon and blindingly bright. We were over the Arctic archipelago, the only assemblage in the world of such large islands lying so close together. Three of the islands below us were each larger than Great Britain, but those ahead of us were of more moderate size and looking very

Christmas-like. Their brown cliffs rose from the frozen sea like chunks of layer cake on the white shelves of Santa Claus's bakeshop. Over the tops of the tabular islands, the snow had blown like frosting; and glaciers, like gobbets of icing, poured in solid streams over the edge to join the frozen, broken, and

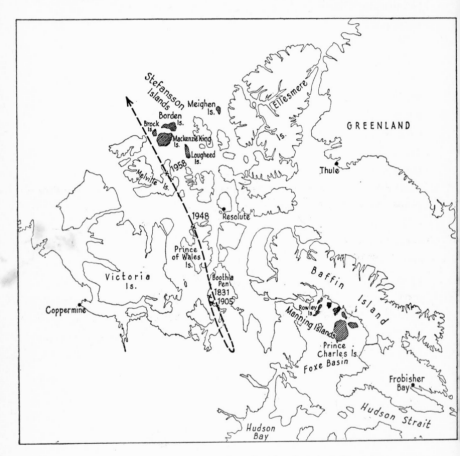

Map of part of the Canadian Arctic, showing the migration of the north magnetic pole. Shaded areas are the last two groups of islands to be discovered in North America, the "Conservative" Islands by Stefansson (1913–8) and the Manning Islands (1936–9 and 1947).

refrozen surface of the white sea below. To the west reared the straight cliffs and flat surface of Somerset Island, off which in 1849 the British explorer Admiral Sir John Franklin had been lost with both his ships and all his men. Beyond it lay, like another great slab, Prince of Wales Island, to which in 1947 the Dominion Observatory had tracked the shifting north magnetic pole.

What do we mean when we talk of the earth's magnetic poles? Like other magnets, the earth has a north and a south pole; however, the effective poles are not on the surface but inside the earth. In 1600, William Gilbert, physician to Queen Elizabeth, pointed out that freely suspended magnets may be used to plot the direction of the earth's magnetic field, which lies in barrel-shaped curves about the earth, pointing towards the poles within. The poles which we call the north and south magnetic poles are simply the two places where a compass points straight downwards.

The north magnetic pole was first discovered by Commander James Clark Ross, R.N., on June 1, 1831. From his camp in an abandoned Eskimo snow house, he described the desolate scene: "The land at this place is very low near the coast, but rises into ridges of 50 or 60 feet high about a mile inland. We could have wished that a place so important had possessed more of mark or note. It was scarcely censurable to regret that there was not a mountain to indicate the spot to which so much of interest must ever be attached; and I could even have pardoned any one among us who had been so romantic or absurd as to expect that the magnetic pole was an object as conspicuous and mysterious as the fabled mountain of Sinbad, that it even was a mountain of iron, or a magnet as large as Mont Blanc. But Nature had here erected no monument to denote the spot which she had chosen as the centre of one of her great and dark powers; and where we could do little ourselves towards this end, it was our business to submit, and to be content in noting by mathematical numbers and signs, as with things of far more importance in the terrestrial system, what we could but ill distinguish in any other manner."

That journey was a hard one. The ship *Victory*, an old Isle of Man ferry with primitive steam engines as well as sails, was beset by the ice and crushed. The crew who had sailed on May 23, 1829, were not picked up until more than four years later, by which time they were "unshaven since I know not when, dirty, dressed in rags of wild beasts instead of the tatters of civilization, and starved to the very bone—gaunt and grim." During the last winter their food ran out and they survived by trapping and eating arctic foxes. At that time the captain wrote in his diary: "Let him who reads to condemn what is so meagre, have some compassion on the writer who had nothing better than this meagreness, this repetition, this reiteration of the ever-resembling, every-day dullness to record, and what was infinitely worse, to endure. I might have seen more, it has been said; it may be; but I saw only ice and snow, cloud and drifting and storm. According to Persius, it is hunger which makes poets write as it makes parrots speak; I suspect that neither poet nor parrot would have gained much eloquence under a fox diet, and that an insufficient one, in the blessed regions of Boothia Felix." Let those who consider it a hardship today to spend a year in the polar regions reflect upon exploration in the days of sail.

We had no such hardships, for our plane landed at the all-weather airfield at Resolute, the central base for weather stations on the Canadian Arctic Islands. Although there were still high drifts of snow, it was melting. The temperature was slightly above freezing, and the sun shone brightly twenty-four hours a day. Inside the base a large mess-hall was open day and night, and a succession of men from the construction and supply crews, meteorologists and airmen, came and went in relays. They were working around the clock to take advantage of the brief summer season. The majority were Canadians, but there were some American meteorological observers and scientists among them.

Since Resolute is so close to the magnetic pole and so far from settled regions, it is not surprising that in addition to the ten-year-old weather station a great number of other scientific projects were in hand. There was a new tide-gauge, built with considerable difficulty to function without damage from the grinding ice. There was an important seismological station. There were cosmic-ray counters and filters to measure the amount of radioactive fall-out in the air. But the chief interest of the scientific colony centred on the magnetic recorders, on the ionospheric sounder for probing the upper atmosphere with radio waves, and on the transparent dome which would shelter an observer of the aurora during the winter darkness.

Here, sitting almost on top of the north magnetic pole, was one of the best places to learn more about the earth's magnetic field and its subsidiary effects on radio communications and on the aurora.

THE EARTH'S
MAGNETIC FIELD

We have noticed a curious feature of the north magnetic pole. It is moving. In 1831 Ross located it on Boothia Peninsula on the north coast of North America. In 1947 P. H. Serson found it to be on Prince of Wales Island 200 miles farther north. In 1959 it was heading across Melville Island and had picked up speed, for it had travelled another 200 miles in much less time.

Such movement is not only true of the magnetic poles but also of the whole magnetic field of the earth, which is constantly changing in strength and direction. This is called the secular variation. It is well illustrated at Greenwich, England, where changes in direction of the compass have been followed since A.D. 1600. What could be moving about inside the apparently solid earth in such a manner as to produce these effects? The first clue is linked to another reason for thinking that the earth should not be considered a fixed magnet like those in hardware shops. At red heat, iron loses its magnetism. There are many indications that the temperature of the interior of the earth is at a few thousand degrees. Thus, the core is much too hot to be permanently magnetized. Indeed, it is thought to be iron so hot that it is molten in spite of the great pressures existing there.

A century ago the first analysis of tidal behaviour of the solid part of the earth also suggested that it reacted to tidal forces not as a uniform solid sphere, but as a hollow one or one containing a fluid core. This also made it probable that the central part of the earth might indeed be molten.

During the last fifty years the study of earthquake waves has revealed the nature of the earth's internal structure in much more detail. Large earthquakes shake the whole earth, imperceptibly in distant places, but enough to affect delicate seismographs almost daily. These seismic waves, deep whispers from some monstrous organ, pass across the whole earth in twenty-three minutes and reverberate within it for hours. They are recorded and precisely timed at six hundred earthquake observatories throughout the world. The records of waves which pass through the earth have been pieced together to reveal the internal structure of the earth, just as X-rays do the human body.

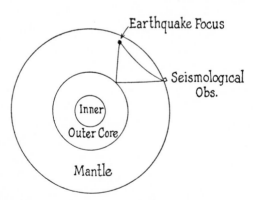

Cross-section of the earth's interior, depicting the inner core, believed to be solid; the outer core of liquid iron; and the solid mantle and crust of rocks of different kinds. Two possible paths of seismic waves from an earthquake to an observatory are shown.

The earth's internal arrangements are like those of a four-minute egg. There is a liquid yolk or core of one composition, a solid white or mantle of another, and a thin solid shell or crust of a third. In the very centre within the liquid core there may be a solid button.

On the assumption that meteorites are broken pieces of a planet, or at any rate representative of material common in the solar system, it has been suggested that the earth's mantle has the composition of stony meteorites. Thus, the core is generally considered to be white-hot molten iron, the mantle to resemble stony meteorites; and the crust is, of course, the part we see. In A.D. 1600 William Gilbert demonstrated that the main part of the earth's magnetic field is generated deep within it; the only place which could both generate a magnetic field and allow it to move about is this great central globule of white-hot molten iron 1,800 miles beneath our feet.

This seething molten mass is believed to be moving in torpid currents, ceaselessly ebbing and flowing inside the earth, just as the hot gases in the sun boil up, ebb, and flow. Applying knowledge that astronomers have gained of the shifting magnetic fields in the sun, physicists have come to believe that the earth's magnetic field shifts with the movement of the currents in its molten core. Astronomers believe that the swirling vortices of ionized gas on the surface of the sun may act like the wires in an electric dynamo to carry electric currents which excite magnetic fields. The earth's core is thought to behave in the same way in generating the earth's magnetic field. If the motion of the core produces currents which rise in some places and sink in others, as in sun-spots or like the currents in a saucepan of boiling water, the earth's magnetic field might be expected to vary and perhaps be stronger above rising currents and weaker above sinking currents. This view is supported by the observation that there are regions of greater and lesser intensity scattered irregularly about the earth. It has also been noted that the spots of higher and lower magnetic intensity move westward around the globe. Evidently, the solid part of the earth is moving faster than its liquid core.

A knowledge of the irregular changes in the earth's field, besides having value in theoretical studies, is of great practical importance for navigation of all kinds. These changes cannot be predicted but can only be discovered by world-wide surveys. The best surveys were those made by the non-magnetic ship *Carnegie* which had no iron on board, only wood and bronze. In 1929 she unfortunately burned at Apia, Samoa, and with the passing of time navigational charts are getting out of date and there is a grave danger that essential data will not be gathered. In some places the declination shown on charts is already in error by several degrees. Fortunately, however, the Soviet Union has recently built another non-magnetic ship, the *Zarya*, and during the IGY this vessel and American and Canadian airplanes made magnetic surveys of the Pacific and Atlantic Oceans and over the Arctic. The Americans have now proposed a scheme to complete an airborne magnetic survey of all the oceans of the world before 1965.

In recent years new light has been shed on the behaviour of the earth's magnetic field through the study of the feeble magnetism of ordinary rocks and old pieces of pottery. When sediments accumulate on the sea floor, when lava solidifies, or when pottery is baked, certain processes act to line up the magnetic elements of the rock or earthenware with that of the prevailing magnetic field, and then lock a record of that direction into the material so that the record is preserved without subsequent change. These studies have shown that the earth's magnetic field was very different in the past and has changed more rapidly than anyone would have believed possible a few years ago. Not only is it changing in direction in a way that corresponds to the observed wanderings of the magnetic pole, but it has also changed in strength and been reversed from time to

time. These studies have been interpreted to mean that the
continents were in different latitudes in past times. It seems
likely that they have moved about relative to one another,
and this slow wandering has been called continental drift.

Odd as it sounds, the earth seems at times to have lost its
magnetism; and when this magnetism has reappeared, it has
been reversed in direction, so that the north magnetic pole
would at times have been in the southern hemisphere. Deter-
minations of the strength of the earth's magnetic field suggest
that such a change is now taking place, because the strength of
the field has decreased by 10 per cent in the past century.
If the trend continues, the earth's magnetic field may pass
through a zero value in a few centuries and then reverse its direction. When it gets too weak, compasses will cease to work,
the aurora and the Van Allen belts will vanish, and long-range
radio channels will no longer operate.

The behaviour of the magnetic field of the earth seems less
surprising when we realize that something similar is occurring
in the sun. The solar cycle of roughly eleven years, which we
have mentioned in connection with the sun-spot cycle, also corresponds to changes in the magnetic field of the sun. Apparently, the sun reverses its magnetism each cycle and the sun-
spots are direct signs of magnetic swirls in the gases of the sun.

The earth and the sun and other stars all generate magnetic
fields in the same manner. But the currents in the liquid iron
of the earth are sluggish and take thousands of years to reverse,
while the sun takes eleven years, and one peculiar star has been
observed to change every nine days.

Besides the main field of the earth, which is generated in the
core, there is another rapidly varying field which is generated
in the upper atmosphere. Like the sea, the air has tides. These
have no more effect on us than ocean tides have on the fish in
the sea. It is at coasts that tides are observed, and it is on the
upper surface of the ocean of air far above us that tides in the

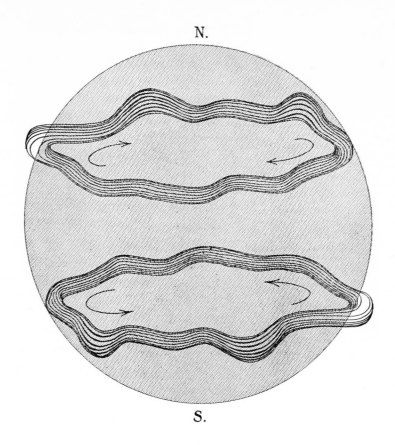

N.

S.

The sun's two toroidal magnetic fields whose existence is suspected. They probably rotate in opposite directions and create sun-spots where they emerge.

air produce noticeable effects. There, on the edge of space, the atmosphere is thin and light and with corresponding ease twice a day it bobs up and down as much as a mile. The effect can be seen even in high mountains. For example, at Chacaltaya Observatory, Bolivia, which at 17,500 feet is the highest permanently inhabited geophysical observatory in the world, the recording barograph shows two tidal waves a day with the greatest regularity.

Higher in the atmosphere, the gases are so thin as to be nearly a vacuum, and they are exposed to bombardment by cosmic rays, solar winds, and waves of ultra-violet and other radiation from the sun. Under these circumstances many of the atoms are stripped of some electrons and become charged ions. These ionized gases can then conduct electricity and are in the same state as the tenuous gases in neon signs and fluorescent lights. The same properties that light up the streets with advertising produce conducting layers high in the upper atmosphere, which because of these properties is called the ionosphere. As tides move these conducting layers up and down within the earth's magnetic field, electricity is generated in the layers. In any limited volume these currents are small, but there is an immensity of air and, collectively, currents of over a million amperes surge above us at heights of 100 miles or so. These produce a smaller secondary part of the earth's magnetic field which varies much more rapidly than the part deep in the core.

Currents are presumably formed in the oceans also, but the oceans are much smaller and more scattered than the core or the atmosphere, and their tides are much slighter than those in the upper air, so that the magnetic effects of the sea are negligible.

The complexity of these variations explains the value of having magnetic observatories at all latitudes to keep systematic records. The main field generated in the core is subject to slow changes over very long periods of time. The secondary field, formed by the reaction of the main field on the conducting layers in the upper atmosphere, is constantly changing in a regular fashion, under the influence of solar and lunar tides, with the time of day, with the season of the year, with the eclipses of the sun. It varies also with latitude.

When outbursts of radiation from the sun strike the upper atmosphere, they cause powerful and irregular currents to flow,

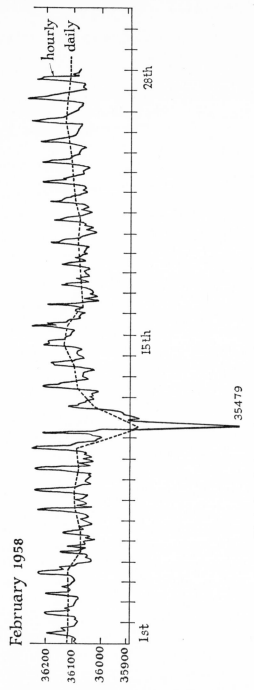

Variation during February 1958 of the horizontal component of the earth's magnetic field at Addis Ababa, Ethiopia. Notice the daily cycle and the effect of the great magnetic storm of February 11, 1958.

and create erratic fluctuations in the total value of the earth's magnetic field. These sudden disturbances are called magnetic storms and are usually accompanied by aurora and disruption of radio propagation. Happily, they do not occur every day. But because they derive from solar eruptions, and because the blast of gas takes about a day to travel from the sun, they can often be predicted.

In each cycle, as the sun-spots increase in number, magnetic storms increase in frequency and severity. They show some correlation with individual sun-spots and tend to recur at intervals of twenty-seven days, the period of rotation of the sun.

All these effects are prominent enough to be readily observed and of such obvious value that it can be well understood why many geomagneticians welcomed a chance to establish new geophysical observatories during the IGY. One example is the Addis Ababa Geophysical Observatory, which was established in 1957 as the first geophysical observatory in Ethiopia. The effects of magnetic storms are plainly shown in the records obtained there in February 1958. These include large daily variations in the magnetic field due to the sun's normal activity and a large disturbance due to the sizable magnetic storm of February 1. This storm was unusually powerful for the tropics. Because the earth's field attracts the solar wind to the polar regions, magnetic storms are more numerous and severe there than they are nearer the equator.

Slowly, by piecing together many such fragments of information, scientists are discovering more about the earth's magnetic field. The field is already known to be asymmetrical, but it will take time to draw a precise map in three dimensions. In any case, such a map will be only an average or instantaneous view because, due to the fluctuations in the ionosphere, the field is constantly changing.

CHAPTER 11

THE UPPER ATMOSPHERE

The earth, like Salome, is shrouded in seven veils. Two we have discussed: the Van Allen belts, the farthest flung and most tenuous, wisps blown by the sun and shot with the colour of the aurora. Now let us admire the other five—the four regions or layers of the ionosphere and the innermost ozone layer, all rising and falling with breath-like tides upon the earth's rotund figure.

These veils are earth's garments, but in rather immodest fashion they are transparent, as we can tell whenever we look up at a cloudless sky. This is scarcely surprising, for the upper atmosphere, of which these layers form part, is so thin and tenuous that for most purposes it could be regarded as a vacuum. Nevertheless, it affords great protection to us from the storms and blasts of outer space; without that protection it is doubtful whether life would ever have developed. Each veil is a trap that stops some particular type of radiation and is, by that absorption of energy, itself created.

In Chapter 7 we mentioned that the outer and inner Van

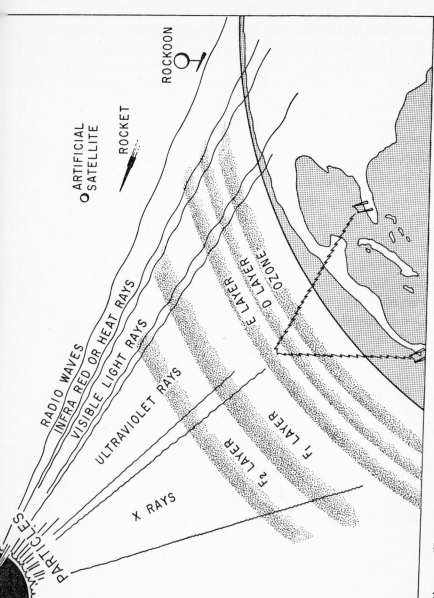

Diagram illustrating the layers of the atmosphere, electro-magnetic radiation from the sun, and current techniques for exploring nearby space. Note how atmospheric layers block the passage of both artificial

Allen belts are magnetic traps which catch and hold the fast-flying particles from the sun and outer space. The main parts of these belts were not discovered until artificial satellites penetrated them at heights of over 1,000 miles, although we now know that the horns of the outer belt may reach down in the polar regions to altitudes of only about 65 miles.

The other five layers were not recognized until this century, although some of the indications that finally led to their discovery have been known longer. As soon as the earth's magnetism was accurately observed, it was noticed that a compass needle moved in a slight oscillation with the time of day. A few scientists believed that strong currents flowing high in the atmosphere could produce these oscillations of compass needles.

This theory was being developed at the same time that James Clerk Maxwell and H. R. Hertz were doing their work on radio waves. They had established that these waves travelled in straight lines and therefore could not be transmitted around a spheroidal earth because they would shoot straight out into space. G. Marconi in 1901 upset all their calculations and predictions by transmitting a radio message over the great hill of the earth's curvature from England to Newfoundland. The only feasible answer to this obvious contradiction was that the radio waves had bounced off some obstruction and angled back to earth; and the only possible reflectors were charged particles high in the atmosphere. No proof of this existed until after World War I, when radio techniques were improved. Sir Edward Appleton and Dr. Merle Tuve by different methods established the presence of three reflecting layers in the ionosphere from which they obtained reflections of radio waves sent vertically upwards. Tuve's technique was similar to that used in timing echoes to measure the distance to an echoing cliff or to the ocean floor. It involves a radio or radar set emitting very brief bursts upwards and recording the time that passes before an echo returns. Since the object of much of this work is to discover a good frequency to use for sending messages, the sounder does not send just one burst, but immediately tunes itself to a slightly higher frequency and sends another. Continuing in this fashion, it sweeps the frequencies from 1 to 25 megacycles (1 to 25 million cycles a second), measuring the height at which radio waves of each fre-

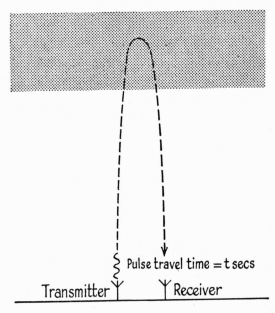

Pulse travel time = t secs

Transmitter   Receiver

The ionospheric sounder reflects signals off the ionosphere to determine the presence of its various layers.

quency are reflected. It then shuts down and repeats the operation automatically every fifteen minutes. The instrument reproduces the results on a photographic film.

Not all the regions produce simultaneous reflections because the layers in the ionosphere are unstable and change. Some of these changes are diurnal and regular; some are irregular and connected with solar outbursts. Anyone who considers the matter can recall noticing the diurnal changes; they make it possible to receive distant radio stations better at night. At less frequent and irregular intervals solar outbursts cause extra ionization which can absorb radio waves on some frequencies and play havoc with international radio, ship, and aircraft communications. Both sorts of change can be predicted, and recommendations can be made as to the most effective radio-wave frequencies to use at any time between any two stations in the world-wide net of commercial radio communications. Such a service is provided by the National Bureau of Standards in the United States.

This sounding board in the ionosphere is formed by the absorption of the intense ultra-violet and X-rays from the sun which strike the upper atmosphere during each day. These rays ionize the atoms and molecules of the upper air; that is, they break them apart into electrons, each carrying a negative charge, and ions, carrying a positive one. As the rays penetrate more deeply into denser air and encounter more numerous atoms, this process increases until all the energy of the ultra-violet and X-rays has been absorbed. At certain levels in the atmosphere the ionization produced by different types of absorption is intense, and layers of charged particles are formed. The process is complicated by the rotation of the earth, which causes the sun's rays to slant at changing angles through the atmosphere. The height and strength of the layers, therefore, varies according to the time of day; and at sunset the source of ionization is cut off. The layers also vary with the irregular changes in emission from the sun and are especially affected by solar flares. Finally, the gases in the upper atmosphere differ in abundance and ease of ionization, so that each of several kinds of gas tends to produce a separate layer. Appleton quickly discovered and named three reflecting layers, one of which is sometimes observed to split, and these he named from the bottom upwards D, E, F_1, and F_2 regions. There is one more layer, the lowest, which is not ionized and does not reflect radio waves. It is, therefore, not recorded by the same devices and not called the C region but the ozone layer, because of the extra ozone molecules present in it.

Although the atmosphere in all of these regions is extremely tenuous, much has been discovered about its probable composition. From the character of the radiation in the farthest layer of the atmosphere (the outer Van Allen belt), it seems to consist almost exclusively of electrons, each having weak energies

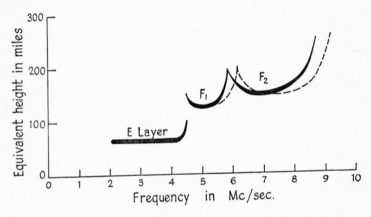

The altitude at which radio signals of varying frequencies are reflected by layers of the atmosphere. Data was obtained by a vertical incidence sounder.

of only 100,000 electron volts, although the particles are multitudinous. The way in which the changes observed in this belt coincide with changes in solar activity would indicate that some of these electrons come from the sun. Whether they are accelerated within the sun and merely trapped in the earth's field or trapped first and subsequently accelerated is not yet clear. There may also be heavier ions present in this belt, but they are not energetic.

The radiation in the more stable inner member of the Van

Allen belts consists primarily of very energetic protons with energies in the order of 100 million electron volts. There are also electrons. Whereas the outer belt is fed by intermittent blasts of solar wind, the inner belt is thought to have resulted from the trapping of particles created by cosmic-ray bombardments of the atmosphere. This may explain why it is more stable.

It is known that electrons, rather than positive ions, reflect radio waves, and these are concentrated in the E, F_1, and F_2 layers, the last two of which often merge. The D layer only forms intermittently at a height of about 40 miles. Electrons in the E layer, at a height of 65 miles, suffice to reflect waves of low frequency, but higher-frequency waves pass through the E layer, especially at night, and are reflected by the F layers at heights of from 100 to 150 miles. Still higher frequencies, such as those used for television, are only reflected under abnormal conditions. Generally they go straight on out into space and are not reflected around the earth, as are radio waves.

In addition to electrons, the ions present are chiefly those one might expect to find in the atmosphere—charged ions of nitrogen and oxygen. Free hydroxyl ions are also present, and very rarely, sodium ions. These sodium ions occur in the ratio of one atom of sodium to every three million million nitrogen atoms, but we know they are present because we can recognize their characteristic yellow spectral lines in the faint air glow at night.

Below the ionosphere, at a height of only about 10 to 20 miles, the ultra-violet light nearest to the visible violet is absorbed by a process that instead of breaking up atoms into ions builds approximately one in every million oxygen atoms (O_2) into an ozone atom (O_3). Although this layer cannot be detected by ionospheric sounders, it is so low that it can be sampled by balloons, and its variations are followed by measuring from the ground the extent to which ultra-violet light is being absorbed. As more opportunities occur to sample the higher regions with the aid of rockets and satellites, more precise knowledge of composition will be obtained.

Since the ionization which produces these layers is due to ultra-violet light and X-rays coming from the sun, we might expect that when the sun is directly overhead the ionization would be strongest and at night it would disappear. In a general way the strength of the ionization of the E and F1 layers follows this predictable pattern with the days and seasons, but it is complicated by the lingering of radiation after the sun has gone, especially in the F2 layer, by large vertical movements of the electrons, and by winds which blow turbulently from one part of the world to another with great speed at those immense heights.

These ionospheric winds were studied during the IGY, as were the implications of the discovery of the outer Van Allen belt, with its horns which project down to disturb the ionosphere. In Antarctica new stations co-operated to study the rather unexpected phenomena found during the long alternating seasons of winter darkness and continuous daylight. Another chain of stations was relatively closely spaced across the maximum auroral belt from the polar regions in Canada and Greenland into the United States. On the equator a group of four vertical sounding stations in Peru and one in Bolivia investigated sizable changes occurring in the ionosphere at sunrise and sunset. Simultaneous comparisons in radio transmission were made across the equator between Antofagasta, Chile; Clorinda, Argentina; Huancayo and Trujillo, Peru; Guayaquil, Ecuador; and São Paulo, Brazil, which proved that conditions were similar in all circuits in daytime but different at night. The strength of the radio signals could be correlated in some cases with the variations in the magnetic field recorded at Huancayo. Variations in both are caused by strong electric currents in the ionosphere over the equator.

I have mentioned that equipment was installed in many places to measure radio noise and to check whether outbursts occurred simultaneously in widely separated places. Some bursts of radio noise are associated with solar flares, but other radio noise is related to local and distant thunderstorms, about five thousand of which are believed to be active at any time over the earth.

An idea of the power and impact of magnetic storms can be conveyed by describing some of the effects a single large storm can have on the ionosphere and on communications. Early in 1958, as the number of sun-spots was beginning to decline from the highest peak ever recorded, the interest of solar astronomers centred on a group of sun-spots covering three billion square miles of the sun's southern hemisphere, one of the ten largest groups on record. The group was active, and on February 8, as it crossed the central meridian, it emitted no less than seven minor solar flares. On February 9 at 2:08 p.m. mountain standard time, or 21.08 hours universal time, the observer on duty at Sacramento Peak Observatory, New Mexico, looking through a solar telescope similar to that which I had seen at Climax, Colorado, noticed the outbreak of a major flare in the form of a bright explosion which spread rapidly in the vicinity of the sun-spot group. During the two hours that the flare lasted he and other observers all over the sunlit side of the earth flooded with messages the branches of the World Data Centres charged with receiving reports of flares. These branches were the High Altitude Observatory, Boulder, Colorado; the Crimea Observatory, Simeis, U.S.S.R.; and the Observatoire de Meudon, Meudon, France. A large flare, centrally located in the sun's disc, appeared likely to blast the earth with particles a day later, and as a routine matter warnings of a magnetic storm might have been sent to cable and wireless companies, to airlines and shipping companies and others whose communications could be affected. But the scientists at Boulder, who, being on the sunlit side of the earth, had received most of the reports, decided that this type of flare would not cause a magnetic storm. The sky at Boulder was overcast, and they could not see the flare themselves; as they freely admitted afterwards, they were quite wrong. Today with our increased experience, the special features of this flare would have been noted and correctly interpreted, and a warning would have been issued.

On February 10 at 8:26 p.m. eastern standard time, twenty-eight hours after the flare began, one of the greatest magnetic storms on record struck the earth. Within a few seconds magnetograms all over the earth quivered. Their recording beams of light or their pens, which had been pursuing a steady course, began to zigzag back and forth across the paper within the non-magnetic huts in which they were housed in scores of places around the globe. Probably at first no one noticed that the earth had been struck by a shock wave of first magnitude which was sending currents of millions of amperes coursing through the ionosphere; geomagneticians do not sit in the dark in their unheated huts with their instruments. But at Hiraiso, Japan, one instrument reacted so violently that a technician thought it was out of order and stopped it for an hour and a half until a scientist recognized the cause of the trouble as an unprecedented storm.

As the solar wind blasted the earth, the outer Van Allen belt filled to overflowing with electrons rushing widely from one hemisphere to the other and exciting the upper atmosphere until it glowed. At eight-thirty a fiery red aurora spread rapidly from the maximum auroral zones across all Canada and the whole United States to Mexico and Cuba and from Antarctica to Cape Horn and South Africa. In Australia it was reported at seventy places and lasted in some throughout the night. Aurora was observed in Japan half a dozen times during the IGY, but the red aurora of February 11, 1958, was outstanding and widely reported. Its fiery brilliance misled the local populace into calling out the fire department to deal with non-existent conflagrations. That night while flying across Iowa at 17,000 feet I watched it filling the sky with brilliant rosy arches which turned from red to a luminescent greenish glow.

At one minute before nine a fresh blast sent magnetometers everywhere off scale. The intense radiation had, without doubt, greatly increased the ionization in the atmosphere and added a D layer. This more intense radiation, instead of reflecting high-frequency radio waves, absorbed them. At nine o'clock all direct radio links across the Atlantic Ocean faded out. Desperately engineers relayed messages south to escape the worst effects and for a time were able to reach Europe via stations in Central and South America and Tangiers, but by eleven o'clock all radio communication between the Old and New Worlds ceased. The effects on airlines can be imagined. When trans-Atlantic radio faded, there were a hundred or so airplanes over the north Atlantic. So long as they were within line of sight of some ground station, they could communicate, but the ionosphere was useless. Urgent messages were relayed from plane to nearby plane by radio operators nervously keeping contact with one another as they crossed the broad stretches of the ocean. Passengers slept undisturbed that night, unaware that trans-Atlantic planes were flying blind like two opposing flights of pigeons in a fog. Over the Pacific lonely planes, too, flew in silence, their whereabouts unknown to anyone but themselves.

The magnetic impulses generated by electric currents in the ionosphere in turn created other electric currents in the earth and in power and cable lines across it. All over Canada and northern United States surges of power swept over transmission lines, tripping circuit breakers and plunging cities into darkness. The trans-Atlantic cable, which after nine o'clock was the only channel of communication across the ocean, al-

ternately faded and squawked as electrical pulses of potentials
as high as 2,600 volts raced through it, straining both the
equipment and the nerves of the engineers. But it continued to
operate fitfully until at dawn the return of sunlight exercised a
tranquilizing effect on the ionosphere. Slowly over the next
two days the ionosphere returned to normal. These then were
the effects of a great solar and magnetic storm. Ironically, it
was one for which no official warning was issued although the
solar flare which caused it had been seen twenty-eight hours
in advance.

CHAPTER 12

AURORA

Among all earthly phenomena one of the most eerie and spectacular is the aurora polaris. Unfortunately, most of its brilliant displays occur over the globe's inhospitable and empty regions. A truly fine show of the aurora borealis is seen only once or twice every ten years over the thickly settled parts of Europe and North America, and over the tropics about once in a century. The aurora australis is almost exclusively a perquisite of penguins, for only rarely does it reach as far north as Tasmania and New Zealand. The glimpses had by most city dwellers, therefore, convey but a poor impression of the magnificent displays regularly seen over the zones of maximum auroral frequency.

In these regions, when the displays are at their best in the spring or autumn nights during the times of sun-spot maxima, the whole sky may at one time be filled with swirling flames of red, pulsating and changing as though blown by silent tornadoes of ineffable intricacy and speed. On occasion, in the Northwest Territories of Canada, I have seen brilliant bands of light dim the stars in the black dome of the sky, while other parallel arches stretched more and more faintly to the distant

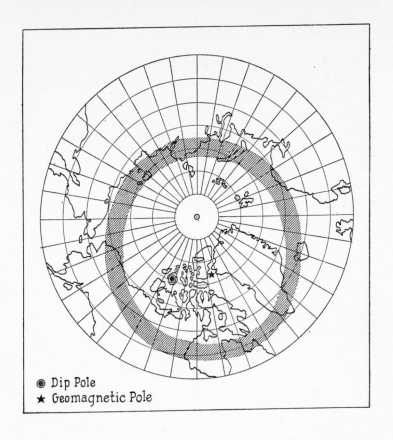

◎ Dip Pole
★ Geomagnetic Pole

Distribution of maximum frequency of aurora borealis.

horizon until the heavens were filled with moving lines of colour advancing like ranks of soldiers into battle. Each band
rippled and shifted brilliantly with a shimmering flicker and
flow, from its dull red base, through yellow, to a crest of palest
green or purple. The whole army of marching lines of light was
matched against its own reflection on the sparkling waves of
the cold lake below.

Seneca, the Roman, knew them, but auroral displays are
very rare in the Mediterranean, and the best early accounts
were by the Norse Vikings and by Polar explorers.

Scientific interest in aurora seems to have been first awakened by the remarkable display of March 6, 1716, described by Edmund Halley of London. He related the aurora to the earth's magnetic field, an observation which was confirmed and extended by the Swedish scientists Celsius and Hiorten a few years later. In the next hundred years further progress became possible through studies, pursued quite independently by two German scientists, of phenomena with which auroral displays are linked—earth's magnetism and the sun-spot cycle. We have already mentioned the discovery of the sun-spot cycle by Schwabe; the earth's magnetism (which the Chinese had discovered long before) first began to be well understood about 1830 through the efforts of the great German mathematician C. F. Gauss. One of the observatories which Gauss was responsible for establishing was at Bombay, and there the Indian geomagnetician N. F. Moos first analyzed the characteristics of magnetic storms, with which the aurora is so generally associated.

The First and Second Polar Years provided valuable opportunities for the study of the aurora. In the course of the former, Herman Fritz produced the first maps of the frequency of aurora by drawing lines to connect places where on the average the aurora was visible the same number of nights each year. More recent and refined versions of these maps have been prepared by E. H. Vestine, a Canadian working in the United States. They reveal that aurora are most frequent along two circular belts or zones which have their centres at the north and south geomagnetic poles and lie at distances of about 1,600 miles away from the poles. Along these belts the aurora may be seen on most nights.

Meanwhile, the Norwegians Carl Störmer and Lars Vegard, by photographing aurora simultaneously from two places some miles apart, provided us with most of the data we have about their height. Aurora are most frequent at a height of about 65

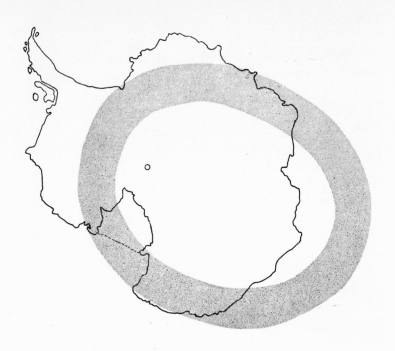

Distribution of maximum frequency of aurora australis in Antarctica.

miles, few being observed at lower levels. They are occasionally seen, however, at heights of as much as 600 miles.

As early as 1733 a Frenchman, M. de Mairan, demonstrated that the early idea that the aurora was due to the reflection of sunlight by high ice crystals was probably wrong. The first notion of the true origin of aurora followed the successful photographing of the aurora spectrum by A. J. Ångström in 1867 in Sweden. At first the lines could not be identified, but further photography of the aurora and successful reproductions of the lines in laboratory experiments (by many workers including L. Vegard in Norway, J. Kaplan and C. W. Gartlein in the United States, and J. C. McLennan in Canada) showed that they were mostly due to molecules and atoms of oxygen and nitrogen which had become excited or ionized in the upper atmosphere. Molecules of both oxygen and nitrogen normally consist of two atoms linked together. Collisions in the near vacuum at heights of 60 miles or more can knock electrons off the molecules or even separate them into individual charged atoms.

The absence of any hydrogen lines was long considered proof that there was no hydrogen in the upper atmosphere, but during observations of a strong display on August 19, 1951, in the United States A. B. Meinel showed that the red colour often observed was at least partly due to hydrogen, and a slight displacement of the hydrogen line towards the violet end of the spectrum could be explained by the Doppler effect.

The Doppler effect in sound waves is familiar to anyone who has listened to a fast train passing a station platform. The effect is particularly noticeable if the locomotive's whistle is blowing, because the note drops to a lower tone, and changes in volume as well, as the train passes. The speed of an express train may be as much as 100 feet a second, a fraction of the speed of about 1,000 feet a second at which sound waves travel in the air. As the train approaches, the speed of the sound waves is increased by the addition of the velocity of the train, so that the waves arrive faster than if the train were standing still. As the train recedes, the sound waves are slowed down, their wave-length is lengthened, and the frequency of the note falls. In the case of extremely fast motions, the same effect can be observed in light waves; those from a rapidly receding body arrive less frequently and hence appear redder than light from the same body when it is still; those from a rapidly approaching body are crowded together and appear more violet. Using this technique, Meinel in 1951 showed that, unlike the light from oxygen and nitrogen atoms in aurora, the frequency of the light due to hydrogen atoms was increased, indicating that the hydrogen atoms were moving towards the earth at speeds of as much as 2,000 miles a second along lines of force in the earth's magnetic field. The earth was being bombarded by hydrogen atoms from the sun.

This was the first definite evidence that aurora might be produced as the result of the bombardment of the upper atmosphere by high-speed nuclei of hydrogen atoms. The reader will of course have realized that the probable source of high-speed hydrogen nuclei is the sun. It was suggested that particles travelling at such speeds could easily give rise to the excitation of other atoms and explain in general terms the cause of aurora.

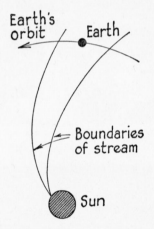

A corpuscular stream from the sun.

But, more recently, the discovery of the Van Allen belts made it probable that the full explanation is more complicated.

The close association of auroral displays and magnetic storms has been known since the time of Halley. Slowly a succession of geomagneticians, mostly working in England, have established some of the details in the relationships existing between magnetic storms, sun-spots, and solar flares. These observations had suggested in a general way how solar outbursts could cause aurora and magnetic storms, and at the start of the IGY a whole series of rather similar theories had been ad-

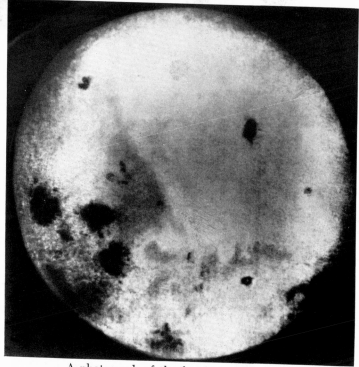

A photograph of the far side of the moon,
radioed back to earth by Lunik III.

The Crab nebula in the constellation
Taurus, the remains of the super-nova of
1054. This photograph was taken through
the 200-inch telescope at Mount Palomar.

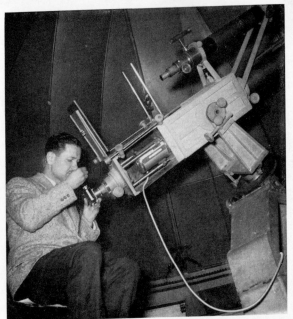

Greek astronomer with small solar telescope
used in co-operation with Moonwatch team
at Athens, Greece.

Moonwatch team tracking satellites at Terre Haute, Indiana. The
row of observers is looking through small telescopes. These point
downward at mirrors so arranged that each observer sees a different part of the sky.

Australian solar radio telescope that produces radio pictures of the sun in the "light" of 21-centimetre wave-length radio waves.

The Baker-Nunn-Schmidt camera at Woomera, south Australia. With this camera Explorer VI was photographed at a distance of 12,000 miles.

The Jodrell Bank radio telescope of the University of Manchester, England, is the largest movable steel structure in the world. It tracked many satellites during the IGY.

The camera mounted at the top of the picture is used to photograph the reflection of the entire sky in the dome-shaped mirror below it.

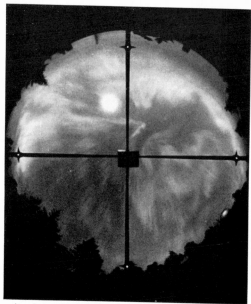

A photograph of an auroral display taken with the camera shown above. The reflections of the camera and its supports form the dark shadows across the photograph.

Auroral forms photographed at College, Alaska, Geophysics Institute in 1957.

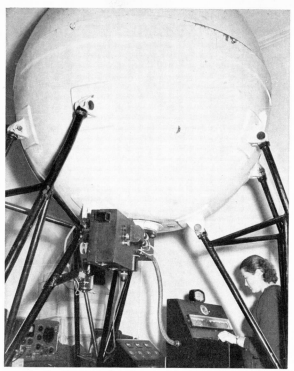

An ionization chamber for counting cosmic rays at the U.S.S.R. Academy of Sciences' Terrestrial, Magnetism, Ionospheric, and Radio-Wave Propagation Institute.

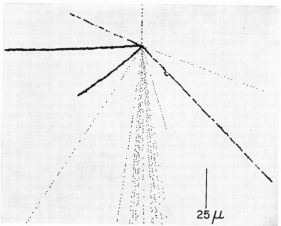

25 μ

A tracing from a mosaic of microphotographs of the collision of a primary cosmic-ray particle with a nucleus in a photographic emulsion. The heavy black tracks are part of the disrupted nucleus. The light tracks are high-speed protons and mesons. The cosmic ray probably consisted of an alpha particle or a helium nucleus.

Observers preparing to release a meteorological balloon carrying instruments which will read temperature, pressure, and humidity and transmit this data. The balloon is tracked by the radio-direction finder on the right.

Indian meteorologists working with a Dobson ozone spectrophotometer used for measuring the total amount of ozone contained in the column of air extending from the instrument to the top of the atmosphere.

vanced in attempts to explain the details. None of them was completely successful. Some vital piece of information about the aurora was clearly missing.

To see just how much was known, let us consider one of the more acceptable theories, that of Sydney Chapman, V. C. A. Ferraro, and F. A. Lindemann, the last of whom became better known as Lord Cherwell, wartime confidant and advisor to Sir Winston Churchill. In the vicinity of sun-spots the sun frequently emits jets of high-speed gases, both as visible solar flares and as invisible weaker emissions. These rush out from the sun like gas from a punctured balloon in jets of electrons and charged nuclei, mostly hydrogen. Because of the sun's rotation, they follow curved paths, sometimes hitting the earth and sometimes missing it, and in any case travelling like a stream of water from a rotating sprinkler. Those that reach the vicinity of the earth are dispersed on so wide a front and are travelling so fast that the blast of this tenuous sheet of solar wind bears down upon the tiny earth as a flat cloud. The geomagnetic field deflects it, so that the wind flows around the earth leaving the earth in a relatively empty pocket several times its own diameter. The surrounding ring of charged particles flowing around the earth acts as an electric current, producing the effects known as a magnetic storm; the particles feeding more slowly into the earth's atmosphere under the guidance of the earth's magnetism disturb the upper atmosphere and cause it to glow, especially in the maximum auroral zones around the poles. The colours are caused by processes analogous to those in neon display signs but differ in colour because the atmosphere is made up of gases other than neon. This was the prevailing theory at the beginning of the IGY.

This theory left a great deal still to be explained. Why, for example, does the aurora flicker and move about so quickly? If there is a fine display in one place, are good displays simultaneously widespread elsewhere? In particular, if there are good dis-

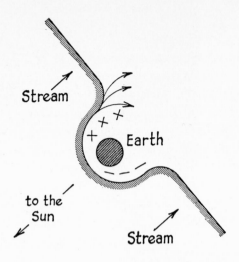

Passage of the front of a corpuscular stream past the earth.

plays in the northern hemisphere, are there also good displays in the southern? Do the displays change in any regular way, for example moving steadily southward or higher in the sky? Why do the colours change? Does the pattern of the displays reveal anything about the shape or nature of the earth's magnetic field or about winds in the thin, high atmosphere which may control the aurora?

On a different theme, scientists were eager to discover the connection between aurora and the mysterious air glow. This unseen phenomenon was discovered on photographic plates that had been exposed to the sky for long periods. Astronomers observed that the same spectral lines which occur in aurora also appear on these plates. Investigation showed that this light is not due to the stars but arises high in the atmosphere. The air glow is so soft and diffused a light that it is not generally visible; nevertheless, it contributes almost as much light to the night sky as do the stars. Little was known about it. Still another mysterious phenomenon, only visible in the tropics, is the faint zodiacal light, a trail or glow seen near the horizon in the night sky after sunset or before sunrise—perhaps a faint vision of the sun's outermost corona.

It was against this background that the program for studying the aurora and the air glow was planned. Thousands of volunteers, including weathermen, amateur astronomers, sailors, airline pilots, and parties of enthusiastic amateurs in all parts of the world, were organized to watch for aurora and to plot its occurrences every fine night. At a hundred or so scientific stations special cameras and spectrographs were installed to photograph and measure particular features of the aurora and the air glow. A special camera was designed which pointed downwards at a convex mirror and could thus photograph a reflection, in the curved mirror, of the whole sky at once. At many sites these were installed to take pictures of the sky, including any aurora, once a minute. At a few stations, arrangements were made to record aurora by radar, or to fire rockets up through aurora, or to take simultaneous pairs of height-finding photographs from positions many miles apart. These programs would, of course, produce literally several million reports and a few million feet of photographic film. To reduce so much data to manageable proportions, ingenious routines and machines were developed and codes of instructions worked out so that electronic computers could compile the results. Once these preparations had been put into effect, the countries involved could begin sending results to the World Data Centres. Needless to say, no such thorough study had ever been instituted before.

Typical of the program for visual observation was the watch agreed upon for North America. Cards showing a simple map of the sky were printed and distributed. On these, observers were asked to plot the aurora every quarter of an hour. A map of the sky should be round; but to see the whole sky involves lying on one's back, which is inconvenient, so the maps were cut like a pie. In this way the observer can stand and face the four cardinal directions in turn, and sketch each quadrant of the sky. A series of guide sketches printed on a separate card make it possible to standardize these observations. Of course, notes about absence of aurora or about cloud conditions are just as important as reports of displays.

Observers are able to identify the forms of aurora by their descriptive names. Arcs are parallel with the horizon or stretch across the sky; rays are elongated in a vertical direction; and spots are diffused. A poorly defined spot is known as a glow, and a strongly developed combination of arcs and rays reaching to the zenith from all directions is called a corona. During any particular display the various forms tend to succeed one another, moving systematically away from the polar regions. When they first appear, they may be below the horizon and only reveal themselves as a glow, low in the northern heavens. Slowly they climb up the dome of the night sky, great arcs and rays increasing in brilliance and movement until they drop below the horizon as a glow. The light is most often a pale, luminous green, but on occasion red may tinge the lower edge, and sometimes even yellows, blues, and purples.

Two lines, labelled 30° and 60° were drawn across the map for convenience in interpreting the results. Since the lowest part of any auroral arc is generally at a height of about 60 miles, a simple calculation shows that auroral arcs appearing to be at angles of 60 degrees and 30 degrees above the horizon would be overhead at places which are, respectively, 35 miles and 105 miles away from the observer.

When data for different areas have been gathered, they will be assembled into maps, which will show the distribution of aurora over the entire globe.

It has been found that great auroral displays occur simultaneously in both northern and southern hemispheres and that they stretch across the entire night sky, for they have been observed all the way from Ohio to the English Channel.

During the IGY there were many brilliant displays, and the aurora was seen unusually close to the tropics in such places as Mexico, Cuba, Fiji, Japan, Pakistan, and as far north in South Africa as Bloemfontein. Aurora were recorded on nearly one third of the nights of the IGY somewhere in Australia. On the other hand, in some countries which had watchers, including India and Taiwan, no aurora were reported.

Aurora are most numerous, widespread, and vivid during sun-spot activity when the emissions from solar flares most fre-

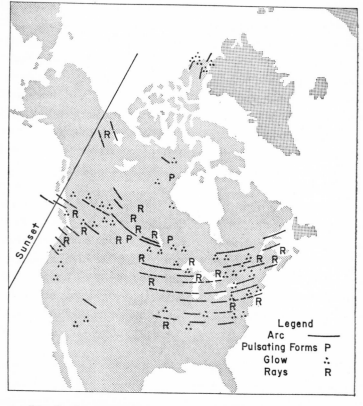

Distribution and frequency of auroral displays at a given time in the evening of February 11, 1958.

quently bombard the upper atmosphere. Since the IGY coincided with the period of greatest activity of the sun ever recorded and since many observers were keeping careful watch, it is not surprising that aurora were more widely recorded than at any previous time. Such elaborate plans deserved success, but it is doubtful that a satisfactory answer would have been found to the detailed mysteries of the aurora if help had not been forthcoming from a totally different source, and if, as we have seen, satellites had not unexpectedly disclosed the existence of the Van Allen belts. The horns of the outer of these great belts of charged particles reach down towards the earth in the neighbourhood of the maximum auroral zones. Clearly the belts play a major part in the story of the aurora; without their discovery we might still not hope to understand the beautiful aurora in spite of our elaborate surface observations. Now we can be confident of making progress. But the discovery of the Van Allen belts is so new that data concerning the belts are still being continuously transmitted by the satellites' radios as I write; at the moment we can only suggest the trend of discovery. There has not been time to assimilate the data, develop theories, and get them published.

We can now understand how the discovery of the Van Allen belts and the production of artificial aurora in the Argus experiments modified existing ideas about the cause of aurora without destroying the old views entirely. In place of rings of current freshly created in space about the earth each time a blast from the sun occurs, we now substitute the permanent Van Allen belts; and we attribute the coincidence of auroral displays with solar outbursts to the disturbance and excitation of the belts by the arrival of solar discharges.

Due to the careful tracking of satellites by radio and optical means, variations in their orbital periods are accurately known. We have already seen how King-Hele used this data to obtain more precise values for the average density of the atmosphere at various altitudes.

Careful studies by Luigi Jacchia at the Smithsonian Astrophysical Observatory have shown how the rates of revolution of satellites are affected by solar activity. In particular, he has shown that although both Vanguard I and Sputnik III are slowed down a day or so after solar flares, the effects are much greater on Sputnik III. The discovery of the Van Allen belts immediately provided an explanation. Vanguard I, whose orbit lies between 34° N and 34° S latitude only penetrates the inner belt, but Sputnik III swings from 65° N to 65° S, regularly passing through the horns of the outer belt. If the particle density in the outer belt is built up directly by the solar wind, and in the inner belt is not, the discrepancy can be explained.

There is other evidence that this is so. Pioneer IV passed through the outer belt immediately after five days of intense solar activity, and it measured particle densities many times greater than did Pioneer III, which passed after a quiet period. S. N. Vernov has confirmed these results with data from Lunik I, which also passed following a quiet period. It appears that the strength and position of the outer belt fluctuates greatly with changing emissions from the sun. This belt is indeed a trembling and shaking veil buffeted by blasts from the boisterous sun. The evidence suggests that the inner belt, on the other hand is quiet and stable. It seems to be the graveyard of many atomic fragments created by cosmic rays. The Argus and Jason projects showed that the flow of particles from one Argus shell, or belt, to another was very slow and that these belts were also stable in position.

As was mentioned in the discussion of the Van Allen belts, rockets fired in 1956 showed that over the auroral zone in the outer Van Allen belt the temperature may be twice that at the same altitude elsewhere. This extra heating, which may reach

4,000° F, could be produced by the collisions of particles where they are most numerous, and this may be sufficient to excite the upper atmosphere and cause auroral displays. R. Jastrow, who has made these suggestions, considers it significant that the loss of particles from the belts to the atmosphere occurs at the tips of the horns. His calculations indicate that the heating thus produced should be greatest at heights of about 65 miles, which is the height at which aurora are most frequently observed. Here then is one possible explanation for the cause of the aurora. Without doubt, it will be proved or disproved and a more detailed picture formed when the results obtained by Explorers VI and VII are available. But we still have no prospect of explanation of why the aurora is broken into many narrow arcs and rays and why they move about so rapidly.

CHAPTER 13

❀

LANDFALLS
IN A FROZEN SEA

JUNE 1958

Continuing our Arctic journey from Resolute, the main base of the Queen Elizabeth Islands, we made three great triangular tours, fanning northwest to the rim of the Arctic Sea.

On those flights we saw very plainly the difference between land ice and sea ice. Some of the islands over which we flew were partly covered by land ice in the form of ice sheets and glaciers. Land ice accumulates where more snow falls in winter than melts in summer. Over the years the snow becomes consolidated into ice often thousands of feet thick. Very slowly these glaciers flow downhill until they melt or reach the sea. Sea ice, or pack ice, forms like ice on a pond and floats on the surface of the Arctic Sea and of the Southern Ocean around the coasts of Antarctica. Although broken and heaped up by the wind, it is never more than a few feet thick, and fish, seals, and atomic submarines can travel beneath it. Icebergs are much thicker. They are parts of glaciers which have flowed off the land into the sea, broken off, and floated away. They may be seen either in the open ocean or frozen as raised ice islands into the pack.

On the first flight we headed west over the main Northwest Passage by Barrow Strait, Viscount Melville Sound, and Mc-Clure Strait. These magnificent ice-blocked channels lie between islands, capes, and passages whose names resound like a roll-call of past explorers, their patrons, and their faith—District of Franklin, Byam Martin Island, Cape Providence, Winter Harbour, Resolute Bay, and Bay of God's Mercy. It was brilliant white over the jumbled ice packs and glaciers, buff and brown over the surrounding hills, and blazing blue above. We turned over Mould Bay, a remote weather station jointly supported by Canada and the United States, and followed north along the low coast of Prince Patrick Island, against which the arctic pack was heaped in ridges. In sheltered places where the ice was broken, seals had come out of the water and lay basking in the sun with their young; here and there a trundling yellow figure or a red splash on the ice showed where the solitary polar bears roam and kill, lords of an empty land.

To the west lay the Beaufort Sea, across whose surface Vilhjalmur Stefansson had walked when he went northeast from Alaska to discover Borden and Meighen and the other "Conservative" islands, which he named after leading figures of the political party then in power in Canada. On this expedition to the farthest frontiers of the Canadian Government's possessions, Stefansson left the north cost of Alaska on March 22, 1914. A blizzard with 80-mile-an-hour winds at 37° F below zero had just blown itself out. Accompanied by Ole Andreasen and Storker Storkerson and equipped only with two rifles, 330 rounds of ammunition, and one sledge drawn by six dogs, he tramped for three months over hundreds of miles of frozen sea, hunting to support the party. On the twenty-fifth of June they reached the northwest coast of Banks Island and continued northwards to discover new lands. After that trip it is not surprising that for the rest of his life Stefansson should be an advocate of an all-meat diet. It is true that Nansen in 1895 and Peary in 1910 made long marches over the polar ice, but they did not depend solely upon hunting for a living.

On the next flight we flew past another joint weather station on Isachsen Island and saw nearby salt domes on the desert plain, great rings of rock, like the tops of sliced onions, with a tumble of gypsum and clay hills in the centres—places which promise oil in abundance, although they have never been drilled. We flew beyond, out over the Arctic Sea—99 per cent with a solid ice cover, but cracked and broken and showing a few open leads of black water—until we reached the large flat iceberg T3. This ice island appears to have broken off a glacier on the north coast of Ellesmere Island a few years ago. In contrast to the shattered surface of the frozen ocean, it appeared massive and unbroken. Upon it the Americans had built the ice station Bravo.

We had hoped to land there and at Isachsen, but the spring sun was already so hot that the ice runways were dangerously soft for a large plane. The pilot contented himself with circling low over the square of huts, the fluttering stars and stripes, and the excited men. Scattered over the ice within a few miles were other flags, vehicles, men, and wires which indicated where experiments were being carried out. Until the United States submarines *Nautilus* and *Skate* cruised under the arctic pack in 1958, our whole knowledge of the Arctic had been derived from a few such ice parties, a few beset ships, and several hundred airplane landings mostly made by Soviet explorers. During the IGY arctic exploration was greatly increased, and the results suggest a possibility of drastic change in North American climate. To appreciate this change, we must consider earlier investigations.

The coasts of the lands surrounding the Arctic Sea were discovered by sledging. In the eighteenth century Peter the Great

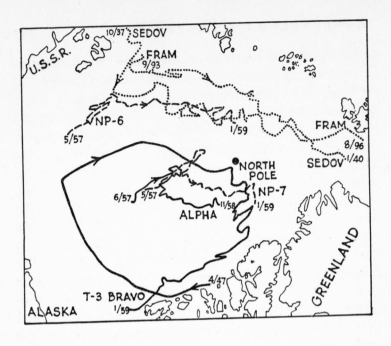

Map of Arctic Sea, showing drifts by American and Russian parties during the IGY.

sent naval parties to the north coast of Siberia, and later others explored Alaska, Canada, and Greenland, but the central part of the sea remained a mystery, guarded by pack ice too thick for ships to penetrate. In the 1870's Joseph Wiggins surveyed far along the northeast coast of Siberia and Baron Nordenskjold completely circumnavigated Eurasia. Fired with enthusiasm, Lieutenant George De Long sailed from San Francisco in the *Jeannette* in 1879, passed Bering Strait, and became locked in the pack. Admiral Clements Markham, a survivor of the search for Admiral Franklin in the Canadian Arctic, had met De Long in England and wrote of him: "He was a good seaman, a scientific officer, and an agreeable companion. Trained to the management and care of seamen, De Long was undoubtedly the best of all American arctic commanders, and he well fulfilled the trust that was placed in him." Misfortune, however, overtook him when the *Jeannette* was crushed and De Long lost, but the survivors, who reached Siberia at the Lena delta, brought back word of the discovery of Bennett and other islands. Thus one of the most remote of Soviet possessions bears to this day the name of James Gordon Bennett, the New York publisher who had financed De Long's expedition.

In spite of misfortune, the expedition indirectly established the course of the drift of the arctic pack, for wreckage from the *Jeannette* was picked up years later in Greenland. This inspired Frijof Nansen to have a stouter ship built to withstand the ice pressure, and between 1893 and 1896 the *Fram* safely drifted right across the Arctic Sea. Nansen, in a vain attempt to reach the pole, left his ship on March 14, 1895, and with Lieutenant F. H. Johansen walked north. Famine forced them to turn back, and more than a year later they were picked up, "wild men, clad in dirty rags, black with oil and soot, with long uncombed hair and shaggy beards, black with smoke," on the Franz Josef Islands. Meanwhile the *Fram* drifted on, her scientists measuring from time to time the thickness of the surrounding ice, the depth of the water, and such other matters as they could observe. Nansen and the crew of the *Fram* continued on their separate odysseys, neither knowing the fate of the other until they reached Oslo within a few days of one another. As the old college song has it:

> *What a glorious day,*
> *For old Norway,*
> *When the* Fram *came sailing into the bay.*
> *To the old fiord,*
> *With the crew on board,*
> *All safely restored,*
> *By the hand of the Lord.*
> *And they shouted "Whoa,*

Is this Skaervoe?"
And they rent the air,
With a loud "Hallo."
And the crowd on skis,
As thick as bees,
Came down through the town,
On their hands and knees.
And oh what cries,
When they recognized,
A man with a pair of sealskin pants on,
And there I declare was Frijof Nansen!

A comparison of modern measurements with the data collected by the *Fram* suggests that the volume of ice over the
Arctic Sea is only half as great now as it was sixty-five years
ago. If this trend continues for another half century, the results
will be spectacular. An open ocean will greatly simplify arctic
navigation, but more important it will provide a source of
moisture and warmth likely to affect profoundly the climate of
all North America.

This sounds so beneficial for Alaska, Canada, and Siberia
that some Soviet scientists have proposed speeding the process
by damming Bering Strait and pumping warm Pacific water
into the arctic basin. Apart from the fact that the sea ice may
melt anyway and that a dam 50 miles long would be expensive,
some American scientists doubt that the results would be as
favourable as seems at first glance. They suggest that an open
Arctic Sea would provide moisture to the north winds, thereby
greatly increasing the snowfall on surrounding lands. At present these lands are very dry, like cold deserts, and the summer
sun barely melts the thin winter snows; the mean temperature is far below freezing and a more abundant snowfall could
probably not be melted. If so, it would pile up in ice caps,
like the ones that melted only eleven thousand years ago, and

an ice age would quickly return to North America and Siberia.

If present warming trends continue, it will be important to watch the Arctic, for remarkable changes could take place there in the next fifty or a hundred years.

Modern scientific investigations of the arctic basin may be said to have begun in 1937 when the first of a series of parties of Soviets and Americans was landed on the floating ice to establish bases by plane like that we saw at station Bravo. In 1948 the Russians discovered the great Lomonosov submarine ridge, running right across the arctic basin from Ellesmere Island to the New Siberian Islands. During the recently increased activity, American parties, by measuring the depth of the sea below their floating ice station, have discovered one and probably two other smaller parallel ridges.

During the IGY two new types of vessels were introduced which will greatly facilitate such investigations in future. Both are nuclear-powered and have tremendous range. They are the submarine *Nautilus* and her sister ships, and the ice-breaker *Lenin*. The use of nuclear power and the consequent reduction in fuel requirements made it possible to build the *Lenin* half as large again as any other ice-breaker and twice as powerful. Launched in September 1957 and commissioned two years later, the *Lenin* has a displacement of 16,000 tons and her engines develop 44,000 horse power. She should be able to cruise at 2 knots through ice up to 8 feet thick and operate for up to a year at full speed without refueling. The submarine *Nautilus* has similar advantages and, in addition, when submerged can operate at high speeds beneath the ice and investigate the thickness and nature of the lower surface of the ice in a way not possible from a surface ship. As the *Nautilus* and her sister ships have demonstrated, submarines can rise to the surface through open leads in the pack and even through thin sea ice. These two types of vessels, each in their own way, open new possibilities for investigating the frozen oceans.

Imagine the difficulty of exploring in any other way the vast area of ice-covered sea around Antarctica in storms and cold, in darkness, and at a tremendous distance from any air bases.

Our third flight went north by the west side and south by the east side of Axel Heiberg Island. A great plateau of ice occupies its entire mountainous centre. But we went farther, entering the heart of Ellesmere Island by Greeley Fiord. There we met a sight of awesome grandeur: from the mountain peaks the low midnight sun cast black shadows far across the tumult of ice fields, and the limitless sky washed with its orange glow those harsh, clear, and desperately barren regions. When we were less than 600 miles from the north pole, our plane landed on ice 7 feet thick on Lake Hazen, named, like other features, for a member of the Greeley expedition which was sent to these remote places by the United States Government during the First Polar Year in 1882. We were warmly greeted by members of a Canadian party, some of whom had wintered there at a meteorological station.

The winterers could be readily distinguished by their fine spade beards, by their tendency to stand apart as a group, polite but slightly condescending towards the new arrivals, and by their rather fixed attitudes concerning camp routine and meals. They claimed that the winter had been uneventful and pleasant. It had been dark for five months but the moon had been so bright that they could travel without any trouble for half of each month. They had recorded 67 degrees below zero, which was the coldest temperature reached anywhere in North America that mild winter, but since there was virtually no wind, the cold did not inconvenience them. We saw that the thin snow had not been blown into drifts and could easily be scraped away by grazing animals.

Other parties were fanning out along the 50-mile-long lake or were climbing the United States and Challenger Mountains beside it to carry out programs particularly concerned with climate and with the history of some of the local glaciers. These glaciers are the highest near the north pole and provide a small but interesting comparison with those of Greenland and Antarctica.

Several biologists had seized the chance to come to this place. It has been so seldom visited that one can walk up to the placid, white arctic hares, watch the arctic foxes playing near camp, and see the strange musk oxen grazing unperturbed upon the hillsides. After supper our air crew, who had visited the party before, lost no time in getting an ice auger, lines, and tackle. By fishing all night, they had caught a total of seventy-nine salmon through holes in the ice before breakfast next morning. Later I tried my hand at this quick but rather primitive way of catching arctic char. Although the lake has an outlet to the sea and is ice-free every August, the fish are so hungry that all one needs is a large auger, a strong line, and a minimum of patience.

CHAPTER 14

GREENLAND AND THE WORLD'S ICE

JUNE 1958

From the Arctic Islands we continued our flight across the ice over the narrow strait to Greenland. If one wants to see scenery that is stark, impressive, and desolate, the easiest way is to fly over Greenland. It is a measure of the change in transportation brought about in recent years that Greenland, once one of the most inaccessible countries, is now crossed every night by planes flying the polar routes from the west coast of North America to Europe, and from Montreal to Scotland. True, these planes do not usually stop, but on a clear, moonlit night one may see as wild and lonely a piece of territory as exists on earth outside of Antarctica. In size, Greenland is four times as large as France and more than a quarter of the area of the United States.

In summer the black-green ocean and in winter the sea ice lap cliffs and mountains of jagged ferocity, rivalling the Rockies or the Alps. Such settlements as exist are hidden in the half-open jaws of rocky fiords. At night nothing is seen of life. The whole interior is a plateau of ice and snow 9,000 feet in height, hemmed in by a rim of mountains reaching as high as 13,000 feet. In gaps between the mountains, rivers of pale-blue ice squeeze and tumble towards the sea. Greenland is like a spoonful of mashed potatoes hollowed on top and filled to overflowing with gravy. Like gravy, the ice, constantly re-newed by snowfall. forever flows out from the centre to break off in the sea as icebergs and drift south to melt in the Gulf Stream. As the glaciers descend into the sea, they become scored with crevasses, fractures along which individual ice-bergs will break off.

In June 1958 it was not this distant view which we had. Instead, we flew to the Thule airbase to see Dr. H. Bader, scientist in charge of a glaciological program on the ice sheet. The brilliance of the snow-covered scenery that morning was the most intense I have ever known, and my light-meter went off scale when pointed in any direction through the plane windows. Viewed through my very dark glasses, the jagged peaks of Ellesmere Island appeared black against the glisten-ing snow around them. We crossed Baffin Bay covered, except for a patch of open sea off Thule, with a frozen swirl of pack and icebergs. In this open place, called the North Water, rising currents prevent ice from forming, and the open ocean creates clouds of vapour.

On the coast at Thule there is a steamer dock. Behind it is a valley in which rows of great hangars and barracks are set among a tangle of roads lying like thread on the gravel. Behind the camp, towering above us as we came in to land, is a smooth white wall of inland ice, poised like a substantial cloud upon the hills. It is a forbidding place, this great United States Air Force base which forms the apex of North American defence; not on account of military display, which is not flaunted, but rather because of the chill and awesome setting, a no man's land of bleak, dark rock between the white ice on the moun-tains and the white ice on the bay.

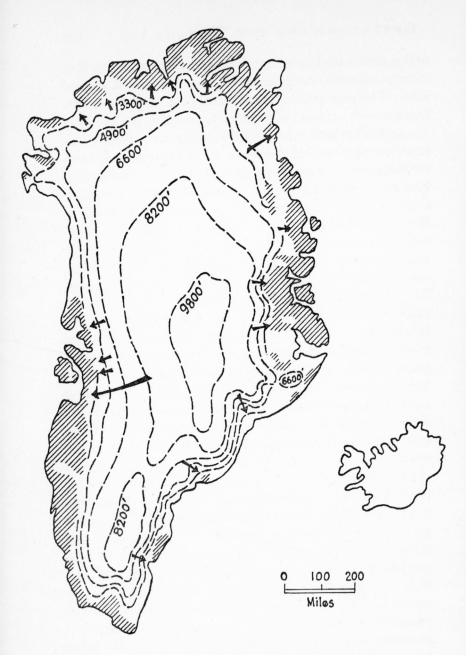

Contour map of the ice surface of the Greenland ice.

We were warmly welcomed by the base commander, and taken to bachelor officers' quarters and a comfortable officers' mess. Whatever defence installations there may have been, they were not evident. What lay behind closed hangar doors was no affair of a party of visiting scientists, but we felt an air of alert expectancy and a sense of front-line tenseness which was illustrated for me by the actions of two very different men. One of the enlisted men who looked after our quarters, his twelve-month tour of duty almost up, longed for home. The loneliness of the winter of darkness among a thousand other men and no women had frayed his fibre to the last strand. He talked darkly of what would happen to Thule if war broke out, and seemed to fear that he might get blasted with the rest of the base before the next month was over and he escaped to the familiar embrace of the United States. The other was the base commander, a very charming and distinguished officer. He also seemed to have the jitters, but for quite a different reason. As a seasoned combat pilot, he was not fearful. Nevertheless, he had a phone in his car; another, so he told us, by his bed; and at breakfast, when the one in the dining hall rang, he ran and answered it himself. His concern was to be ready at whatever instant S.A.C. headquarters might call. In his decisions, seconds counted. During his tour of duty there were no days off, no office hours. He did not allow himself the respite of one single minute of complete relaxation. While it is indeed reassuring to know that defence services are maintained in the alert and efficient manner so evident everywhere at Thule, it is also a matter of concern that in other countries the same scenes are without doubt being enacted with the same grim and dedicated earnestness. So long as this tenseness prevails, it is always possible that some weak link, like the overwrought enlisted man, may panic and set in motion an irreversible sequence of blows and counterblows which would very effectively solve the world's problem of overpopulation.

We drove up the hills to the ice. The road was longer than it had looked from the air, and we bumped and lurched over lifeless gravel, stone, and snowdrifts. At short intervals there were safety shelters where any driver caught in a blizzard could find fuel, food, and blankets until the storm passed or help came. Where the road ends, the ice begins; not gently like the sea on a beach, but as a bulging white wall dwarfing the operations at its foot and rendering the ascent on to the ice steep and dangerous.

In one place an adit, or passage, had been driven from the base 1,200 feet straight into the ice wall. The previous year heavy coal-mining machinery had been used to cut this opening to a height of 7 feet and a width of 20. At intervals along the roof and walls square grids of precise dimensions had been inscribed and dyed on flat surfaces in the ice. In the ensuing months the great weight of the ice had very slowly caused it to flow off the plateau, and its movement had reduced the size of the passage. The resulting distortion of the grids provided an exact measure of the flow. Near the head of the tunnel the reduction had become so great and the roof was so low that we could walk only with difficulty in a stooped position with our hands clasped behind our backs and our heads or shoulders bumping at intervals on the roof.

Even more spectacular were the effects to be seen in larger rooms which had been cut in openings off the main passageway. Here, mass flaking had led to the collapse of the roof. It was unsafe to enter these rooms, but from the doorways we could see a succession of huge slabs, 10 feet or more across, broken off the roof and hanging like the petals of inverted rose blossoms, or heaps of ice which had fallen from the roof lying in shivered blocks about the floor.

At another place a few miles away, where the ice face steepened less precipitously, a ramp had been built and a road climbed up it on to the inland ice. The surface of this road was, of course, of snow; the ice is only formed in glaciers below a depth of several hundred feet, when the weight of fresh snow above and the passage of time have squeezed out air and caused the snowflakes to congeal. As a consequence, this road could only be used by snowmobiles and over-snow tractors, both of which have wide tracks to support them. The great tractors used for hauling equipment to the interior of Greenland were particularly impressive, as the steel tracks on some were as much as 6 feet wide. These tractors pulled 10- and 20-ton loads on heavy sleds and also wanigans, as the bunk houses mounted on sleds are called.

The glaciologists told us of a further difficulty which they had to overcome in getting up to the ice plateau so many thousand feet above. The margins and indeed some patches of the interior of any ice sheet are cut by crevasses, great cracks as much as 200 feet deep, many feet wide, and miles long. The ever-drifting snow is able to build bridges across most of these and hide them completely from view. These hidden crevasses are dangerous enough for men on skis or dog-sledges, although the snow bridges can usually support such relatively light loads. If they do not, the custom of roping a party of men together enables them to arrest the fall of any one of their number so unfortunate as to fall through. Such techniques are even of value in stopping the fall of snowmobiles, but they will not do for large tractor trains. Before these can cross the ice sheet, roads must be established and marked. All crevasses must be found and at the road crossings they must be filled with snow by bulldozers.

Once well up on the ice, other difficulties present themselves. The weather on top of ice sheets is cold; blizzards are frequent, and there are no landmarks to guide the parties which break trail and mark the routes. They have to "hole up" during blizzards, dig themselves out afterwards, and navigate across the featureless snow plains like ships at sea.

With utmost labour they had manoeuvred a large drilling rig on to the ice cap to drill holes 1,000 feet deep. Just as archeologists slice through the site of an ancient city to discover from the layers of broken fragments the history of an ancient civilization, so glaciologists, by studying the annual layers, the orientation of crystals, and the debris in the ice, trace the history of the ice cap. By measuring the thickness of annual layers, they can estimate the precipitation; by observing the extent of melting, they can tell the summer temperatures; and by locating traces of ash, they can identify former volcanic eruptions. These operations and those we were to see later in Antarctica provided an insight into the formidable task faced by explorers of the world's two great ice sheets, and they formed an interesting contrast with the very different operations we had just seen in the mountains of Ellesmere Island and on ice island T3. All had a common basis in man's desire to investigate the world's ice, whether in continental sheets, in mountain glaciers, or in the frozen surface of the ocean.

The first extensive area of glacial ice to be explored was Greenland, which Nansen crossed in 1888. Since then a succession of American, British, Danish, French, German, and Swiss expeditions have added greatly to our knowledge. The area of ice in Greenland has been surveyed. Its thickness has been measured in many places by firing small shots of explosives on the surface and timing the echoes reflected from the bottom. Its behavior has been explored by drilling and by digging pits and tunnels. Of the 840,000 square miles of Greenland, glacial ice covers more than 700,000. Beneath it, the surface of the bed-rock is shaped like a dish rising to over 13,000 feet along the eastern rim but lying close to sea level in the central parts. This dish is filled to overflowing with ice, which reaches a maximum thickness of 11,000 feet and which has a total volume of 620,000 cubic miles. This volume is steadily, if slowly, diminishing, as can be seen from the recession of the edges of the glaciers and from calculations of the total balance sheet of the ice. The average snowfall over all Greenland is equivalent to 12 inches of rain, which would contribute 118 cubic miles of new ice each year. Fourteen ice rivers have been mapped, and each year these carry an average of 57 cubic miles of ice to the sea, where they break off as icebergs. Melting of the lower parts of the glaciers in summer causes a loss of another 83 cubic miles of ice yearly. If these estimates are correct, Greenland is losing an average of 22 cubic miles of ice a year. Should this rate of shrinkage continue, all the ice would melt in about thirty thousand years.

The ice sheets of the last glaciation disappeared from Europe and America in about one tenth of this time. The shrinkage of the Greenland ice cap is thus comparatively slow, but the circulation of ice through the ice sheet is faster. The addition of 118 cubic miles of snowfall each year will completely replace, or rejuvenate, the Greenland ice cap in about five thousand years. This is the average time of circulation of ice through the sheet.

One of the methods commonly used to gather information is to dig pits. On the upper reaches of an ice sheet the climate is too cold to cause any melting, even in summer, so that a vertical section of the ice contains a sample of all the snow that has fallen. The annual layers can be counted and measured to determine the average annual snowfall, and the mean annual temperature can be recorded. In Greenland and on mountain glaciers, it is usually possible to distinguish the summer and winter layers in the ice by sight, but in Antarctica this is difficult. Fortunately, the entrapped oxygen contains two isotopes—oxygen-16 and oxygen-18—the ratio of which varies with the temperature at which snow was deposited. If the ratio is measured, the summer and winter layers can be determined.

It is not practical or safe to dig pits by hand to greater depths than about 100 feet. During the IGY a 5-inch oil-well drill was adapted for drilling in ice to extend investigations to greater depths. At a place on the ice sheet about 200 miles east of Thule, a hole was drilled to a depth of 1,350 feet, and cores of ice were recovered from it. The annual layers show that this ice had taken over eight hundred years to accumulate. At a depth of 100 feet the core contained a layer of fine volcanic ash identified as coming from the eruption of 1912 in the Valley of Ten Thousand Smokes at Katmai, Alaska. It is expected that small amounts of volcanic dust from the great eruption of 1883 at Krakatoa, Indonesia, may be found in cores all over the world. Measurements of the radioactivity of ice in different layers can provide comparison of the rate of natural and artificial fall-out at different times in the past.

The drill was later taken from Greenland to Antarctica, where I saw it in use. There, with a slower rate of accumulation, a 1,000-foot core may provide a frozen record of two thousand years of history, but greater depths cannot be reached with present techniques because the release of pressure produced by drilling causes the ice to fly to pieces.

In 1959, to learn more about the dynamics of ice sheets, Expéditions Polaires Françaises sent the largest glaciological expedition ever launched, a party of sixty men with several aircraft and helicopters and many over-snow vehicles, to make an exhaustive study of an active part of Greenland ice sheet which lies between latitudes 68° and 74° N. The ice there is flowing seaward at the rate of about 450 feet a year. Markers that will last for ten years have been placed every 6 miles along a 500-mile traverse of the ice cap. Accurate ground and aerial surveys of the region and of the stakes have been made and will be repeated in order to determine how the ice sheet is renewed, how it moves, and how it is dissipated. The study and publication of the results of this work will lead to improvements and refinements. It is in the Antarctic, which was least known, that recent efforts have produced the most marked changes in our knowledge.

Most of the ice in the world is in Antarctica. Before the IGY the outlines of much of the coast had been mapped, but no one had seen or even flown over the greater part of the interior. A single line of surveys by the Norwegian-British-Swedish expedition of 1949–52 had suggested that along this route Antarctica was a continent covered with ice a mile thick, but it was still possible that Antarctica might either be an archipelago of rock islands linked by ice or a continent with only

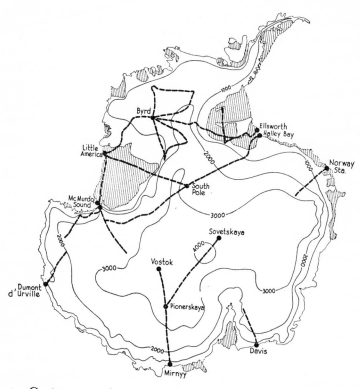

Contour map of the ice surface of Antarctica. Broken lines indicate routes of the major traverses across the ice sheet up to the end of 1959.

a frosting of ice over the rock. If the first were true, there would
be twice as much ice in the world as if the second were so.

During the IGY twelve nations operated fifty-five stations
on the Antarctic continent and adjacent islands, and in 1959
another nation, Poland, proposed to take over one station
from the U.S.S.R. American, Australian, British, French, and
Soviet parties carried out major traverses across the interior
making geophysical soundings. From preliminary accounts of
these ventures, from reports of the earlier inland journeys of
Amundsen, Scott, Shackleton, and the Norwegian-British-
Swedish expedition and from observations made on flights,
rough sketch maps were prepared. They show the contours of
the top and bottom surfaces of the ice. The bottom surface is,
of course, the rock beneath. These maps suggest that the
volume of ice in Antarctica is about 4,000,000 cubic miles.
Because the traverses have been few and a long way apart and
the maps are merely rough sketches, the results are preliminary
and unprecise. Other estimates range up to 7,000,000 cubic
miles. That possible errors would be large is indicated by the
difference in the results of three seismic measurements of
thickness of ice made at the south pole. American seismologists, who were flown to the south pole on Operation Deepfreeze, obtained a thickness of 8,900 feet; G. Pratt, the glaciologist with Vivian Fuchs's Commonwealth Trans-Antarctic
Expedition, found 6,300 feet; and a Soviet party, which made
another traverse reaching the south pole on December 26,
1959, found 9,500 feet.

Only Greenland and Antarctica have large ice sheets, but
small ones are to be found on a few polar islands, including
Ellesmere Island and Novaya Zemlya, and on high mountains in all latitudes. In the tropics these mountain glaciers
can only form at altitudes greater than 16,000 feet, but they do
exist in New Guinea, East Africa, and South America. Because
mountain glaciers are widespread and because their melt water

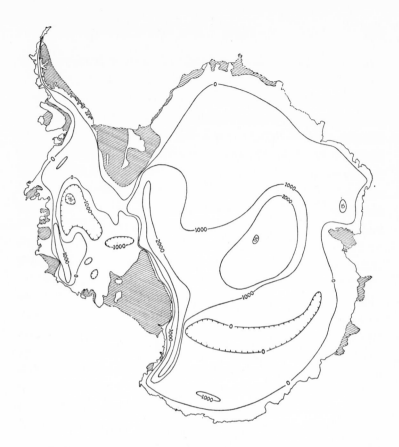

Contour map of the bed-rock of Antarctica below the ice sheet as deduced from soundings.

provides a good summer flow of water, they are of immediate interest and consequence to people in many countries. Without glaciers to store the winter snow, many rivers now used for irrigation would flood in spring and run dry in summer. Examples of rivers fed in part by glaciers are the Colorado, the Saskatchewan, and the Rhine. During the IGY, expeditions were sent to investigate many mountain glaciers. An important example was the joint Swedish-Finnish-Swiss expedition to Murchison Fiord, North East Land, Spitsbergen, where thirteen men wintered. Poland established another station nearby.

In Mexico there are glaciers on the three highest peaks. J. L. Lorenzo, who studied them, has described the difficulties glaciologists encounter. Concerning the glaciers of Mount Orizaba or Citlaltepet (at 18,620 feet, the highest peak in Mexico), he points out that there had only been one previous report, in 1910, and that it was quite wrong. Lorenzo's party camped above the 16,000-foot level for twelve days, and under conditions of snow storms and high-altitude fatigue, they mapped 3.8 square miles of glaciers. On Popocatepetl the party were troubled by smoke and fumes from the volcano but completed the mapping of several small glaciers. About the third volcano, Iztaccihuatl, he writes: "It is a volcanic range, the silhouette of which recalls the figure of a sleeping woman, whence its name, Iztac, white, and cihuatl, woman, the white referring of course to the white of the snow and ice covering it. It is curious to note that Iztaccihuatl is the mountain with the most ancient references as to its glaciers. Sometime between 1781 and 1789 Father José Antonio de Alzate Ramírez in taking some barometric measurements noticed 'a great wall of ice, which because of its great width must have been formed since time immemorial.' "

Since the end of the war, the whole of Canada has been photographed from the air. Examination of these photographs and of maps made from them revealed that Canada has many more glaciers than had been supposed. About 5,000 separate valley glaciers and many small ice sheets have been plotted, in all covering 70,000 square miles, an area equal to England and Wales or as large as all the New England states plus New Jersey.

We have already quoted calculations of the annual increment and losses of the Greenland ice sheet and the estimated net loss of 22 cubic miles of ice a year. During the IGY attempts were made to extend this to the world as a whole.

Among others, F. Loewe and H. Lister have published preliminary estimates of the changes in Antarctica. Lister suggests
a gain of 125 cubic miles a year, but his figures (although
attained by the same methods used by Bauer for Greenland)
must be treated with great caution because, as he points out,
they are based upon observations made on one crossing only
and involve a good deal of guesswork. Similar estimates or
balance-sheets have been drawn for the changes in some of
the world's mountain glaciers. Almost all are diminishing, but
we do not yet know the total figure. Since the mountain glaciers cover a relatively small area, we can be fairly certain that
the loss is no greater than that for all Greenland.

Using these estimates, we can try to arrive at a balance for
the whole world. The total amount of water on the world's
surface is nearly constant, so that whatever water melts from
the ice sheets and glaciers will increase the volume of sea water
and raise sea level. We have figures to make a very rough calculation. Think of it in terms of water gained and lost by the
oceans each year:

Water gained from Greenland (from 22 cu. miles of ice)	+19 cu. miles
Water gained from mountain glaciers	+19 cu. miles
Water lost to Antarctica	−125 cu. miles
Total volume of water lost each year by the oceans	−87 cu. miles

A volume of 87 cubic miles spread over the whole area of the
world's oceans, which is about 150,000,000 square miles,
would result in a lowering of sea level by 0.037 inches annually
or 3.7 inches a century. However, direct estimates of the
change in sea level suggest a quite different result. Tide-gauges
show that on the average over the past many years sea level has
been rising, not falling. Estimates of the rate vary from 2.5 to
6 inches each century. Studies of the rate of submergence of
marine beaches in middle latitudes also suggest that through-

out the past 3,000 years sea level has been rising at an average rate of 4.8 inches a century.

It is obvious that the two sets of results are in direct contradiction to one another. The changes in sea level are based upon world-wide observations made over a long period of time and are almost certainly approximately correct, although many new tide-gauges recently established will in a few years refine our knowledge. The view that the oceans are deepening and that the land is diminishing is also supported by the existence of many dry valleys in Antarctica. There is much evidence that these valleys were formerly filled with ice and that the height and volume of ice in Antarctica has diminished during the past few thousand years.

The discrepancy in the figures is thus considered to be due to an error in the measurement of snow accumulation in Antarctica. Recent discussions in London suggest that, in addition, the rate of flow of ice off Antarctica may have been seriously underestimated. It also seems probable that the few places measured for the rate of snow accumulation in Antarctica are not typical of the continent as a whole. These factors may have contributed to the discrepancy. We have much to learn, indeed, before we can accurately explain the causes, and thereby predict the onset, of climatic changes.

That these changes can be very great and could have a profound effect on human destiny is hard to accept, but it is certainly true. It is now well established that large areas of Canada, northern United States, northern Europe, and Siberia were covered with ice sheets which began to melt with great rapidity only eleven thousand years ago. For tens of thousands of years before that, all these lands resembled Greenland in the extent and thickness of their ice cover and in the bitterness of their climate. This load of ice locally depressed the land, which is still rising rapidly. Indeed it is probable that the shallow Baltic Sea and Hudson Bay only exist because they were depressed by the loads of ice. Everywhere else the melting of so much ice has caused sea level to rise by a height of over 100 feet. This melting appears to be still in progress. The rise of land in some places and of sea level in general are causes of anxiety to harbour masters throughout the world.

It would be of the greatest importance to mankind to be able to predict whether the ice age will return, whether conditions will remain as they are, or whether the remaining ice sheets will continue to melt and inundate all coasts to a depth of scores of feet. But until more is known of the behaviour of ice sheets and the influences which affect them, we cannot tell what will happen or at what rate changes in climate are likely to occur.

CHAPTER 15

BRUSSELS
TO MOSCOW

JULY 1958

On July 16, 1958 I flew to Europe with a party of Iowa farmers, whom I met again in Moscow, and an American archery team, who fell to earth I know not where. I was on my way to attend meetings in Moscow, but I stopped for twenty-four hours in Brussels to see the World's Fair and in Helsinki to call on colleagues.

At the World's Fair I went directly to the American and Soviet pavilions. The United States had erected a light and splendid circular building, easily the finest in the fair. The huge hall was bright and well proportioned and rose to a great open skylight in the centre, but it was almost devoid of exhibits. It looked like an empty stage, waiting for the actors. There was a lake, open fields of grass, and a few gaunt trees. It was beautiful, but appeared to have little to do with the vibrant life of the United States. The lonely emptiness was more a foretaste of Siberia.

A more careful search revealed a collection of abstract paintings, a movie about atomic energy, a voting machine, a glass box containing six tumbleweeds, and a room in which hi-fi records were being played. In another darkened hall there was a good display of the program of the IGY. The whole was restrained to the point of bleakness, and what finally made it seem clear that the exhibits were intended to advertise Siberia and not the United States was an exhibit of wooden farm implements used by the pioneers three hundred years ago, and a collection of enamel campaign buttons from past presidential elections. Americans only wear lapel buttons at service club luncheons and during political campaigns. On the other hand, throughout Asia in the summer of 1958 the well-dressed Communists wore lapel buttons all the time, and the more of them the better!

It seemed curious to me that the American nation had become so sensitive to public opinion (and let us be candid—to public envy) that they had staged an exhibit of exactly what they were not. Artistically it was a great success, but it did not convey much impression of the abundance, the exuberance, the freedom, the exultant joy of living which seems to me to be the essence of America.

I went across to the Soviet pavilion. From the moment that I bought an ice cream "Morozony" and entered the big, stark, rectangular modern building until I was at last disgorged from the aisles within, I felt I was back in the New York which I had left only twenty-four hours before. The building was crowded with people and lined with displays of Sputniks, sleek automobiles, vast machines and towering piles of food and clothes. During the ensuing months in Russia and China, I was never to see such abundance again. Strange that these nations, both so powerful, each wanted to be esteemed not for what it was, but in the image of the other: the Americans as simple, hardy pioneers; the Russians as lavish providers of the world's goods.

Out of curiosity I went for supper to the Canadian building.

It was a skeleton of a place, a lot of girders held together with wire and decorated with excellent photographs, plans, and models. To a much greater extent than the designers had intended, it typified the country, half empty and half finished. In the restaurant upstairs I had what was advertised as a typically Canadian meal: pea soup, stuffed tomatoes, green beans with chunks of bacon, maple-syrup pie, and rye whisky. I was glad to get coffee and not Labrador tea or stewed spruce roots. All the individual ingredients were authentic but the menu was not, and I can appreciate why so few restaurants at home advertise Canadian cooking.

The exhibition had a superb setting in a royal park. The Belgians had gone to great trouble; I was sorry not to have seen more, but I had to catch a plane and fly to Finland over the peaceful lands that border the North and Baltic Seas, with their trim fields, neat forests, and compact villages of red brick. Europe, like most of the more fertile parts of the world, is getting so full of people that the cities sprawl together, devouring the countryside.

After two days in Helsinki I boarded a two-engined Soviet plane, rather like a DC-3, and flew south over the Gulf of Finland and the Russian forests to Moscow. During the flight a large and attractive stewardess with a mass of fair curls plunked a tray of caviar, smoked salmon, cheese, bread and butter, fruit, vodka and wine before me and dealt out coloured brochures in several languages explaining the wonders of the Sputniks.

At Moscow the vice-president of the IUGG, Professor V. V. Beloussov, a gracious, wise, and ponderous man built to the dimensions and colour of a brown Russian bear, met the plane and whisked me through immigration and customs and into a waiting VIM, the Russian version of a 1950 Buick, for the 15-mile drive to the Moscow Hotel.

In the course of our drive I was guilty of a social error: I lowered the window of the car to throw away the butt of a cigarette I had been smoking. "There are ash trays in the arm rests of our cars," said Beloussov. Today in Russia it is important to be *culturny*. Hatless, dishevelled, with bags deliberately chosen for their battered condition, travelling "tourist," and throwing butts out of windows, I was clearly not living up to the precise and formal standards of behaviour required in the new Russia. I felt like a revolutionary visiting the country of the czars.

We entered Moscow, that huge forbidding city, the Chicago of Eurasia and the melting pot of Russia. Here the peasants of the steppes come to gawk, here the elite of satellite countries are royally entertained and impressed with the wonders of the new Russian fatherland; from here the mass of Communist orders and propaganda issues forth; and here, ironically, the Western influences of education and science are most strongly felt. It was the infiltration of Western ideas and defeat by Western armies that caused the Russian revolution, and the Western influence has remained strong. Today in Russia there is a level of popular education and of material progress that would have astonished the czars.

Our meetings were held in the University of Moscow, new, ornate, and the tallest building in Europe. Some of its professors complained about the difficulties of getting up and down in the elevators, but our meetings went well. At some meetings everyone spoke English; at others, Professor V. V. Beloussov acted as chairman, and himself carried on a three-way translation into English, French, or Russian as required. After breakfast Ludmilla, Natasha, and other efficient Intourist guides would pick all of us visiting scientists up at our hotels and drive us to the University, and then would reappear each afternoon, offering to show us the sights. With their help and with a gradually growing confidence in my own ability to find my way about alone, I saw what I could of the city.

The hotels which I saw fell into three classes. There are three old czarist ones, the National (the most comfortable), the Metropole, and the Savoy. There are the new skyscrapers: the Ukrania and the Leningradskaya for tourists, and the Sovietskaya where the party elite congregate. This last has much the best service and the best orchestra in town. Lastly there are two oddities, the Peking and the Moscow. The Peking is small and has a good Chinese restaurant. It seems to be the place where junior officers and officials like to go for a good time and it gets pretty riotous. The Moscow, where I stayed, is the largest and most unusual. Its forbidding appearance, the bad service, and the close surveillance of its guests remind one that it was built by Stalin in the 1930's. In addition to the watchful doorman and the girl on each floor, I regularly received an incomprehensible phone call at eleven-thirty each night and once, returning unexpectedly, I caught a man emerging from my room. Perhaps he was inspecting the plumbing.

On the top floor is a café—accessible from the street, not from the hotel—frequented by the rock and roll teen-agers who also gather on the square in front of the hotel in great numbers each evening to watch an open-air stage show, listen to the loudspeakers, dance on the pavement, and jostle the girls.

One of the interpreters took us to the Tretygof Gallery—the Moscow counterpart of the L'Hermitage Gallery in Leningrad, but devoted solely to the work of Russian artists. Although the Russians have never been as distinguished in painting as in writing or music, the gallery is a splendid review of the social history of the country. A French scientist who had praised L'Hermitage to the skies said: "Ride a bicycle through the Tretygof, but spend hours in its basement among the old ikons." We did. I had no idea until I saw them how superbly colourful and imaginative these religious paintings could be, and how many facets of the life of the times could be packed into the background of a saint's portrait.

Seeing our interest in the ikons, our interpreter asked: "Do you believe in God?" One of us replied and returned the question. "No," she said doubtfully. "We have no need. Science is our God." I considered advising her to spend more time on her scientific catechism, for her knowledge of science was slight, but realizing that she was an Intourist guide, not a technical translator, I held my peace.

Another night she took us to the State Central Puppet Theatre. We were late because the service at the Moscow Hotel was so slow that it always took two hours to get dinner. It made no difference whether the Intourist guides were there to browbeat the waiters, or whether we were unattended and free to try cajolery and tips; the service was uniformly bad. The endless delays were compounded by a chronic shortage of menus. The more farsighted waiters had small caches of them hidden under the tablecloth, but they usually managed to produce the wrong one. They had three to choose from: tourist, first class, and de luxe. We scientists all sat together, but we were travelling in varying degrees of grandeur and the changes that could be rung on three classes of meal tickets and menus led to endless confusion.

That night, when we had at last got our salt fish in jelly, partridge with jam, tomato salad, coffee with lemon, and excellent bread, we made our way to the theatre, which stood in a garden like the Tivoli in Copenhagen. The production was directed by People's Artist of the U.S.S.R., S. V. Obreztsov, whose puppets seemed to be able to lampoon the regime in a way no actors would have dared. The tickets, at 17 roubles (officially $4.25), were beyond the means of any but the more prosperous and sophisticated Russians, and most of the audience were tourists.

I sat between my interpreter, Natasha, and a businessman

from New Haven. He mentioned that during the day he had
driven into the country to a Greek Orthodox monastery and
that he had been unfavourably impressed by the number of
empty trucks he had seen bouncing along the roads. I later
learned that this apparent inefficiency and waste was due to
the fact that the peasants, having no cars of their own, seize on
any sort of an errand as an excuse for a joy ride in a truck.

An enthusiastic choir of puppets began the first chorus,
which was translated for me:

> *Drink more vitamins,*
> *All drink vitamins,*
> *Vitamins A B C D.*
> *Only those who drink more vitamins*
> *Will live to their death.*

I probably looked rather blank, but Natasha thought it very
funny and daring. "Don't you see," she explained, "that they
are laughing at the ridiculous laws and edicts which the Government is always issuing?"

There followed a quick succession of clever acts from old
fashioned vaudeville:

MAKEIT BETTEROF—*Cellist*
ALLEGRETTA TRALALALOVA—*Coloratura Soprano*

Also an infant prodigy, a lion tamer, an illusionist, a waltz
team, and at the piano Sufferin Victor. The jazz quartet of
"Boogie, Woogie, Jeep, and Creep" roused shouts of enthusiasm because at other places jazz is frowned upon as decadent.
Best of all was the gypsy choir. As the program had it: "Just
imagine that we are in a restaurant. Enter—the gypsy choir.
Around us rises the smell of the steppes and schnitzel— Whatever anyone may say, for me this is real art: *Ochi Chernize.*
. . . I have not enquired too closely into their family backgrounds. I wouldn't like to say that they are all gypsies, but

don't let's be too particular. I do know that one of them has a gypsy sister-in-law."

The puppets had faces and dresses of a completely oriental cast—obviously from Turkestan and Central Asia. They danced and sang gypsy choruses interspersed with solos. Each time another slit-eyed Turk or Uzbek was introduced, Natasha was convulsed with laughter. I became more and more puzzled. "Don't you see," she whispered hysterically, "how they are laughing at the fuss the Government makes about the national minorities? Don't you hear how completely Russian the names are that they have given to all those extraordinary-looking people from the south? Don't you hear," she sobbed between her laughter, "what those horrible gypsies are singing? They are saying: 'Money is everything, money is everything.' "

Perhaps this show was put on for the benefit of tourists. If so, this particular tourist missed the finer points, but the Russians in the audience didn't miss a thing, and they loved it.

I went to many scientific institutes, several with very fine new buildings. But whether new or not, all were full of eager and able scientists who showed great interest in exchanging ideas with the West. Some of them asked us to their homes, a fairly new venture I believe, because only recently have suspicions been relieved and the standards of living raised sufficiently to make this possible.

The living standard for full professors in Moscow is comparable with that in North America; they have rather fewer rooms, and fewer cars, but they have more books. They have good food, summer holidays on the Black Sea, the chance to travel over half Asia, and for the fortunate, occasional trips to underdeveloped countries or to Europe.

The fact of the matter is that I thoroughly enjoyed my time with the Russian scientists, and I found them not fundamentally different from ourselves. Another Canadian scientist in Moscow summed up our views on Russian progress by remarking: "Only a fool could fail to be impressed." Why then is this picture so different from what we imagine? Were these scientists typical? Was my view of Russia genuine?

It was genuine enough. We went into well-known institutes, met well-known scientists, saw their laboratories, and talked about science. Countries don't build jet airplanes and launch Sputniks without a very real and large body of able engineers and scientists. These scientists came from many classes and held many beliefs, not always what the Communist party would have wished. One cannot easily be specific in these matters, but the diverse backgrounds are illustrated by two scientists whom I met. One was Urey Goudin, Stalin Prize winner and devoted Communist, skeptical of foreigners and brought up entirely in the pattern of the revolution, but an able oil-finder none the less. The other was the late Academician Ivan Bardin, vice-chairman of the Academy of Sciences of the U.S.S.R. and chairman of the Soviet IGY Committee. At a reception in Moscow he said to me in good English: "Professor Wilson, I'm glad to see you again. We enjoyed our visit to Toronto last year. It was good to be back in North America." When I asked him about his previous visit, he said: "Yes, in 1910, when I was a young man, I worked for a year as a metallurgist for the Illinois Steel Company in Gary, Indiana."

The young engineer of czarist days who was able to go abroad and round out his education is hardly one's idea of the successful revolutionary, but because of his ability that wise old man had remained to render great service to his country.

❀

CHAPTER 16

GRAVITY AND THE EARTH'S WOBBLE

Gravity is the power of attraction of the earth. It is what keeps men's feet on the ground. In doing so it provides us with a strong sense of direction. Being upright feels the same everywhere, although a moment's reflection about people around the globe shows that the vertical direction is not uniform, as it feels, but is always radial to the earth.

This power of attraction is not confined to the earth but is a universal property of matter. We don't know why it exists, but we do know that it cannot be generated like magnetism and that it does not vary with time. Its study is therefore much easier than is the study of geomagnetism. Once the value of gravity has been measured at any place, that value is fixed. There is no need for gravity observatories as there is for magnetic observatories.

Broadly speaking, geophysicists concentrated during the IGY's year and a half span on phenomena which fluctuated rapidly with significant and measurable changes. Gravity was certainly not one of these, and was not a major program but it was included because the IGY offered gravity specialists so many good opportunities to get to out-of-the-way places and speed the regular collection of data.

To measure gravity two means are employed: deflections of delicate spring balances called gravimeters and variations in the rate of swing of pendulums.

The earth is slightly flattened at the poles. Thus, anyone sitting at the north pole is thirteen miles closer to the centre of the earth than he would be if he were sitting at the equator. The fact that the earth may also be somewhat pear-shaped would have less effect than the flattening.

Since the closer a body is to the centre of the earth the greater is the pull of gravity, a heavy man weighs about a pound more at the poles than he does at the equator. This change would not show on a steelyard because the balancing weights would be equally affected by the change, but it would show on spring scales because springs are not affected by gravity. By using special spring balances called gravimeters, we can measure variations in gravity with extreme accuracy, even to one part in a billion.

Pendulums swing because gravity attracts them. Therefore the rate of swing of pendulums is affected by changes in the value of gravity. The astronomer Pierre Bouguer discovered this when he was sent by the French Academy to carry out surveys in Ecuador and Peru in 1735 and found that his pendulum clock ran slower over the equatorial bulge. Pendulums used in this work can now be timed so precisely that even the slight aging which occurs in any material after it has been worked during manufacture affects their length and time of swing and causes errors. Thus, old pendulums, which have been through a long settling-down period, so to speak, tend to be better than new ones. It is generally agreed that the two best sets are those made twenty-five years ago by the Gulf Oil Company and the University of Cambridge. Measurements have now been made by these instruments and by sensitive gravimeters at stations all over the world.

The IGY, with its many bases in remote places, provided an excellent chance to measure gravity more extensively than ever before. The United States took a lead in linking existing surveys by networks around the world and from pole to pole. One of the latter lay through the Americas and another lay through Japan and New Zealand. A third network extended from the Arctic through Europe and South Africa.

When plans had been made to complete the land network for the measurement of gravity, concern was expressed about how to supplement the scarce observations over the seven tenths of the earth's surface covered with water. The motion of waves has always made measurement difficult, and observations had only been made by instruments lowered to the bottom in a few shallow places and from submarines submerged below the waves. Both methods were necessarily limited. Italian, Swedish, and Finnish scientists urged that underwater gravimeters be widely used on continental shelves during the IGY, and much of the Baltic Sea was covered in this fashion.

The idea of using a submerged submarine as a quiet place in which to measure gravity at sea was first put into practice in 1923 by the Dutch geodesist F. A. Vening Meinesz. The Americans wished to make no less than two thousand observations from submarines, but since all navies seem to share a reluctance to lend their submarines the proposal did not prove feasible. J. L. Worzel, of Columbia University, found a way out of the impasse by developing a method of measuring gravity from surface ships. In November 1957 he succeeded in adapting a new German Graf instrument to record gravity continuously on shipboard as long as the weather was reasonably calm. He achieved this by placing the instrument exactly at the centre of buoyancy of the ship, where the motion

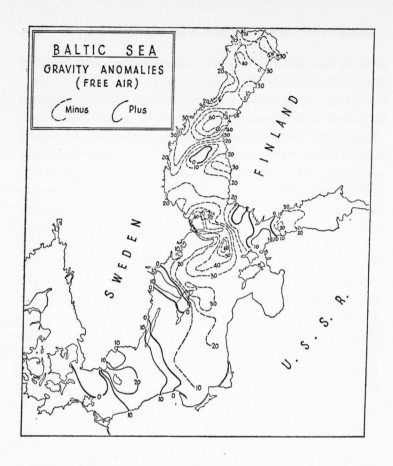

Map indicating variations in the strength of gravity in the Baltic Sea. Survey was made by Dr. Honkasalo, who lowered underwater gravimeter to the bottom of the sea to obtain measurements.

is least, and setting it, dampened with viscous oil, on a stabilized platform so that it did not respond to rapid wave motion. In this way it has become possible to measure gravity over the oceans and so complete a gravity survey of all parts of the world; but this will take several more years.

Gravity is an inherent property of all matter, and the

amount of matter near any spot determines the value of gravity there. For most practical purposes, the earth is so much the largest piece of matter in our vicinity that its attraction outweighs all else. That is why the value of gravity is said to be constant. If, however, large masses lying close by are moved, then a detectable change can occur. The movements of the sun and moon can also produce small but regular tidal effects.

Extremely sensitive gravity instruments can detect so minor a change as a wash-out under an apparently sound pavement. They can also disclose a body of heavy ore in the ground or show that in general tall buildings weigh less than the earth excavated from their basements.

Just as the sea rises and falls with the tides, so does the land; but whereas the great pulse of the tides of the sea is measured in feet, the rhythm of the rise and fall of the land is measured only in inches. Nevertheless, increases and decreases in the distance from the surface to the centre of the earth cause very small variations in the value of gravity which can be detected by delicate gravimeters. The most sensitive can record changes in elevation as small as one eightieth of an inch.

Both the U.S.S.R. and the United States proposed that earth tides should be recorded at fixed stations which would provide information about the rigidity of the earth's interior. Such stations were established all over the world, including one at a depth of 4,000 feet in a mine at Pribram, Czechoslovakia.

Due to the preponderant influence of the earth, the value of gravity at different places is related to the size and shape of the earth. The study of the earth's vital statistics, or the figure of the earth, is called geodesy. This word puzzles a great many people, but one can remember it if one understands that geodesy bears the same relation to an appreciation of the earth as the figures 35–25–35 bear to the judging of Miss Universe. Geodesists confine themselves to the main features and leave it to the topographers and hydrographers to fill in the detail.

A knowledge of the shape of the earth is of course essential to any broad-scale mapping, and that is chiefly why countries have geodetic surveys. To survey a one-acre field, it makes no difference whether the earth is a large sphere or a flat slab borne on the back of a turtle; but to survey very large tracts, to navigate across oceans, or to determine boundaries between countries, it is necessary to know the shape and size of the earth as precisely as possible.

Geodesists use three types of measurement: observations of stars; surveys of distances and directions; and measurements of changes in the value of gravity from place to place.

It is surprising that such good astronomers as the ancient Babylonians and Egyptians were hypnotized by the uniformity of the feeling of uprightness and failed to realize that the earth is spherical, not flat. The Greeks were the first to discover this truth and thereby explain such well-known phenomena as the round shadow cast by the earth on the face of the moon during eclipses, the sinking of distant objects below the horizon, and the apparent change in the heights of the sun and stars between temperate and tropical latitudes.

To an Eskimo the Pole Star appears high in the heavens; in Ecuador it is close to the horizon. There, on the earth's waist line, I have seen the Great Bear and the Southern Cross on opposite sides of the heavens at the same time. The Patagonian cannot see the Pole Star at all because the bulge of the earth hides it from his view. By making a precise series of such observations from different places on the earth, we can chart the curvature of the earth and so discover its shape and size. It was in this way that Eratosthenes measured the size of the earth fairly accurately. Geodetic surveys were among the first scientific measurements to reach a high degree of precision, and in the two centuries since the initial French expeditions preliminary surveys have been executed in most parts of the world. It has been discovered that if the topographical details are smoothed out the general shape of the earth closely approximates a flattened spheroid. Since 1924 the figures adopted by international agreement for this spheroid have been: polar diameter, 12713.824 kilometres; equatorial diameter, 12756.776 kilometres.

Given these figures and the elevation of any particular place, it is possible to calculate what the value of gravity should be at that place. This calculated value can be compared with the measured or observed value. Any difference between the two is called an anomaly and is attributed to irregularities within the earth. This is one way in which gravity measurements help us understand the earth's interior.

In a few years, when there has been time to calculate and collect all the results obtained during the IGY, it is probable that the official figures for our standard spheroid will be slightly revised and improved. If, as J. A. O'Keefe has postulated, the earth is very slightly pear-shaped, and if the equator is indeed somewhat elliptical, then small modifications may be introduced in the equation.

Since we have already described how irregularities in the motion of satellites are used to study irregularities in the shape of the earth, it will be understood that local variations and anomalies in gravity affect the paths of long-range missiles. If the dimensions of the earth are in error or the distances between continents and islands are not precisely known, then the aim of missiles will be correspondingly affected. These military implications have on the one hand intensified the study of geodesy and gravity, and on the other they have led to some reticence in the exchange of certain information. Fortunately, most of these measurements were known fairly accurately before the missile age so that only limited refinements are possible.

In addition to observations from satellites, precise clocks

and ingenious telescopes have been introduced to increase accuracy in the measurement of the stars. In 1958 at Wellington, New Zealand, I saw a Danjon astrolabe, a telescope developed in France for fixing the direction of stars. Later in São Paulo, Brazil, I saw the American Markowitz moon camera, which makes it possible to photograph perturbations of the moon with great precision. The principle is very simple. The path of the moon past the stars each month can be calculated, its average speed is known, and for any instant of time its position relative to stars can be predicted precisely. Photographs can then be taken to determine whether the moon is on time. If it appears not to be, slight irregularities in the rate of rotation of the earth are probably the cause. This process involves practical difficulties, however, because the moon is moving relative to the stars and because it is so much brighter than they are. With a fast exposure only the moon shows on a photograph; and with a long exposure, which would show the stars, the moon's image is fogged by its greater brilliance and both moon and stars are blurred by their motions. To overcome these difficulties, the Markowitz camera is driven by a small motor in such a way that the images of the stars remain fixed on the plate and can be photographed without apparent motion during long exposures. To reduce the glare of the moon, a round dark filter is positioned in the barrel of the telescope so that it just covers and darkens the image of the moon without interfering with the light from the surrounding stars. The moon filter incorporates a prism that is rotated at the rate required to hold the image of the moon steady against the stars, thereby effectively "stopping" the motion of the moon relative to the stars.

The importance of these geodetic and astronomical measurements to gravity studies has already been indicated, but they are also vital to another related program of the IGY, one called Longitudes and Latitudes, which was aimed at discovering how much the earth wobbles during its rotation. Astronomers have observed for a long time that the earth is not entirely uniform in either its direction or its speed of rotation; its axis wobbles like a top and its speed is also slightly irregular. Small fluctuations might have been predicted and can easily be explained. The interesting questions are whether systematic changes are moving the direction of the axis of rotation about and whether the earth is speeding up or slowing down.

Everyone knows that a skater spins faster when he hugs his arms close to his sides than he does when he holds them spread out. In the same way, shifting of the earth's cargo of water, ice, and air can cause it also to wobble about on its axis. These changes in distribution can be brought about by great storms or by variations in the pattern of persistent winds. Thus, the speed at which the earth is spinning varies according to whether the waters on its surface are piled up around the equator or driven towards the poles. W. A. Munk has suggested that such changes are also due in part to movements in the liquid core of the earth.

These effects have long been known. Observations collated at Naples, Italy, show that the wobbling of the axis causes the north and south poles to move with an irregular circular motion about 10 feet in diameter. But we have been observing this phenomenon for so short a time that no one can yet say whether the poles are migrating or whether the continents are drifting. Likewise, the speed varies so much that some days are one thousandth of a second longer than others, and this can easily be measured on atomic clocks precise to one part in a billion. There is also good evidence that the earth is slowing down. This theory is the result of work on historical records of old eclipses by an astronomer named J. K. Fotheringham.

Fotheringham searched the old Babylonian records and from time to time found references such as: "On the twenty-sixth day of the month of Sibellu in the seventh year, the day

was turned to night and there was fire in the midst of heaven."
From his knowledge of the records he was able to interpret this
to mean: "On the thirty-first day of July, 1062 B.C., there was a
total eclipse in Babylon." Working with modern astronomical
tables, he established the fact that there had indeed been a
total eclipse on July 31, 1062 B.C., but that the narrow path of
totality for that eclipse should not have passed near Babylon.
He found similar discrepancies between calculations and observations throughout, which he could only explain if the
earth had slowed down by four and a half hours in the past
three thousand years. Inasmuch as there are a great many days
in three thousand years, and since the changes in rate are
cumulative, this discrepancy could also be explained if the
days in each century were on the average only about one
thousandth of a second longer than the days of the preceding
century.

Several of the matters discussed in this chapter are related
to a fundamental question which has not been fully settled.
This is the problem of whether the earth has permanent
strength or not; of whether it behaves like a true solid and
holds its shape indefinitely against applied forces or whether
if these forces are applied for a long time it will flow slowly
like pitch or tallow and adjust itself to them. For short periods
we know the answer. The earth is more rigid than steel. Large
earthquakes make the earth ring like a bell and daily tides indicate a similar rigidity to brief forces, but there is still no
agreement as to whether the earth flows in response to forces
which are applied for thousands and millions of years.
O'Keefe's discovery that the earth is slightly pear-shaped led
him to believe that the maintenance of this shape indicates
permanent strength, but we have seen that other geophysicists
consider the pear shape a relatively temporary deviation caused
by ice loads applied during the recent ice age. The discovery
that the rate of rotation is changing also suggests that the

earth is capable of flow, for the present shape of the earth is just what it would be in a fluid body rotating at the earth's speed. If the earth is able to flow, this is to be expected. But if the earth is rigid, it is a remarkable occurrence that we should be living just when its unyielding shape exactly corresponds to that of a liquid body rotating at the same speed.

A sufficient knowledge of gravity might also help us settle this problem. If over the whole earth the calculated and observed values agree closely, then the earth is in equilibrium and has probably flowed slowly to reach adjustment. If, on the other hand, these values do not agree, then it can be concluded that the earth has not adjusted to its irregularities and hence probably has permanent strength which enables it to resist adjustment. The settlement of this question is fundamental to an understanding of the causes and nature of mountain-building. Because the enigma has not been resolved, there are many theories of mountain-building, each supported by some evidence and apparently contradicted by other observations. Some theories have depended upon a strong earth, others on a plastic one.

By coincidence, another theory which had not been taken very seriously before was raised during the IGY. It is that the earth is expanding due to a weakening in the force of gravity. Astronomers have observed that the distant galaxies are receding; this is referred to as the expansion of the universe. In 1931 P. A. M. Dirac suggested that this expansion might be the result of a steady and universal decrease in the attraction due to gravity. If so, not only would the universe be expanding, but also the solar system and the earth and indeed everything in creation. At that time the origin of the universe was widely believed to have occurred two billion years ago. It was soon pointed out that the resulting rate of expansion would, a comparatively short geological period ago, have placed the earth so much closer to the sun that evidence of the higher temperature would be evident in the older rocks. Such evidence was not in fact there. Dirac's speculation was shelved until 1957, when R. H. Dicke recalled it and pointed out that the universe is now believed to be far older, that the rate of expansion need not have been so great, and that the heating effects would not be noticeable in the geological record. He also pointed out that the interior of the earth is greatly compressed by the weight of overlying material and that any reduction in gravity would lighten the load of overlying matter, thus causing the earth to expand. Dicke could think of no experiment that could be performed in a physics laboratory to prove or disprove this hypothesis, so he appealed to astronomers and earth scientists for help. "It would," he said, "be truly remarkable if geology and astronomy could answer such a fundamental physical question about the gravitational interaction."

It had not occurred to many geologists before that the earth might be expanding, and it is still difficult to see how expansion could push up mountains. But the IGY disclosed the existence of great cracks in the ocean floor, and B. C. Heezen, who noticed the cracks, adopted this idea as an explanation of their existence. He considers that the rate of expansion is of the right order of magnitude to have produced the cracks.

I shall return to this question again and present evidence from other fields. However, as yet we have not been able to solve the problem of the degree of permanent strength of the earth. No one knows with any certainty how the earth behaves, why mountains are uplifted, how continents were formed, or what causes earthquakes. We know some anatomy of the earth, but no real physiology. Earth scientists are as ignorant of their patient as doctors were of theirs before Harvey disclosed the circulation of the blood. But earth scientists are knocking on the doors of discovery; they await the answer.

CHAPTER 17

THE SOVIET UNION

For any nation to have launched a satellite would have been a remarkable feat, but it was a particularly great achievement for the Russians. One hundred years ago the majority of the Soviet people were illiterate serfs, chattels of the czar, of great landowners or of independent Oriental khans. Their emergence from ignorance, poverty, and defeat during the last forty-five years has been rugged, and they have not yet attained Western standards of freedom. Why were these people backward for so long? And how did they so quickly assume a leading place in science, as made manifest to all the world when they launched the Sputniks as part of the IGY?

From time immemorial one of the outstanding geographical features of Eurasia has dictated the history of Russia. This is the great natural highway which extends across central Asia and southern Russia, from Mongolia all the way to the gates of Europe. This belt of fertile grassland, the steppes, skirts the northern flanks of the mountains of central Asia and Kazakhstan, sweeps through a passage between the Urals and the Caspian Sea, and flows over the great plains of the Ukraine

and Romania. It finally ravels out in a tangle of passes through
the Polish marshes and the Carpathian Mountains. From ear-
liest history by this route have come the invaders: Goths,
Huns, Magyars, Turks, Mongols, and Tartars. Not until after
the Tartar Empire of Genghis Khan had finally collapsed were
the scattered nomads of these ravaged plains able to develop
settlements and unite.

To the north of these great steppes vast forests engulfed
and held prisoner isolated pockets of Slavs and Scandinavians.
Slowly and ruthlessly the princes of one city, Moscow, extended their autocratic domination in spreading rings about
their capital, swallowing one isolated community after another until their dominion stretched over the Urals to the
Bering Sea and across the great southern plains. In 1884, with
the conquest of the farthest deserts of Turkestan, the great
Russian Empire was complete, stopped from further expansion to the south by mountains and by the armies of British
India, to the west by Germany and Austria, and to the east
by the Chinese in Manchuria. The Russian Empire, which is
now the Soviet Union, is thus a comparatively new country.

This vast land is far from homogeneous, for it incorporates
many varied and restless peoples, including 25,000,000 Mos-
lems. They speak a great variety of languages. They have never
known freedom or democracy. Until this last generation few
could read or write or travel farther than they could walk from
their native village. Their history had been one of unmitigated
horror and misery. It seems fair to say that today the average
Soviet citizen is better educated, freer, and wealthier than
his ancestors ever were. He certainly has better hopes for the
future. For this, two tyrants are chiefly responsible: Peter the
Great and Stalin. Peter introduced European civilization to a
small group of aristocrats and professional men; Stalin introduced it to the Russian masses. He may have killed millions
and been hated by tens of millions, but he was cast in the

old tradition of the czars who ruthlessly imposed the greatest and most significant changes upon Russia. The success of the Soviet revolution was demonstrated to the world by the launching of Sputnik.

Because of this success, the IGY was acclaimed in the Soviet Union by government and people alike. Anyone coming, as I did, in connection with the IGY was free to meet Soviet scientists and to see their work. As a consequence, it was my good fortune to visit geophysical parties working where the forest meets the steppes in the oil fields of the Volga plains, to see earthquake observatories in the Caucasus, to examine institutes and universities in Peter's City, Petrograd, now renamed Leningrad, and to attend conferences in Moscow, the ancient capital, which Stalin restored as the heart and centre of all the Russias. Finally I left the Soviet Union by the slow length of the Trans-Siberian Railway. From these various points of vantage I caught intimate glimpses of both Russian science and Russian people—many of whom struck me as ebullient, forceful, modern reincarnations of the Horatio Alger hero.

Soon after my arrival I arranged, through the good offices of Dr. V. Fedynski, who had visited the Alberta oil fields the year before, to see a deep-sounding seismic party investigating the crust of the earth around the Tuimasi oil fields, the largest in the U.S.S.R. Very, very early on an August morning, in spite of the assurances of the Canadian Embassy that no Westerner would be allowed to visit the provinces of Tartaria and Beskeria, I flew from Moscow with Vladimir Orichenko, a cheerful and sophisticated technical interpreter, and Michael Davidchev, a shy engineer. At dawn, as we circled to land at Kazan, we saw the great Kuibishef Sea, a hydroelectric storage lake on the Volga River, and the Kazanski Kremlin, an ancient fortress of the forest edge.

At Ufa, where the foothills of the Urals are still scarcely

perceptible, we landed again to be met by three members of the Tuimasi Expedition. In the Expedition's two small YAK-12 planes, flown by U.S.S.R. Air Force pilots (there is no other kind of pilot in Russia), we were taken to the head-quarters, a collection of wooden buildings on the edge of Tuimasi, a new town whose dominant features are brick blocks of flats, several sprouting refineries, and a lamp-black factory.

For the next four days Urey Goudin, the Communist Stalin Prize winner, showed Tuzo Wilson, the capitalist professor, everything about his expedition. He told me that he had never had a non-Russian visitor before, and his attitude suggested that he regarded me, a representative of capitalism, as axio-matically an effete and dangerous exploiter of the downtrod-den. Nevertheless, orders had come sifting down to him from the upper reaches, and he showed me everything I wished to see of his party and its work. He was forty-six years old, capa-ble, and hard-driving. He had been an oil man all his life and seemed not a little surprised and put out when I told him that I, a capitalist, had started summer work when I was fifteen years old—two years before he had.

He had 1,100 people, 200 vehicles, and a budget of 20 mil-lion roubles a year (equal to $5 million at the official rate of exchange and not less than $2 million in purchasing power.) These he directed in the investigation of geological formations of the largest size—scores and hundreds of miles across—hidden beneath the plains. Other parties followed to look for the oil pools themselves. In the winter the whole party moved south to continue similar researches in the deserts of Turke-stan. Crustal studies of a like nature were undertaken in many areas of the world as part of the IGY seismic program.

For four days we travelled by jeep and by plane, visiting his work parties. From the air we could spot the special ve-hicles and lines of instruments which made them unmistak-able. We landed in stubble fields beside several, and I have no doubt that the geophysical exploration which we saw was genuine and unstaged. The most interesting and picturesque party was one at which we had not intended to land at all. We did so because due to rain and a late start our timetable had been disrupted, and by evening we were still far from base and had not had a bite to eat or a drop to drink for twelve hours. It is possible that Goudin was expecting his capitalist visitor to collapse, but I was so fascinated at watching his scientific teams at work that I had not noticed the passing of time. At seven o'clock we landed to see a party and took a swim at the junction of the Belaya and Kama Rivers. After that Goudin radioed ahead to one of his prospecting parties that we would land in twenty minutes and wanted supper.

The pilot set down our light plane in a field beside a threshing machine. Men and women were working together to bring in the harvest, and a tractor provided the power. Geophysicists met us with a jeep and drove us a couple of hundred yards to a camp at the edge of the forest where a party of twenty were living in tents. The cook asked whether we wanted our eggs boiled or fried, and while she cooked them, we looked at each tent. All had aluminum cots, reasonable bedding, and in the dining tent were a table and some folding chairs. As we sat down, I noticed that each place was set with a bowl and a mug, a big spoon and a small one. We had black bread, soup made of cabbages, potatoes, and dried meat (there being no refrigeration), and ate boiled eggs in their shells. The tea was sweetened with huge lumps of sugar and a syrup made of boiled wild cherries. The Russians said that they liked their tea "hot, strong, and sweet like kisses," to which I suggested that they should add the word "often." The cook continued to protest that she had not had time to prepare a proper meal, so we had clearly had what was left from the workers' supper. I would not have minded working in the camp and indeed, thinking of my own days in the Canadian woods when we travelled by canoes, not trucks, I said: "We didn't have beds in our camps." To this they replied: "But you did not go prospecting in 1958." I do not think that they have long had such comforts.

The fine-looking people who inhabit this region are, I was told, Tartars, descendants of the Golden Horde. "They are the best workers," said the leader of the expedition. Some had been trained locally for prospecting. Half were men and the other half shy, pretty girls who retired into the background after being introduced. Everyone was in Western dress—shirts and trousers for the men, and slacks or simple dresses for the girls.

It was peaceful standing at the forest edge after supper and looking out at the slanting light of the evening sun. The leader of the Tartars was a stalwart man with almost orange hair, light blue-green eyes, very red cheeks, and the bull neck and rather flat upright face we associate with the word "huns."

When I remarked to him on the beauty of the rolling fields of grain, he replied: "We are not ashamed to admit that this is our country. All races are equal in the Soviet Union now!" I felt that his obvious enthusiasm owed nothing to Communism, but that his feelings were the same as those of the natives of Texas, of Alberta, and of Arabia when the discovery of oil brought new jobs and new wealth to local people.

During these four days we flew back and forth for 1,000 miles through the heart of the Russian steppes—the vast tract that lies between the Kama River and the Urals. As I travelled over those endless plains, my first impression was that the country could have changed but little in the centuries since it was first settled. The scattered and isolated villages are all alike: Identical mud roads are lined with little log cabins with thatched roofs and tiny windows brightened by frames of painted fretwork. Behind each cabin, enclosed by a picket fence, is a tiny barn, a chicken yard, a cabbage patch and as long a field of potatoes as a man can dig and harvest in the evenings. The wide and muddy street is the stage on which the life of the village is played. Children swarm over it all day, and in the evenings their elders stroll along it or sit and gossip on the benches before their houses. They build their houses on it. These cabins are fashioned of fir or aspen logs. In the course of time, as the logs rot and the cabin is in imminent danger of collapse, a new one is built in the middle of the village street. One day the old one is knocked down and the new one shoved into its place.

Each nightfall the life of the village street rises to a crashing crescendo when the small boys return from the uplands driving the flocks and herds before them. Stampeding down the street, the cattle come; and glorious chaos reigns until each animal is sorted out and herded into its proper barn.

As we flew over the plains, I saw the little villages edging the streams, and between them the flat uplands marked out in fields of wheat and rye, oats and barley, and occasionally corn and sunflowers. In the south on the Orenburg steppe are broad stretches of wheat country like our own prairies. Farther north the ground is wooded. The villages are surrounded by dense forest, a great, green carpet only occasionally marred by a clearing, like a moth hole, each with its wood-cutter's cottage surrounded by neat piles of cord wood. All this we saw, hour after hour, in unending repetition. I watched the geese rear up and flap their wings, saw the sparrows whirl from the threshing floor, waved at the little boys swimming in the river, and marked the lone thatcher harvesting his reeds in the swamp. I watched the sheep and goats stampede amongst the unconcerned cattle beneath the shadow of our plane.

A question that greatly interested me was how far the Russian form of Western industrial revolution had affected the villages of the steppes. First and most striking is the fact that every field I passed gave evidence that the whole task of plow-ing, harvesting, and seeding had been mechanized. I saw hundreds of tractors working in the giant fields. I counted thirty-eight in one half-hour, but I did not see a single plow or combine drawn by horses. In only three cases did I see men reaping by hand and all were in odd corners, river banks for instance, where tractors could not penetrate. Horse-drawn carts were used for drawing crops and for family transport, but there were also many large farm trucks. There were no private cars, but a few bicycles and motorcycles.

The recent abolition of the State tractor stations was mentioned two or three times and was evidently regarded as important. I gathered that it was not only a sign of an increasing liberal attitude on the part of the Government but also a sign that there were plenty of tractors and that all farmers were accustomed to their use. The tractors were rather rough-looking, but they pulled a span of five plows through the rich black soil without any trouble.

The second thing I noticed was the widespread rural electrification in these remote plains. At least half the villages we passed were reached by rows of wooden poles carrying a three-wire electric system very far from the power houses on the Volga and the main steel transmission lines. The electricity was carried down each street on poles, and we were often low enough to discern the two wires leading from the poles into the tiny thatched cabins. It is true that by our standards the power was limited, with only one street light for a whole street and only a bare bulb in each room, but it was an enormous advance over candles, and it meant power in the barns and in village workshops. The harnessing of the Volga had brought comfort to the people of these remote villages as well as power to industry.

The third thing I noticed was the change in housing. The smallest and most remote villages had scarcely been affected; the cabins in those places had not changed much in style.

But in the larger villages and especially near towns tar paper and metal roofs were replacing the thatch and bark of old. Perhaps a third of the cottages had modern roofs and a few in the most prosperous villages were brick. More conspicuous in every large settlement were the new sheds in the shape of an H or a T, which I supposed were for cattle owned by the State. In most cases these sheds supplemented older thatched sheds.

In the larger villages there were also schools or halls and occasionally a church. As far as I could make out, many of the latter were abandoned; some may have been continuing with a much reduced activity. One we passed on the ground was a ruin. I remarked on this, and my companion replied: "Of course, what would you expect?" But he did add: "A few are now being restored," and this was indeed true.

Outside the villages were cemeteries in which the graves were individually fenced in the Russian fashion; some were painted blue and some had crosses on them. More had plain tombstones; the choice was apparently optional. I also saw this mixture in a cemetery outside Moscow, but there the most ardent party members had added grave markers shaped like obelisks, surmounted by a vertical pointer and star—the whole painted bright scarlet. They certainly brighten up a graveyard.

I avoided getting into discussions about such controversial subjects as politics, religion, and economics, and so did not discuss the organization of life in the country, but from what I could see the villages were where they had always been, neither growing nor diminishing very much. The towns and cities had grown enormously, but in the villages the difference was one of organization. What had been called a village was now a collective farm with a different arrangement of ownership and payments.

The unending procession of villages on the seemingly infinite plain appeared to explain a great deal about Russia, for suddenly I realized that most of the people governing the U.S.S.R. today must have grown up in such surrounding as this. I thought that their isolation had much to do with their suspicion; their poverty with their toughness; and their hardship with their crudity. For centuries these villagers had little to thank the world for. Until 1861 they had been landless serfs. Governments were represented only by tax collectors. Shops and industry had scarcely existed for them. Foreign affairs meant but the recruiting and often the loss of their men at war. The nobility and the wealthy were envied and hated where they were known, but in these remote plains the owners of great estates and their castles were as scarce as they are in Saskatchewan. The Church gave solace to the aged, but it failed to educate the young or to mitigate the hardships of life on this earth.

We in the West have been so horrified by the many excesses of the revolution and so often frightened by the threats to peace made by its leaders that we do not realize that the revolution was essentially a Western movement. Its creed was written by a German living in England; Marx never visited Russia. In 1917 its first leader, Lenin, was brought back to Russia by the Germans from years in exile. His aim was a complete industrial and political revolution along lines developed in the West but going much further. As we passed the hydroelectric developments, my colleagues recited Lenin's creed in his own words: "Soviet power is socialism plus electrification of the Russian State." In Russia today this desire for Western ways is apparent everywhere. It is a sincere compliment to us, if a wry and undesired one.

The Western influence is not the only non-Russian one in the Soviet Union. Anyone who has seen the Moisiev Folk Dancers is aware that there are Soviet people other than Russians. Indeed the performances which I have seen of the Moisiev, Romanian, and Chinese folk dance troupes suggest that no Russians, Romanians, or Chinese ever dance, only Byelorussians, Ukrainians, Poles, Uzbeks, Moldavians, Bessarabians, Bulgars, Tartars, Mongols, Tibetans, and other border folk. It seems probable that the directors of all these troupes have been trained in the same school for the same propaganda purposes.

Not only does one see these national minorities on the stage, but one meets them when travelling; and I discovered how strongly these people feel when I flew from Moscow for a week-end to Tiflis, capital of the Georgian Republic, now magnanimously enough called by its Georgian name, Tbilisi. I had not been there five minutes when the Georgians made it quite clear even through the filter of a Russian Intourist interpreter that they were not Russians, never had been Russians, and did not like to be mistaken for Russians. With considerable hauteur they explained that the Georgian kingdom had been founded six centuries before Russia existed, that they had been converted to Christianity and had developed a written language with its own exotic alphabet five centuries before the Russians had become acquainted with either, and that they had only joined Russia a hundred and fifty years ago to save themselves from the Persians.

I went to Georgia because I had been baulked in an attempt to go to Samarkhand and Bokhara. Intourist had told me flatly that because of the crisis which then existed in Jordan and Lebanon all of Turkestan was closed except for Tashkent and that it would be quite impossible for me to go to Samarkhand. I gathered that Tashkent had little historic interest and less charm, and was not a place the discriminating traveller would choose to spend a week-end. I had, therefore, settled for Georgia. The week-end in Georgia came in a neat de luxe package at $30 a day, which included an interpreter and a car to drive up into the Caucasus. It was a very rewarding $60's worth.

On a Friday morning early in August my interpreter drove me to Moscow airport and dutifully stood waving until the TU-104 took off. She had been instructed to see me safely on my way to Georgia, and her mission could not be considered accomplished until I was airborne.

The interior of the jet had all the stuffed opulence and comfort of a Victorian Pullman car, and my travelling companions, to judge from the script of the newspapers they were reading, were almost all Georgians. They are an exceptionally handsome people: the women tall, serene, and dark; the men with a fine, swashbuckling air, well fitted to be the prototypes of the Caucasian race.

Until we reached the Caucasus the land was but an unremarkable pattern of hazy green and yellow squares cut by streams, so I gave my undivided attention to my lunch: caviar and biscuits, chicken with tomatoes and rice, wine, brandy, and tea. The meal took on the element of the Mad Tea Party when the woman sitting across the aisle from me washed her finger tips in the dregs of her tea.

Two hours and 1,100 miles later I looked down from 33,000 feet on the great peaks of Elbruz and Kasbek, the tallest mountains of Europe, 18,000 feet of craggy magnificence.

The descent to the airfield at Tiflis was hair-raising, a succession of tilted glimpses of wild chasms and inhospitable hillsides that appeared through breaks in the great thunderheads that puffed and mounded all around us. Eventually, the pilot found a hole in the clouds that suited him and down we went to slam to a stop with smoking tires at the exact end of an undersized concrete runway.

Several seismologists, one of whom had been at the Toronto meetings, met me with an Intourist car and interpreter, and together we toured the sights of the town: various old forts and ancient churches, a university with large new dormitories, a champagne factory, and a fine amusement park reached by an ancient funicular railway. All the churches there, unlike those in Moscow, were full of people morning, afternoon, and night. They were not shy in showing their devotion but got down on their knees and waved their arms in exhortation before silver ikons and elaborate altars. Alone in the evening I sought out the academy at which Stalin had trained for the priesthood. It slightly resembles a Greek temple and is now a museum devoted to Stalin's life. Many of the men in Tbilisi wore Georgian jackets cut in the style worn by Stalin, but everyone else was in drab, Western dress, except a few Kurdish women dressed in yellow, orange, scarlet, or pale-green skirts and blouses. With scarves in their hair and many bangles, they looked like gypsies strayed from some opera.

My hotel, in which I had been granted a suite, was like a Moorish palace with poor plumbing, but the restaurant was excellent, with good food and wine. The atmosphere was boisterous and the company lively; corks popped, toasts rang out, and waiters streaked through the room with meat sizzling on skewers, filling the air with smoke and the smell of good food. On my first appearance in the dining room, I was hailed with delight by an ancient man who still had some remnants of English left to him from a trip he had made many years before to the United States. He dragged me over to his table to have a drink. His companions, brawny, uninhibited types with gargantuan appetites, did not share my new-found friend's enthusiasm for me and one stormily refused to drink with me. I eased gently away and promptly became involved with a company every bit as intriguing as the one I had just left. It was a group of Americans, led by an earnest old gentleman who told me that he was a close personal friend of John Foster Dulles and that he was leading a peace mission through Russia. I found this a very entertaining idea and suggested that we should drink to the success of their mission. They were politely shocked when I offered them a glass of wine and, like the Georgians before them, refused to drink with me. I regretted that to make the best use of my stay in Georgia and to enjoy the excellent red Haranschara, I had to become a solitary drinker.

Sadly I retreated upstairs to the Moorish splendour of my suite. I pulled back the faded velvet curtains from the tall windows of my sitting room and looked by moonlight into the gardens and the graveyard of the cathedral set with cypresses and hibiscus plants. Whatever my lack of appeal as a drinking companion, at least I could take comfort from the thought that my rebuffs had taken place in a corner of the world I had long hoped to see. Southward over the mountains of Armenia and Ararat lay Persia; to the west, past the orange groves of the Circassian shore, lay Byzantium; while eastward, past the oil fields of Baku and the Caspian Sea, were the fabled cities of Turkestan.

My nostalgia was for the romantic Orient described by the adventurers who had opened it to Western eyes—stories which glossed over the cruelty, the disease, the poverty, and the stagnation of those lands. The inhabitants, whose experience was more bitter, looked on Western progress as a dream. Now awakened, they were pursuing this dream. They gratefully followed Communism, not for its ideology, but for the lead it had given them and for the path it promised, through science, to a better life.

Next morning, when the geophysicists of the Georgian Academy of Science took me to see their library, their seismographs, and their maps, and discussed with me their work on drought and irrigation, we felt for a time that we were following the same path. For the moment it did not matter that we came from different beginnings and were pursuing different ends.

The building in which the Academy was housed was new but already beginning to show signs of disintegration, for the parquet floor had shrunk, the railings were loose, and the concrete poor; on the other hand, the instruments were adequate and the library and the scientific work excellent. On fine maps of the region they had plotted the locations of all the many earthquakes, and they followed the changing centres of seismic activity with care. They knew that earthquakes occur more frequently at some places than at others, and they had discovered that the locations at which earthquakes occur most frequently move about. Recently the worst areas had been Socchi, Mount Ararat, and a line along the Caucasus Mountains. All this they duly reported to the World Data Centre in Moscow for international exchange.

The library, as I said, was excellent, and I noticed *Nature*, *Proceedings of the Royal Society, American Journal of Science, Annales de Géophysique* and many other well-known Western journals. Their own publications were printed in both Russian and Georgian. I admired the handsome antique script of the latter so much that they gave me copies of each edition.

At noon when I returned to the director's office to make my formal farewells, a sight confronted me such as I have never seen before in a geophysical laboratory. A table was spread with bowls of peaches, plums, pears, nectarines, apricots, and great bunches of grapes, and bottles of champagne and brandy. We sat down and toasted one another, our countries, our friends, and our work with the greatest gaiety and enthusiasm, nor would they let me leave until I had sampled every one of their delicious local fruits and much of their excellent wine. Their system beats coffee breaks.

With my three attendant seismologists and the interpreter, I climbed heavily into the car, supplied with my de luxe ticket, and rolled off toward the Caucasus Mountains. For many years there has been a military highway that stretches across the heart of the mountains between Tbilisi and Ordjonikidze, and we drove up this road to the pass. Overcome by the unaccustomed laboratory supplies, I slept peacefully for an hour and did not waken until we reached Mtskheta, the ancient capital of Georgia. According to tradition this city, now only a small town nestling at the foot of the hills, takes its name from a grandson of a great-grandson of Noah. Mount Ararat, suitably enough, lies 200 miles to the south. Certainly it is a very old town, for it was known to Alexander the Great, Pompey, Trajan, and many other invaders who at one time or other conquered the country.

We went through the cathedral, first built in A.D. 330 when the Georgians were converted to Christianity. Its fortified walls bear evidence of its long history of invasion, for they show signs of repeated damage and rebuilding. A few artisans were rather casually cleaning off the plaster and restoring the ancient frescoes and mosaics in the interior.

We continued on our way up the narrow fertile valleys to the bare slopes of the mountains, the country becoming increasingly more rugged and beautiful as we climbed. Alongside the road ran a telegraph line which, they told me, was the old line that once linked Britain with India. Our way wound up through little villages entirely built of stone and tile, with here and there an ancient watch-tower. The fine, handsome residents were diligent but unhurried; the old men stopped working on the roads to watch us pass, and the handsome girls set down loads of hay and faggots that they were carrying on their backs down the mountain and tossed free their thick black braids of hair.

We stopped for supper in one of the villages. On the outskirts a group of children were encamped, Young Communist Pioneers, the Soviet equivalent of Boy Scouts. The inn and its ivied porch were crowded with local people, but we sat in a pavilion in the garden and dined surrounded by the sight and fragrance of flowers and blue wood-smoke drifting up the sunset hillside. It was a festive ending to my week-end in

Georgia. We started with sliced tomatoes covered with fresh mint, parsley, onions, peppers, and herbs, and a cool drink made of tangerines; then hot bread in flat slabs, thick and crusty from a stone oven and spread with salty goat's cheese instead of butter; next, mutton soup with tomatoes, spices, and rice from Azerbaijan, washed down with white Tetra wine. After a pause the cook came running through the inn door and across the court, brandishing smoking fillets of veal on two long skewers. The next time he appeared he bore a great platter of broiled chickens, surrounded by potatoes and cucumbers and more wine, a sweet red Kinsmarhuli. The feast ended with a compote of stewed cherries and plums and cups of black Turkish coffee.

Early next morning I flew back to Moscow, well content with my trip. I had met a charming and individual people and seen the beauty of their country. My brief examination of their rugged and magnificent mountains had confirmed my own belief that the Caucasus, like the Carpathians and the Rockies, are made predominantly of sedimentary rocks and thus differed fundamentally from the Apennines or the Sierra Nevada, which are composed of volcanic and plutonic rocks. The Caucasus had their birth in the ocean, the Apennines and the Sierra Nevada in the heat of the earth's interior. Such volcanism as there has been in the Caucasus is incidental.

During another break in the Moscow meetings, I went to see Leningrad. Several kind Moscow geophysicists escorted me to the Red Arrow Express. They boarded the train and saw me safely ensconced in a comfortable two-berth sleeping car. As there was plenty of time, I asked them to sit down, and they gladly helped me polish off my remaining Scotch whiskey. As the train pulled out, they left me in the capable hands of interpreter Orichenko and an engineer. The porteress on our car brought us caviar sandwiches. These finished, we slept peacefully in this, the crack Russian express. For those not

familiar with the colour of the Soviet scene, I might remark
that the Red Arrow is the only blue train in the U.S.S.R.; the
others are green.

More geophysicists met me in Leningrad with a Zim car,
and after installing me in the old Astoria Hotel, insisted
that we tour the city before seeing any institutes. This was
not because they were holding back, for later I had long formal tours of institutes, but because Leningradians love their
city. It was founded by Peter the Great. Peter was a giant in
stature, 6 feet 7 inches tall and possessed of demonic energy.
When he came to the throne, Russia was a backward and semi-
Asiatic autocracy. Forty years later when he died his kingdom
was even more surely an autocracy, but the elements of Western education, industry, and military strength had been introduced. He had broken the power of the orthodox church and
made it subservient to the czars.

In 1702 this formidable man captured the coast of the
Gulf of Finland from the Swedes and started the building
of this western European city. With his own hands he built a
hut and a rowboat with which to explore the delta of the Neva
and choose the sites for his city, for his shipyards, and for the
great fortress of St. Peter and St. Paul. Proudly they showed
me all these and many other relics of Peter which are venerated
and carefully preserved today. Although the name of the city
has been changed to Leningrad, it is still the city of Peter
and the czars to its inhabitants. The scientists often used the
czarist names for bridges and parks rather than the new and
colourless revolutionary names.

It is indeed a beautiful city, built like Paris on the banks of
a river, in much the same grand style, at the same time, and
by many of the same western European architects. The inhabitants' affection for the city does not stem from enthusiasm for the great writers and revolutionaries who fought the
czars in the last century. They were scarcely mentioned. Nor

is it associated with the Great October Revolution of 1917 of which Leningrad was the scene. True, the *Aurora* was pointed out to me as the cruiser from which the first shot was fired, but I was not taken aboard. We visited the Smolni School for Daughters of the Nobility, in which Lenin had declared the revolution. They pointed out the Kirov factory, in which he was shot, and we watched the naval vessels moored in the river and dressed with flags to celebrate Red Navy Day. All these struck me as casual references to local sights of no more intrinsic interest than the occasional battle scars from the German siege. What fascinated the Russian mind were the great monuments left by the later czars during the two centuries of autocratic tyranny when they tried the impossible feat of changing Russia to a Western state while retaining a completely dictatorial form of government over an enslaved population.

The whole mockery was exemplified by Peter's fortress in the Neva River. Two tremendous walls, one within the other, ring a whole island and enclose a rough greensward on which stand the golden-spired cathedral, the Russian mint, and a blacksmith's shop. In the cathedral are buried Peter and his successors. In the mint they still coin money. In the blacksmith's shop political prisoners of the czars were manacled for transportation to Siberia. The walls of the fortress are lined with cells. These three buildings mark the keys to czarist control: a subservient church, ruinous taxation, and brutal oppression.

The gates to the fortress and the doors to the prisons have been symbolically removed, but all else has been refurbished, gilded, and put on display for tourists.

Sunday we devoted to the Peterhof, summer palace of the czars, founded beside the Baltic Sea by Peter, captured and destroyed in 1942 by the Germans, but now completely rebuilt in replica of the original plans of Le Blanc. My colleagues introduced me to the chief engineer who described the plumbing of the 129 fountains which he had just finished rebuilding. He mentioned that 160 pounds of pure gold had been used to gild the hundreds of statues in the gardens. The rebuilding of such a palace had nothing to do with Communist doctrine. It was pure nationalism.

We toured the Winter Palace, designed by Rastrelli for Peter's daughter, the Empress Elizabeth. It is now a museum of the czars, full of their relics and particularly the relics of Peter: his tools, clothes, maps, and the mechanical gadgets in which he revelled.

We saw the moated Micaelovski Palace, built as a safeguard by the Emperor Paul when he feared revolt. His fear was indeed justified because he was strangled in the palace a week after its completion in 1801. His executioners were his personal Semenovsky guards, the governor of his palace, and his own son, Alexander I.

We spent an all-too-brief afternoon in L'Hermitage, generally acknowledged to be the greatest collection of Western art in the world. I marvelled at the gallery of thirty-six Rembrandts, the little-known Leonardos, the many rooms each devoted to one of the greatest French, Flemish, or Italian masters. I discovered that my hosts, although scientists, not guides, were thoroughly familiar with many of the paintings and their artists. L'Hermitage was built a century ago by Nicolas I, successor to Alexander and inaugurator of the formal police state in Russia.

Pent-up antagonism against the czars exploded in the bomb which in 1881 killed his son, Alexander II. "The Cathedral Built on Blood" now marks the spot of the assassination. Its sombre bulk, topped by multi-coloured bulbous domes, blocks what had once been a main street as effectively as horror at the murder blocked any chance of reform.

After I had seen these palaces, after I had been taken to

one terminus of the subway and had had to get out to admire
every one of the ten stations before being picked up again at
the other end, and after I had been scolded by an old woman
gardener for walking on the grass to take photographs of a
well-kept park, I began to appreciate the affection the people
of Leningrad have for their city. I found myself stopping to
pick up a cigarette butt I had carelessly thrown away on the
sidewalk.

The institutes were very proud of their old czarist tradition,
but even more so of the progress they had made. As the director of the All-Union Geological Institute pointed out to me
during the six hours I spent with him: "This is the old Geological Survey of Russia founded in the last century, and our
headquarters are still in the original building. Of course, we
have expanded a great deal. Whereas there were one hundred
geologists, there are now ten thousand in Russia; or counting
hydrogeologists and geophysicists, twenty-two thousand."

I visited several of these institutes. They were engaged in
training young geologists to prospect for oil in Siberia or for
metals in European Russia, to develop new techniques, and
so on. Their buildings were rather shabby, but their equipment
was adequate and their libraries splendid, all catalogued in two
alphabets, roman and cyrillic. These shabby buildings were
crowded with a bright and eager lot of students, and always
there were anywhere from four to twenty scientists to show
me the laboratories and discuss their work. At the Arctic Institute I talked with P. A. Gordienko, G. M. Nikolski, and
Ya. Ya. Hakkel, all of whom had been recently in the Antarctic or the Arctic. They told me of the latest findings by the
stations drifting in the Arctic Sea, of the discoveries by the
research ship *Ob* between Greenland and Spitsbergen and
their interpretation of the geology of the ocean floor based on
soundings.

In all these institutes the scientists were very generous with

their time. Many showed me their work and went to great
pains to explain it. Mme Deminitskaya, for example, had been
considering the geology of the whole earth at once. She had
made maps and sections of the crust so as to study it in three
dimensions to a depth of 50 miles. I found her studies of some
fundamental aspects of geology very exciting. She had brought
her own translator, of whom she was very proud—her sixteen-
year-old son, kept out of school for the day. He had great
ability and translated our technical conversation fluently both
ways. In Russia some pupils are much better taught than others, for the children I was shortly to meet on the Trans-Siberian
Railway had no such abilities, or at least did not show them.

The Soviet scientists were as enthusiastic about developing
their vast country and as excited about scientific discovery as
are North Americans. Being well treated in material ways and
much better off than they had ever been before, and having
a strong and successful government which satisfied their national pride, they were content.

In only two respects did they seem to be at any great disadvantage, but both were vital. Since, in effect, they all worked
for the same state monopoly, they were frightened of doing
the wrong thing, afraid of the boss, and inclined to be secretive and cautious, contrary to their natural impetuosity and
warmth. Also, their studies of the earth had given them a great
curiosity about other lands, which the state would rarely permit them to satisfy. It was difficult for them to get an internal
passport to travel within the Soviet Union and virtually impossible to get permission to travel outside unless they were
bolstered with the excuse of an international meeting or an
invitation to lecture. For such opportunities some of them
asked my help.

The Soviet State may be likened to an adolescent. From
the point of view of older and more mature nations, it is
sloppy in appearance, secretive in behaviour, unpredictable,

sensitive, and brash. It is also inclined to show off, which is annoying when, on occasion, it happens to be right. But we must remember that the Soviet Union is experiencing the jubilation of youth, the satisfaction of newly won prosperity, the sense of importance, and the enjoyment of relative freedom, while to other members of its bloc it has the appeal of a cocky leader. Fortunately, even as it flexes its muscles, the Soviet Union shows signs of a growing maturity; and nothing is better calculated to hasten a more co-operative and cautious attitude than the emergence of an even more populous rival in the east.

CHAPTER 18

EARTHQUAKES

The study of earthquakes is called seismology. This is another subject which has been stimulated by military developments since the instruments which detect earthquakes can, under favourable circumstances, also detect large explosions. Great efforts are therefore being made to improve the sensitivity of the instruments and the methods of interpreting the results so that shocks caused by earthquakes and shocks caused by man-made explosions can be differentiated.

Of all the vibrations which shake the earth, the largest and the most numerous are earthquakes, but volcanic eruptions, large explosions, storms, and winds can also cause characteristic, if minor, disturbances.

The earth is not immobile. Cracks, or faults, form in its upper parts. The slipping motion of one side of a fault relative to the other gives rise to an earthquake. Whenever a slip happens, the ground is shaken and waves of vibration spread outwards and downwards in all directions. A single slip may move as much as 50 feet and cause tremendous havoc in the surrounding countryside. If the focus of the earthquake is deep within the earth, it will be less noticeable. Every year thousands of earthquakes shake the whole earth. The great majority are imperceptible and can only be recorded with instruments called seismographs. All those of any consequence are now recorded.

Ideally, a seismograph should not rest on the ground, but should be set in space ready to record the passage of vibrations beneath it. This is not practical, so the principle of inertia is employed.

Anyone who has ever been swinging on an old farm gate when others have shaken the fence will recall that the gate does not at once respond to the movements of the fence. Seismographs use this principle. A pen or electrical recorder is attached to a large weight suspended like a gate, or delicately balanced on springs. When the ground starts to move, the weight does not respond quickly and the pen can trace a graph of the movement of the earth.

When seismographs were first invented, it was discovered that pulses were produced not only by waves coming directly from the earthquake but also by other waves, which have bounced around and been reflected inside the earth. For example, fifteen minutes after an earthquake occurs in Japan, the first direct wave may be recorded in California, but after twenty-five minutes another pulse may be produced by a wave which has gone from Japan to the core of the earth and been reflected back from there to California. Thus, seismograph records contain many pulses, large and small, set against a background of irrelevant noises due to wind, waves, and human disturbances such as traffic. It is the task of the seismologist to pick out the pulses from the noise. By studying records obtained at many places from many earthquakes, seismologists have been able to interpret the significance of the successive pulses and piece together the results to add to our

knowledge of the nature of the earth's interior. In this manner
the thickness of the crust has been measured and the depth to
the hot, liquid core has been determined.

Like gravity, seismology was a rather marginal activity of
the IGY. There were several reasons for this. In the first place,
unlike the weather, severe earthquakes are not a universal
complaint. They are of crucial interest only in regions that
suffer from them, and large ones occur infrequently and in a
scattered fashion. In the second place, there already existed
a world-wide network of six hundred seismological stations recording continuously; they already sent their reports regularly
to Cambridge and Strasbourg, and they were simply requested
to make special efforts to submit complete reports punctually
to the World Data Centres in Washington, Moscow, and
Strasbourg. To simplify and speed these reports, a special tele-
graphic code, "Seismo," was developed and published. To supplement the information from existing stations, new stations
were established in out-of-the-way places, especially in Antarctica and the Arctic. All countries were asked to undertake
any special programs they could to measure the thickness and
nature of the crust and to investigate the effect of wind and
storms, which at stations near the sea produce continuous
small vibrations known as microseisms. These are disliked by
seismologists because they hide the pulses due to small earthquakes. In Patagonia microseisms are so severe and continuous
that a seismological station opened at Punta Arenas by the
Chileans was closed when it was found to record microseisms
nearly all the time.

On the other hand, microseisms may be useful in meteorology, as J. MacDowall suggests in this report: "At Halley Bay,
Antarctica, microseisms were only active during three summer
months, particularly during on-shore winds. It was therefore
concluded that the microseisms originated at the ice front and

that the cover of sea ice damped out this movement for three quarters of the year and stifled microseismic activity."

Crustal investigations are by their nature local, and ordinary explosive charges can be used to supplement the records obtained from earthquakes and speed the investigations.

It was on such work that the Tuimasi expedition was employed when I visited it on the Volga plains. By firing explosives at some camps and recording the echoes at other distant ones, they were plotting the echoes received from deep within the earth's crust and upper mantle to depths of 60 miles. Other countries were engaged in similar investigations. Parties from the Carnegie Institution of Washington cooperated with local scientists in investigating the Colorado plateau and the Andes in Bolivia, Chile, and Peru. The removal by blasting of Ripple Rock, an obstruction to navigation between the mainland of British Columbia and Vancouver Island, was recorded across the Rocky Mountains by Canadian Government parties and in Alberta by oil-company parties. Three large explosions of between 50 and 100 tons each were fired during construction of hydroelectric projects in the Snowy Mountains of Australia. Records obtained at distances as great as 200 miles were interpreted to mean that the crust was 23 miles thick in that region. New Zealand seismologists were very active, using explosions to measure crustal thicknesses in their islands and using natural earthquake waves to estimate crustal thicknesses in Antarctica. They concluded that the larger, or eastern part, of Antarctica was a true continent and not just an archipelago.

American parties measured the thickness of the layers beneath the ocean floors in the Pacific and Atlantic, and with the help of Argentine, Brazilian, and Chilean vessels explored the Scotia Sea, Drake Passage, and the coastal seas of South America. American and British parties co-operated in coastal studies in the Red Sea and the Gulf of Aden. French and Italian parties worked in the Mediterranean. Russian parties explored the floors of the sea of Ockotsk and the Kurile Trench.

It is now well established that the crust of continents varies in thickness between 20 and 40 miles, but that beneath the oceans the crust is only about 3 miles thick. The crust is composed of rocks with which we are familiar. They are lighter than those of the solid mantle beneath.

In the closing years of the last century John Milne started the first world-wide network of seismological stations by writing privately to friends all over the world. During the IGY seismologists relied for most of their data upon the great network of six hundred stations which had subsequently developed, but they became very conscious of its limitations. The operators of these stations had installed whatever instruments they had been able to make, buy, or borrow, with the result that there was a remarkable diversity of types. Obviously it would be of great advantage to have a uniform network of modern instruments, both to find out more about the inside of the earth and to enable even small nuclear explosions to be detected. There was not time during the IGY to introduce a complete new network nor even to agree upon the most suitable instruments to use, but some progress was made.

Maurice Ewing of Columbia University installed his own sets of uniform seismographs at twenty stations scattered about the world, and the Communist countries had already settled upon two standard designs that they installed at all their stations. The ingenious proposal was made that seismographs of special design should be placed on the sea floor. At present they are habitually installed in underground vaults to protect them from the noise of buffeting winds and the rumble of traffic, but the deepest vault cannot duplicate the quiet of the cold, still depths of the sea. The problem of an economical method of recovering records from the sea floor has still to be perfected.

Also under active consideration was the replacement of the old method of visual examination and measurement of records with some technique involving the use of computers to examine the records more quickly and efficiently.

Inherent in all these proposals were two questions: who would pay for the new and expensive installations, and would the world's seismological network by international agreement also form part of a system for detecting nuclear explosions.

Thus, the close of the IGY saw unprecedented activity and interest in new methods for seismology; a start had even been made on the design of lunar seismographs to be placed on the moon by rockets. Old fashioned as the existing system of seismographs now appears, it has nevertheless disclosed a great deal of useful information about the earth's interior and it has shown that most of the world's greatest earthquakes occur along one of two very definite zones. The chief of these, which has been called the continental fracture system, lies in the shape of an inverted T folded about the earth. The stem encircles the Pacific Ocean from Antarctica to Indonesia through the Andes, the Cordillera of North America, and East Asia. The cross of the T extends from the Alpine mountains of the Mediterranean through the Himalayas, Indonesia, and the Melanesian Islands to New Zealand. The system is scalloped into a series of great arcs of which the Aleutian Islands, Japan, and the Himalayas are examples. The earthquakes lie at depths of up to 450 miles on downward extensions of these arcuate fractures. Along this system are also found most of the world's greatest volcanoes. Most of them are composed largely of a rock called andesite after the Andes Mountains. It is generally agreed that volcanoes are fed by lava rising along these faults. Faults and earthquakes show that the earth to at least the depth of the deepest earthquakes breaks in a brittle way.

The only way to harmonize this behaviour with flow in the mantle is to suppose that pressures producing earthquakes build up much quicker than those producing flow, and that like pitch or ice the earth fractures under rapid forces but flows under the pressure of slower ones.

During the IGY several nations took the opportunity to refine their knowledge of the distribution of earthquakes. Maps were prepared of Ecuador, Colombia, and Mexico, for example, showing the location of all known earthquakes and of large faults. These maps suggest which regions future earthquakes are most likely to affect.

In the course of American preparations for the IGY, Maurice Ewing and Bruce C. Heezen made the remarkable discovery that another continuous major belt of earthquakes and volcanoes exists under the sea, and that these are associated with a great submarine ridge. Some parts of the ridge, like Iceland, the Azores, the Carlsberg ridge in the Indian Ocean, and the Hawaiian Islands, had been known for a long time, and had been recognized to be seismically active. But no one had realized that they are all part of the same system and that it constitutes the greatest mountain range on earth. The tracing of this vast system was diligently pursued, and the discovery that it is continuous was one of the most notable achievements of the IGY.

The mid-ocean ridge lies in the centre of the oceans midway between continents. The main ridge extends from the Arctic Sea right down the Atlantic Ocean and south of Africa into the Indian Ocean, thence south of Australia into the Pacific, where it forms several branches. This mid-ocean fracture system is different from the continental system. The lavas of its volcanoes are basalts and have a different chemical composition, with more iron and magnesium and less silicon than the andesites of the continental fracture system. Earthquakes along the mid-ocean ridge occur to depths only one tenth as

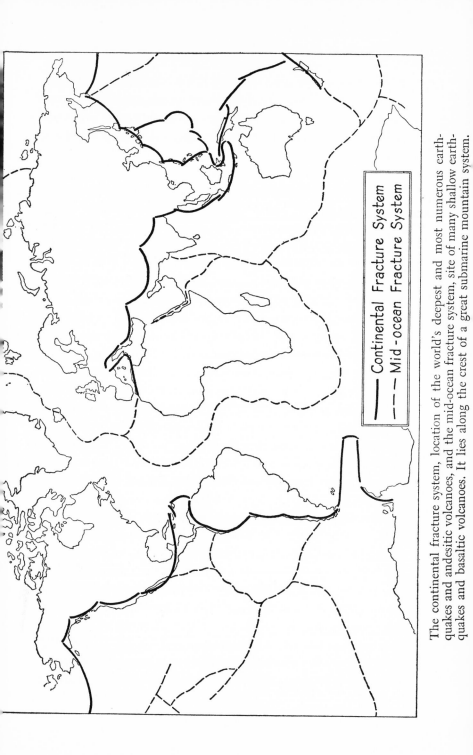

The continental fracture system, location of the world's deepest and most numerous earthquakes and andesitic volcanoes, and the mid-ocean fracture system, site of many shallow earthquakes and basaltic volcanoes. It lies along the crest of a great submarine mountain system.

great as on the continental margin, for they are never deeper than 45 miles. There are no scalloped island arcs like the Aleutians or Japan. The discovery of this second great fracture system has given impetus to the search for the cause of volcanism, earthquakes, and the building of mountains.

It was not part of the program of the IGY to try to formulate new theories for the behaviour of the solid earth, but the work done during the IGY made evident the need for revision of existing notions and provided bench-marks to measure future changes against. The discovery of the greatest mountain system on earth hidden beneath the oceans demonstrated how little we really know about our home, how much better we need to co-ordinate our studies.

The many theories of the way mountains are built may be divided into four groups. These represent different ways of looking at the earth.

The oldest theory, said to be due to Newton, has been championed by Sir Harold Jeffreys and may be regarded as deriving from a photographic image of the earth. The earth, like a photograph, retains a hard sharp image. It may be torn or crumpled, but it doesn't flow. According to this view, the earth is strong and brittle. Traditionally, it was once hotter and is still cooling and hence getting slightly smaller. This contraction of a rigid earth is held to cause wrinkling of the surface, as does drying in an apple, but in the earth the wrinkles are called mountains. A. E. Scheidegger showed that this process could give rise to scalloped fractures and other details of the continental mountains and island arcs, and in this respect the theory provides a more complete explanation of mountain-building of the continental type than any other theory. Unfortunately, it was advanced before the discovery of the mid-ocean ridges and it has not been extended to explain them, nor is it compatible with the idea that the earth is recoiling from

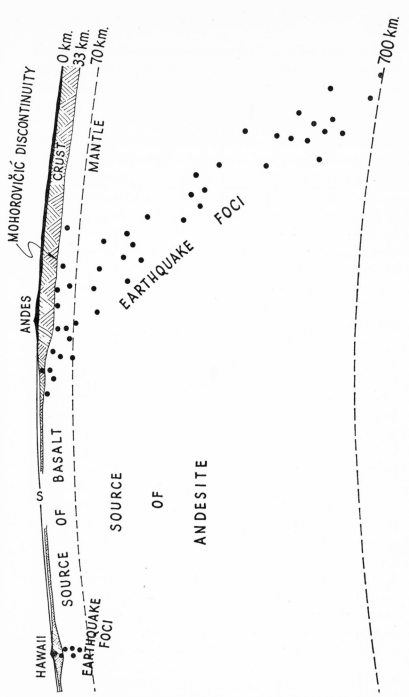

Cross-section of the crust and upper part of the mantle, showing the distribution of earthquakes below the continental and mid-ocean fracture systems.

ice loads and adjusting to changes in its rate of rotation by a slow process of plastic flow.

A second very different view about the earth was advanced about 1910 by A. Wegener. His view of the earth is like a painting by Picasso in which faces have been turned around or heads displaced relative to bodies. Wegener thought that the surface of the earth had been moved about and displaced by drifting of the continents. In particular he noticed that the continents had the same profile on opposite sides of the Atlantic Ocean and that the shores of the Red Sea were nearly parallel, and he suggested that these lands had been pulled apart in these places. No explanation was offered of the cause of these movements, and the idea of drift was not at all acceptable to the proponents of a strong earth. In the last few years, however, the apparent flow after ice loading, the shifting of the poles suggested by the different directions of magnetization of old rocks, and the apparently tropical aspects of some fossils from polar regions have again revived ideas of extensive movements. Some geophysicists support this idea of continents drifting about, but others hold that the relative position of the continents has remained fixed and that only the crust as a whole has been displaced relative to the poles of the earth, or, looking at the question in another way, that the axis of rotation has moved about relative to the earth as a whole.

A third theory was proposed by the Dutch geodesist F. A. Vening Meinesz. His view of the earth, like a painting by his compatriot Van Gogh, is one of swirling motion. He believes that the mantle of the earth below the crust is like pitch and that it is flowing in very slow convection currents which push up mountains. At present many geophysicists and geologists are rather attracted by this idea, but so far no one has developed it far enough to explain in any detail the structures found in mountains. Nevertheless, with this theory it may be possible to explain the existence of two kinds of mountains, for the continental mountains would have been pushed together where slow converging currents meet and descend, and mid-ocean ridges would have been raised and pulled apart where rising currents upwell and separate. Some features suggest this, but again no one has been able to fill in the details.

We have already mentioned the most recent proposal of Dicke and Heezen that the earth may be expanding. This view can only be likened to an abstract painting of the earth. I don't know whether any anarchist in the last century drew pictures in which everything was exploding. If not, it would seem an appropriate theme for the avant-garde of the nuclear age to try. Such a painting would show what this school of geophysicists thinks may be happening to the universe and the earth. In any case, it is not a very fast expansion; a rate of increase of only one fiftieth of an inch a year would have added 1,000 miles to the earth's waist line since the oldest rocks were formed three billion years ago.

To be frank, all of these theories, like diverse schools of art, have their good points and their weaknesses, and no one is yet quite sure where the truth lies. Probably it is more complex than any of the theories suggest. Deep convection currents and mobility of the poles relative to the earth's surface may cause blocks in the more brittle crust and upper mantle to move and jostle. The earth at the same time could be expanding. Mountains and continents may in part be formed by the extrusion of lava and its conversion to crustal matter. That may indeed be the origin of the whole crust—a scum squeezed from within the earth and reconstituted by the long-continued action of the weather and by mountain-building.

A major handicap in these speculations is that we do not know much about the mantle. No one knows with certainty whether any samples of it reach the surface unaltered. So important is this question that at the close of the IGY a group of American scientists proposed that a hole be drilled through the crust and into the mantle to obtain a sample. With samples of the mantle we may be able to understand why its melting produces different kinds of lava in different places, and we may be able to discover whether it is likely to be capable of flow or not.

The project has been called the Mohole after the Mohorovičić discontinuity, as the boundary between the crust and mantle is called in honour of the Jugoslav seismologist who first found evidence of it in earthquake records. Because the crust under the oceans is so much thinner than under the continents, the drilling must be done on the floor of the deep ocean. In April 1961 a short preliminary hole, 601 feet deep, was successfully drilled off the Pacific coast of Mexico, but it will be some years before all the engineering difficulties can be overcome and a really deep hole is put down to the mantle.

In the meantime, some geochemists think, though they cannot yet prove, that they have discovered samples of the mantle in diamond pipes. There two rare materials are found which have not melted and flowed like lava but which seem to have been shot up from the depths of the earth as solid fragments in volcanic explosions. These substances are the peculiar rock eclogite and the mineral diamond. Both are formed as a result of very high pressures, and they may be samples of the mantle.

Is it not strange that the only substance from the dark interior of the earth which most people ever see is the brilliant diamond?

CHAPTER 19

CHINA, TAIWAN,
AND JAPAN

SEPTEMBER 1958

I had plenty of time for reflection as I left Moscow, for I spent the next eight days and nights in a lower berth on the Moscow-Peking Express of the Soviet State Railway. For nearly a week the train followed the line of the famous old Trans-Siberian Railroad. No one on board admitted that he could understand or speak a word of English or French, but Georgi Khimish, an engineer, his wife, and son, with whom I shared the compartment as far as Omsk, were kind and polite. At intervals we smiled at each other, made signs, or laughed over the Russian lessons they set for me, but the result hardly amounted to conversation. When their places were taken by a rather starchy Air Force officer and his family, silence fell on our compartment. Any desire I had for conversation had to find expression in the few Russian words I had culled from a phrase book to order my meals from the plump and cheerful waitress in the dining car.

Most of the passengers were Army and Air Force officers and their families. They paid no attention to me, or I to them, but

when they all got off on the sixth day, as we were approaching
the Chinese frontier, the train suddenly seemed deserted and
empty. Siberia is barren and desolate enough, save for the large
cities artificially created beside steel bridges that carried our
train over the wide and turgid rivers, but at least Siberia has a
few stunted trees, whereas the windswept hills of the north
Manchurian border are bald-headed prairie. The departure of
the officers, resplendent in dress uniform, epaulettes and med-
als, left me to speculate why so many officers chose so bleak a
spot for their destination. The only clues vouchsafed to me
and to the handful of Chinese students remaining on the train
were a few empty sidings and half-concealed spur lines, a collection of gasoline tanks, and a large power station. Nothing
was to be seen but the hills, the sky, and the herds of cattle,
the same now as they were to Genghis Khan's advancing
hordes.

The formalities at the border, which anywhere else would
have seemed tedious and lengthy, excited me in this desolate
spot, for they effected an abrupt transition from a remote but
unmistakably European outpost into an Oriental station full
of Chinese. By the time we reached Peking two days later, I
had mastered chop-sticks and learned the Chinese for the three
phrases handy in any country: "Please, thank you, and good
day." A welcoming party of scientists from the Academia Sinica met me at the station. Being discerning and considerate
people, they offered me a bath, lunch, and a chance to catch
my breath before discussing what I would like to see of Chinese geophysics.

A few months earlier they had received my letter asking if I
might return to Canada through China and see what they were
doing in the IGY. My visit had been prompted partly by sheer
curiosity and a desire to travel, and partly because the rival
Academy in Taipeh had applied to join the IUGG as the representative of all China. The executive of the IUGG had

agreed that I should attempt to discover the facts of the situation before any action was taken. No doubt the men in Peking were aware of this, although they never mentioned it. They were determined to prove that they controlled Chinese geophysics and were doing a good job of promoting scientific work. That this was the case did not greatly surprise me. For the past few generations we have been so accustomed to the spectacle of a backward and prostrate China that it is easy to forget that they can make a good claim to have developed the foundations of science.

Certainly this is true in geophysics, for their chronicles contain accounts of 8,165 earthquakes since 1189 B.C.; no other country has comparable records. In A.D. 132 Chung Hung invented the first seismoscope to register the occurrence of earthquakes and indicate the direction to the centre of the disturbance, and he also produced an anemoscope for measuring wind direction and speed. About A.D. 233 a Chinese named Yuan discovered the magnetic compass and soon afterwards mounted this instrument on a cart, along with another resembling a speedometer, for the purpose of executing a road survey of China. By A.D. 1424 the Ming Emperors had equipped all the districts of China with rain-gauges. The flow of rivers and all floods were recorded systematically. These developments, together with the invention of paper in the first century A.D., of printing with movable type in the eighth century, of the first clock with accurate escapement mechanism, and of explosives (essential in seismic methods of prospecting), helped lay the foundations of geophysics. This has not been forgotten by the modern Chinese, for during my travels I frequently saw models of the early instruments in museums.

This was all ancient history. What I had come to see was the state of geophysics in 1958, and I wanted to be sure that what I saw was genuine. The scientists told me that they had arranged a tour which would take me to universities and insti-

tutes in Peking, Shanghai, Nanking, Hanchow, and Canton. I
welcomed the chance to see Peking, and I had no objection to
visiting Canton, since I was to leave from nearby Hong Kong.
But at the risk of a rebuff I told my hosts that I did not think
there were great opportunities for geophysics in the other cities
and that I thought the trip included too much sight-seeing. I
gently explained that since my sole object was to see geophysics, I should prefer to go to the west, to Sian and Lanchow,
where there was more geophysics and less mud. After all, I was
a physicist, not a farmer. This proposal they accepted with the
utmost calm, and without any demur they changed all their
plans to accommodate my wishes.

When we had safely negotiated these preliminaries over
countless cups of tea, we set about an examination of geophysical installations in Peking. It started with a formal dinner with
Dr. Li-shan Pei, the secretary-general of the Academia Sinica,
a formidable man, austere, cold, and of a commanding presence. He spoke no English and was most reserved, so that I
discovered nothing about him except that he was an agricul-
turist and hence probably of peasant stock. He seemed a dog-
matic Marxist, although we did not discuss such matters. He
was very conscious of his power and proud of the grandeur of
his country's history and civilization, but I felt that he was ignorant of the West, distrusted it greatly, and felt a strong re-
sentment of the indignities inflicted on China in the past. His
two chief concerns were to see that I had a good dinner of roast
Peking duck, and to make it plain that the Academia Sinica of
Peking was willing to co-operate with international bodies in
scientific matters, provided that such bodies had already shown
that they would have no dealings with any Chinese organizations not under the control of Peking. He did not ask me to
agree with his views, and I did not debate them.

The next day, I started out to visit universities, observatories, and Government institutes, and I shall briefly describe a

few which were typical of all. The Institute of Geophysics and Meteorology of the Academia Sinica in Peking is the headquarters for most geophysical work in China. It is located amid many other institutes in a newly developed region of Peking. The main building, which was still surrounded by temporary huts, was a solid, three-story one and well equipped. Like most institutes which I was to see, it had an excellent library. This one had been started many years before but now, according to the count I made in the reading room, subscribed to about four hundred scientific journals, mostly standard Western ones. I noticed, for example, recent issues of all the well-known geophysical journals from Britain, France, Germany, Italy, Japan, Sweden, and the United States.

I had talks in English with the director, Dr. Chin-chan Chao; the vice-director, Dr. Tsung-chi Chen; and the chief seismologist, Dr. Shan-pang Lee. All had studied in Europe or the United States. I had already met another research worker from this institute, Dr. Cheng-yi Fu, a graduate of McGill University and the California Institute of Technology. He was the only Chinese scientist whom I met in Russia. I did so because the Soviet scientists, when it was known that I was going from Moscow to Peking, suggested that I call on him in the Moscow Seismological Station.

All the men I have mentioned are well known in the West. They publish books and technical papers. They are competent scientists, and there is no question that they are in charge of the technical work which they displayed to me with such enthusiasm. For example, Dr. Lee showed me the instruments he had designed. I went through the workshop where they are built, and I saw the results of their use in maps charting the areas subject to earthquakes of varying intensity and frequency. An account of this work has been published and reviewed favourably in the Bulletin of the American Seismological Society.

These men are leaders among China's few experienced geo-physicists. They held similar posts under previous governments, but their work is appreciated by the present regime and they are being supported to a far greater extent than was ever possible before. It should be emphasized that this support is generous and is not merely a consequence of the advantages offered by peace after years of civil war and invasion. Everywhere scientists have new buildings, many assistants, Government cars for transport, and above all, excellent libraries. Of course, they don't have freedom, as we understand the word; but their programs were sensible and useful, they had probably had a say in determining what they were to be, and they certainly felt that what they were doing was good for China.

They told me that they now operated almost two dozen seismological stations and would soon be increasing the number. While in China I visited four such stations. Before the revolution, I believe, there had only been two in the whole of China, and I have subsequently discussed these changes with the late Father P. Lejay, s.j., who was director of one of them.

The Central Geophysical Observatory of China is located in the foothills near Peking, 10 miles from the town of Chufan. There I entered the vaults and saw twelve seismographs operating. All were of Chinese manufacture, but nine were based on Soviet designs. I also visited three large, non-magnetic buildings housing a magnetic observatory under development. I looked at the sun through a solar-flare patrol telescope, which had been made in the German Democratic Republic and which was being used to carry out part of the IGY program. I was told that five seismologists at the observatory examine the records from all twenty-three Chinese seismograph stations, and that cosmic-ray observations, which I did not see, had been started.

While in Peking, I visited several other institutes and uni-

Czech scientists observing earth tides in a mine 4,000 feet beneath the earth's surface.

Magnetic surveyor in the field for the Royal Thai Survey Department.

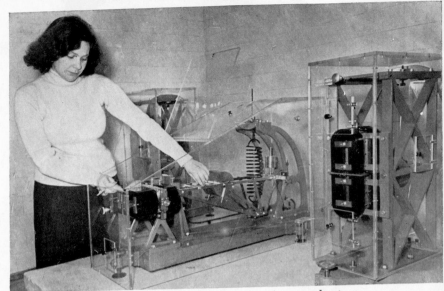

A Soviet observer adjusts a seismograph at Pulkovo Observatory at Leningrad, U.S.S.R.

Inside the great crater of Mount Vesuvius, which is being filled in by eruptions from the small active cone.

Professor Lloyd V. Berkner, who suggested holding the International Geophysical Year, is shown at Little America I, sitting on top of a radio mast which he had erected in 1929. By 1958 the lower 65 feet of the mast had been buried in snow.

Young Soviet scientist observing solar radiation at Arctic drifting-ice station NP-6.

Professor Sydney Chapman, president of the Comité Spécial de l'Année Internationale Géophysique (CSAIG) with academician I. P. Bardin, chief of the U.S.S.R.–IGY Committee.

The author discussing geophysical and geological maps with Soviet scientists and engineers at the Tumasi Deep-Sounding Seismic Expedition of the Ministry of Geology, U.S.S.R.

Drifting ice station NP-6 on the Arctic pack ice.

Ice-coring on Blue Glacier, Olympic Mountains, U.S.A.

Henrietta Glacier, Ellesmere Island, Northwest Territories, Canada, flowing from interior ice fields toward Lake Hazen.

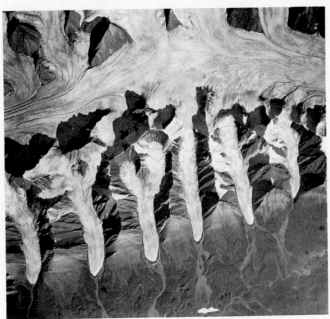

A series of valley glaciers in the mountains of Ellesmere Island. The six tongues of the valley glaciers are separated from the larger glaciers by a mountain ridge.

H.M.C.S. Labrador breaking a passage through spring ice. The dark pattern is of melted water lying on the surface of the frozen sea ice.

This tunnel, built under the Greenland ice cap by U. S. Army engineers, is part of living quarters suitable for year-round occupancy. Rooms and buildings have been built from snow, ice, wood, and corrugated steel. The tunnel shown here has a self-supporting snow roof.

R. W. Mason, glaciologist, examining the walls of a crevasse in McCall Glacier, Alaska.

versities. One of them was the Institute of Geological Prospecting on the outskirts of Peking, a brand new institution still surrounded by the remnants of vegetable fields. It had been formed in 1952 out of the old department of geology of Peking University. On the campus I visited six large new buildings and many small temporary ones, and saw two more large ones under construction. Geophysical prospecting is one of six departments and is taught in adequately equipped laboratories. I saw a truck equipped for electrical prospecting, chemical and spectroscopic laboratories, a teaching museum and workshops, but the library had not yet been built. I was met by the vice-president, C.-T. Chung, and by Professors L.-H. Shu., F.-L. Yuan, and Kai Chow. They explained that within the past six years they and about twenty-five other experienced professors had trained technicians and five hundred inexperienced colleagues and started to teach a five-year college course to six thousand students. They had had to collect equipment and translate text-books. Most of the staff and students were away, on seventeen field parties, by means of which the students combined field experience in the summer with lectures and laboratory work in the winter.

In spite of this tremendous load placed on so few experienced professors, they said that they had been able to undertake some research and had published two works. Obviously, the literature now emanating from China does not reflect the full state of activity there.

After my ten days in Peking, I set off for the west with my interpreter Mr. Yu-san Tien. In order to see everything at as close range as possible, I travelled entirely by train and by automobile, spending five more days and nights in sleepers. I ate nothing but Chinese food, becoming quite proficient with chop-sticks.

To give some idea of the extent of this journey from Moscow, back and forth through China, and on to Hong Kong, let me translate into North American terms. It was as if I had travelled from Hudson Bay to Alaska and back again, then crossed into another country near Winnipeg, and on down south to Tampico, Mexico. The side trip to Lanchow would have taken me from St. Louis into the mountains at Denver and back.

Lanchow is an ancient walled town that in past centuries was regarded as lying on the utmost fringe of the old Chinese Empire, an outpost on the old Silk Route to the West: dusty, windswept, cold, and rigorous. Only fifteen years before I arrived in Lanchow, Mr. Tien, my interpreter, had had to walk for fifteen days, his luggage loaded on an oxcart, to reach Lanchow from Paochi. Now the railway bores through a mountain range, by way of 187 tunnels, to reach Lanchow, and it extends beyond, crossing the Gobi Desert and the Altai Mountains to complete the link with Alma-Alta and Moscow.

The old town has burst through its walls and sprawls over the surrounding countryside in a chaos of construction, noise, and dust. Day and night the building goes on, under floodlights and to the accompaniment of hearty music blared forth from loud-speakers hitched to the street lights. The population has increased eight times in the last ten years, from 100,000 to 800,000. I visited the branch of the Academia Sinica and the new university. They are most impressive displays of idealism and practicality: a library designed to house a million books, the Multilithed copies of original texts open only to the student who has command of the Western languages in which some of them are written; a curriculum specializing in land use, reclamation of deserts, irrigation schemes, and meteorology; laboratories equipped with good but simple instruments.

Outside of Lanchow I was taken through a large oil refinery which was nearing completion, and I was told that the oil came from "the west." The Tsaidam depression near Lake Koko Nor between Lanchow, Sinkiang, and Tibet is the probable source, for it is said to be a very rich and productive area.

All in all I was agreeably surprised by what I saw in China. The Government clearly believes in and supports education and science. The many scientists from the old regime who have remained, although overworked, have never before had so much support, and they are enthusiastic at the material progress being made in China.

The students are selected by examination, and many are given scholarships. They are polite, well disciplined, enthusiastic, and hard-working, even though they spend a great deal of time on political activities. As part of their program they have to take some physical exercise and do some practical work, but as far as I could make out the basis of their education in science and languages is sound. It would be foolish to believe otherwise.

From Canton I took the short train journey to the border and said good-bye to Mr. Tien, my constant companion of the past month. I had come to like him, to appreciate the good care he took of me, and to enjoy his company, although in most respects we were opposites. For him, with his hard upbringing, life was as serious and as clear in its purpose as a burial service. For me, the trip was like a visit to a theatre, where amid a feast of colour and sound, and in a spirit of gaiety and humour, I could nevertheless look for the playwright's underlying serious message. We got on well because we both fully enjoyed each day's investigation of the new China, he displaying it with pride and I examining it in fascination.

I then flew on to Taipeh, where I was warmly greeted as a guest of the other Academia Sinica. I was taken to the headquarters of the academy in a peaceful village 10 miles south of Taipeh. It is housed in four or five small, new brick buildings, all devoted to the social sciences and the humanities, except a chemistry building, which was still under construction. There were no physics or geology buildings there. A museum was devoted to displays of ancient Chinese writing on pieces of wood, of auguries on bone, and of the costumes and arts of the 18,-000 Malay aborigines of Taiwan. There was a small library devoted to similar subjects. I was shown a locked door behind which I was told that copies of recent publications from China were stored. They were said to be reserved for intelligence purposes and not to be available to others.

In Taipeh I visited the headquarters of an active and competent meteorological service. Here they plotted the paths of hurricanes and prepared weather maps, using data broadcast from the mainland. Five radiosonde stations were said to be operated. At this building there was also a seismological station equipped with three Weichert, three Omori, and some other Japanese instruments. Since there are many severe earthquakes in Taiwan, the director of the station needed new modern instruments to supplement those left by the Japanese, but the necessary $50,000 was not forthcoming. He told me that there was no magnetic observatory in Taiwan.

On the roof of the city hall I saw a regular IGY Moonwatch station equipped to track artificial satellites.

At the National Taiwan University I gave a lecture, speaking very slowly in English and showing slides. The professor of geology was an enthusiastic man, but his library contained far fewer periodicals than did those on the mainland. There was still much evidence of Japanese influence, and very little new equipment. In the department of physics the elderly professor asked me whether I could ask the National Bureau of Standards to replace his ionospheric sounder, since it was the oldest instrument in the Western world and he was trying to co-operate in the IGY program. It was still manually operated. I duly delivered the message when next I was in the United States, and I must agree that their reasons for withholding the new equipment are only too sound; he obviously did not have the capacity to cope with anything more complicated.

I was driven to Miaoli, where I met the Chinese geophysicists and geologists in charge of prospecting to extend an oil field there. These men had been trained in the United States, and with modern equipment were obtaining good seismic records. I believe that two seismic crews were operating and that this was the chief effort in prospecting on the island.

I felt very sorry for the scientists in Taiwan. They are few in number, and some of them seemed to be dejected and homesick. It is a myth that all the best Chinese scientists escaped to Taiwan. This is simply not so; most of them are still on the mainland. The chief difference between the two groups is in the degree of support they receive.

To my mind, the mainland Chinese are now undergoing an awakening comparable in our history to the Renaissance. When I was in China I felt that they were looking back to the civilization of their magnificent past, which grew and enriched itself without a break for 2,700 years until it was overwhelmed by the Mongols in A.D. 1270. From that point the cultural and intellectual life of China slowed down until their civilization, once far in advance of the West, fell far behind. The dark ages had descended upon them as they did upon the West after Rome fell to the Vandals. Just as in the West the old learning returned, enriched, in the wake of a new invader, so it happened in China. We of the West are to China what the Moors and the Arabs were to medieval Europe. The Westerners have pushed their way into China, and under the pressure China is reasserting herself and reviving in improved form the sciences she founded. In this process the Communist revolution is but one phase. Were not the Chinese Boxers just as terrifying when they tried in 1900, with some success, to kill every Christian convert and every foreigner in China? Were not Sun Yat-sen and Chiang Kai-shek just as anxious to resurrect their country's greatness when they overthrew the Manchu Empire and fought the Japanese invaders? To regard the Communist capture of China as an isolated phenomena is to give undue credit to a foreign and fallacious dogma and to underestimate the rabid feeling of nationalism that is one of the chief supports of the government in China.

The Communist revolution in China has caused untold suffering, misery, and death; but one is entitled to ask whether any country has ever lifted itself from centuries of poverty, sloth, ignorance, incompetence, graft, and foreign self-seeking, without bloodshed. The pattern of revolution has always passed from the idealist and the intellectual to the extremist, and so it has in China.

Now China is racing to make up the time she has lost and catch up with the West. Some of us have expressed the fear that the scientific education stressed in Communist countries will produce nations of robots. To my mind this is nonsense and a direct negation of our noted belief in the power of education. It was abundantly clear to me that the Chinese scientists had done their best to re-establish contact with the West through the IGY.

In science, as Sir Eric Ashby has pointed out, "truth is not something final, revealed, sacrosanct; it is tentative, constantly being modified, enlarged, adjusted to new knowledge." Communist dogmatism and the free spirit of scientific enquiry cannot long exist together. One will destroy the other, and I welcome the spread of sound scientific education in Communist countries, for I am sure that free thought will prevail. At the moment, in China as in Russia, the gullible can embrace Communism as the partner of nationalism, and the sceptical can tolerate it, confident that the worst features will be and indeed have already been modified. In the meantime, its success and its sense of urgency have inspired many with John Ruskin's "idea of self-denial for the sake of posterity, of practicing present economy for the sake of debtors yet unknown, of planting forests that our descendants may live under their shade, or of raising cities for future nations to inhabit."

I saw much in China to admire. I wandered through beautiful old temples and palaces that are now being restored and opened to the public. I liked the theatres and the food, and the quiet, polite, and good-humoured Chinese people among whom I constantly mingled as a solitary Western traveller. It is very rude and quite wrong to liken the Chinese people with ants on an anthill on the grounds that they suffer under a Communist dictatorship. Was not the old empire equally dictatorial? It was simply less efficient. I sympathized with the gargantuan efforts the Chinese are making to reorganize the life of their nation and improve the lot of the people. Some of these efforts have been misunderstood in the West by reason of insufficient knowledge or special pleading. The commune system is a case in point. As I saw it on travelling through the countryside, it is not a matter of rehousing people in barracks, but of reorganizing village life. A moment's reflection will make clear the impossibility of rehousing in barracks a population three times that of the United States. The peasants, instead of each working his own plot to pay the landlord, have been formed into groups to work much larger tracts, and they have established communal dining halls and day nurseries to economize on labour. The uprooting caused untold misery, but now everybody works, some enthusiastically and some because they have to. Whether willingly or unwillingly, the activity is prodigious, and because of it new railways, new factories, new dams, new universities, and new cities are sprouting up all over China.

There is no doubt that this material progress is spurring widespread national enthusiasm. We would do well to remember how different life in China has been from life in the West.

Conditions in a commune, which might seem poor, dictatorial and unpleasant to us or to the wealthy Chinese who have been displaced, mean security for peasants who before faced only poverty, famine, disease, and civil war. Now, after a decade of peace and strong government, material progress is being achieved.

In the process, many grievous hardships and injustices have been inflicted, but we can be confident that the Chinese will gradually moderate the present system. In the meantime, it would be salutary for us in the West to admit that a modern, awakened China does exist and that since China is the oldest, most populous, and second-largest country on earth, it is a power to be reckoned with. Soviet scientists are aware of Chinese progress, and regard it with mixed feelings of admiration and fear. We may have reason to fear it, too, but we cannot dispose of it by shutting our eyes and refusing to recognize that it is there.

The fervour of nationalism that has effected these accomplishments is spurred on by periodic outbursts of anti-Western hate-fests. I was engulfed in anti-Western parades on various occasions. In every case, each column was led by one or two shouting, sweating Communists, but most of the marchers clearly regarded the whole thing as an excuse for a good junket. It was ironic to stand on the kerb, as the parades swept past, and realize that the political philosophy which these anti-Western marchers supposedly professed had been developed by a refugee German working in the reading room of the British Museum. The resurgent modern China is the child of Western culture, and we cannot disown her just because we regard her as a changeling.

So ended my investigation of Chinese science. Two Chinas, two academies, each claiming to represent the whole and neither having intercourse with the other. This great rift in Chinese science affects not only science in China, but in the world as a whole. One cannot do global research by studying only three quarters of the earth, any more than one can settle the affairs of the world by pretending that one quarter of it does not exist. As a scientist, I was disturbed to discover that the Government of Taiwan, which is the government of China recognized by my country, does so much less to support academic and scientific work than does the People's Republic of China, which we choose to ignore.

I went on from Taiwan to pursue my round of calls on universities, institutes, and historic sites in Japan. The plane was late, but even at two in the morning Professor Chuji Tsuboi, of Tokyo University, and Dr. Tatzuso Obayashi, a former graduate student of mine, were waiting to meet me, smiling and cheerful.

Through Japan I went, shepherded by my old and warm friend, Tats Obayashi, being proudly introduced to all that was best in Japanese science and culture, and staying in the quiet, exquisite, little Japanese hotels. And it never stopped raining. Whether we were visiting institutes, contemplating stone gardens, or rushing through the countryside in a train, the rain sluiced down. Typhoon Ida was sweeping in from the Pacific, bringing with her the heaviest rainfall recorded in Tokyo's modern history, seventeen inches altogether, twelve of which fell in one day.

In the country, rain washed the rice fields to freshest green, and wind blew damask patterns through the waving grain. The villages, each a close cluster of wooden huts about a larger temple, did not need the wooden fire towers which rose as observation posts above the black-tile roofs. Between high dikes swift torrents, opalescent with the splash of falling drops, poured back the water to the ocean. We were shut in by clouds above and by steep and dark mountains rising into the mist on every side.

In the Ryoanji Temple at Dajun-Zan, the stone garden was

so wet it looked like a sea set with islands. The rain splat-
tered on the pebbles, rattled on the tin-roof gutters, and
gurgled as it ran away in streams under the pavilion where
we sat for the tea ceremony. The coloured umbrellas of the
visitors, as they mounted the mossy steps between stone lan-
terns and laurel bushes, looked like irridescent bubbles
bobbing on the flood—green, blue, pink, yellow, and black.

In the city the rain sluiced off the roofs, blew in gusts around
the street corners, flooded through the streets, drowned cars
in the lower gullies, and poured into basements everywhere.

At the Imperial Hotel servants held back the flood with
carpets and sand bags as long as they could, but eventually
the water cascaded down the stairs and turned the cocktail
lounges in the basement into swimming pools, short-circuited
the generators, drowned out the kitchen, and sent all the
guests early to bed by candlelight, with a cold supper to comfort them amid the trembling, gurgling, swishing sounds of
the buffeted hotel.

Typhoons, floods, storms, earthquakes, volcanic eruptions,
tsunami waves racing in from the sea, and even the rising
sun on the national flag are reminders enough to the Japanese
of the importance of the elements, and their awareness of the
natural world may explain their active part in the IGY. Their
scientific work is of the highest standard, and they entered into
every program with enthusiasm, even dispatching an expedition to Antarctica.

I had long discussions in the Earthquake Research Institute
and in departments of the University of Tokyo and Kyoto. I
visited many well-known scientists, some of whom I had met
before, and I admired the skill with which, on small budgets,
they keep in the forefront of scientific work.

On my last day it cleared, and at the airport I had the good
fortune to see the President of India arrive for a state visit.
From the roof of the new Hameda airport we saw the Im-

perial Guard, in their cream uniforms and with their brass band blowing furiously, drawn up on one side, and on the other, the diplomats and government officials in black morning coats with yellow chrysanthemum boutonnieres. A great pink Constellation settled down neatly on the runway beside them. Turbaned Indian aides, tall and slim, with their swords and buttons glistening, emerged, followed by the President in his white Indian cap and coat. Together he and Emperor Hirohito walked arm in arm to inspect the honour guard and to climb into the Emperor's maroon Pierce Arrow. As the rulers of these ancient nations left the modern scene, the full moon rose from the Pacific and the orange glow of sunset bathed the airport. I wondered if the full moon had in fact replaced the rising sun as a gentler symbol of the new Japan.

CHAPTER 20

THE OCEANS

The oceans cover 70.8 per cent of the earth's surface and form a single body so extensive on this planet and so unusual in the universe that impartial space travellers observing the earth for the first time would certainly christen it "The Water."

Most people's knowledge of the oceans is limited to a familiarity with their general shape, as shown in atlases, and a vague notion that they are deep and contain most of the world's water. Many are not even aware of the outstanding mysteries which the seas present. What is the origin and history of the great basins in which the oceans lie? Where and at what rates do currents flow, especially the deep ones by which sea water circulates within those basins? What are the processes of exchange of heat and moisture between sea, air, glaciers, and land which regulate the climate and make the world habitable?

Inasmuch as the oceans contain 97 per cent of the world's water, they are the greatest reservoirs of moisture and of heat on the surface of the earth. Until we know more about the currents that carry warm water towards the poles and bring cooler water to the tropics, we cannot expect to forecast the world's weather correctly or to exploit ocean fisheries to full advantage. The surface currents, such as the Gulf Stream, which produce these moderating effects are relatively well known, but the deeper currents, which are equally important, have been little studied. Submarine ridges and sills exercise strong controls upon deep currents, and the shape of the ocean basins affects all currents.

The history of the exploration of the sea floors is brief and simple, and it can truthfully be said that the enormous task of studying these cradles of the sea was first faced in an adequate manner during the IGY. This is less surprising when one realizes that the job of making accurate maps of most of the land surface was only started during the Second World War and has not yet been completed.

Throughout the centuries of great geographical discovery no one knew or investigated the shape of ocean basins beyond the shallow continental shelves. To sound any great depth by the traditional method of lowering a weight on the end of a hemp line was not practicable because the ropes broke and were lost. It was not until 1840 that Captain James Ross made the first soundings at depths of over a mile.

Shortly afterwards, a cheaper and more practical method was introduced by Captain Matthew F. Maury, a United States and Confederate Naval officer of great enthusiasm and scientific ability. He made soundings by dropping a cannon ball to which was attached a length of twine. He measured the rate at which the twine was paid out and assumed that the shot had reached bottom at the moment when the rate became slower. Having noted this depth, he cut the twine and cannon ball away. In 1855, from data thus collected, he made the first hydrographic chart of the north Atlantic.

A few years later, proposals to lay trans-Atlantic cables made a knowledge of the ocean floor important and gave these investigations great impetus. On Christmas day, 1872,

the British ship *Challenger* set sail on the first great oceanographic expedition to explore the world's oceans and particularly to investigate the nature of their floors. A hundred other
oceanographic expeditions have followed. The world's navies
and hydrographic services, working out from civilized coasts,
have made charts, but progress was slow, for the efforts were
unequal to the task. By 1914 only eighteen hundred soundings
had been made in the deep parts of the north Atlantic and
fewer elsewhere. The greatest depth that had been found was
31,600 feet in a trench close to Guam. The floor was considered to be everywhere gently sloping and covered with a
thick layer of clay and ooze, as fine organic remains are called,
which had slowly settled from the sea. Only three ships had
been built specifically for oceanographic research: Nansen's
Fram, Peary's *Roosevelt*, and Scott's *Discovery*. One general
bathymetrical chart of the oceans had been published by an
international institute in Monaco (established by Prince Rai-
nier's grandfather), but these charts were admitted to include
"the widest generalizations." Some progress was made between the two World Wars, but the failure to recognize the
continuity of the mid-ocean ridge until 1956 is one indication
of our continuing ignorance about the little-travelled parts of
the ocean. Real progress awaited the development of new tools
with which to explore the oceans, and the availability of funds
for expeditions to exploit these tools.

The first need was for good charts, which require precise
measurements of depth, latitude, and longitude. Since about
1920 scientists have been able to measure depth by sending
sound signals into the water and timing the echoes received
from the bottom. This is known as echo-sounding and can be
used to determine depth accurately within a few feet. Before
this development, a ship's position at sea could only be determined by sun or star observations, accurate to the nearest mile

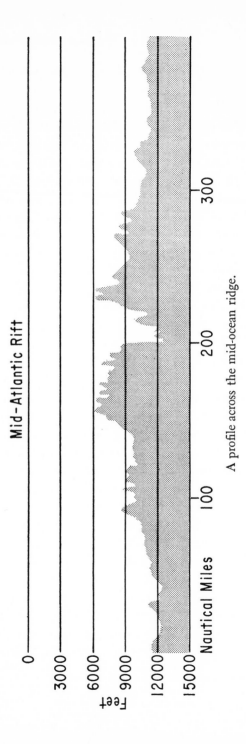

A profile across the mid-ocean ridge.

or so but not good enough for exact mapping. It is now possible to achieve greater precision by using radio and radar devices on ships and coastal installations. This equipment is expensive, however, and was not available in many parts of the Indian Ocean and of the Southern Ocean, which surrounds Antarctica, until after the IGY was over.

During the IGY the Soviet vessel *Vityaz*, operating in the Pacific, carried out systematic charting, by echo-sounding, of the deepest trenches in the Pacific Ocean. On January 23, 1960, shortly after the close of the IGY, two men, Lieutenant D. Walsh of the United States Navy and J. Piccard, sank to the bottom of the Mariana Deep in the western Pacific to the greatest depth known, 36,800 feet, in the bathysphere *Trieste*. There they spent thirty minutes before releasing ballast and floating back to the surface. This special submarine, invented by the Swiss professor, Auguste Piccard, consists of a strong steel sphere, 6 feet in diameter, made buoyant by having attached to it a large tank full of gasoline. The depth reported by the *Trieste* was 1,000 feet greater than the depth measured by the *Vityaz* using echo-sounding. Why the *Trieste* seemed to exceed that depth by so large an amount has yet to be explained.

In addition to improvements in the fundamental task of making good charts, the last fifteen years have witnessed the development of many devices for exploring the nature of the sea floors. As an extension of echo-sounding to determine water depths, Maurice Ewing in 1938 demonstrated that firing small explosive charges produced echoes that indicated the thickness of sedimentary beds, lavas, and crust lying below the ocean floor. The method, which at first involved exploding single charges, has been widely applied. During the IGY it was extended by the development of a whole series of "sparkers," "bloopers," and "thumpers." These devices, which are towed behind vessels, emit loud bangs periodically. Just as echoes from weak signals can be used to plot a continuous profile of the surface of the ocean floor, so the stronger signals from these loud bangs can be used to plot continuously the beds lying beneath the ocean floor, even to depths of thousands of feet. Now a ship can cruise at a steady speed, mapping the stratigraphy of the ocean floor thousands of feet below, for as long a time as the crew can stand the racket of several loud explosions a minute close behind the ship.

But echoes do not provide samples, and to obtain them dredges and coring devices have been developed. The *Challenger* expedition used dredges, but they only skimmed the uppermost layer. In 1936 C. S. Piggott of the Carnegie Institution devised a double-coring tube that could be lowered to the bottom and the inner tube fired as from a gun into the floor. Rapid improvements followed. B. Kullenberg of Sweden, and Soviet inventors, showed that in many places the oozes on the ocean floor are so soft that a heavily weighted tube of appropriate design can penetrate as much as 80 or 100 feet when dropped into the ocean floor. Cores up to that length can be recovered, but 100 feet seems to be the limit for free-falling corers. Thousands of such cores have been collected in the last few years.

We have mentioned the Mohole project by which it is hoped to drill through the crust under the ocean floor to the mantle. The project, which is sponsored by the United States National Science Foundation, will take several years to complete. The first short experimental holes, made in the spring of 1961, penetrated 601 feet into the floor of the ocean off Lower California. The deepest core pierced 557 feet of clays and oozes deposited about 25,000,000 years ago and then drilled 44 feet into a layer of basalt lava of unknown age. Since the rate of sedimentation on the ocean floor is slow, these cores and the much longer ones that are planned should reveal much about the history of the oceans. They may also help to determine the age and origin of the oceans and to decide whether the continents have drifted about or not.

Much of the floor of the ocean basins consists of great, flat, smooth plains. It had been taken for granted that the floors were smothered in a carpet of ooze, which had slowly sifted down through the sea since the beginning of time. Unexpectedly, coring not only showed that the rate was wrong but disclosed layers of coarse sand hundreds of miles from the nearest land. How did sand reach places where there should be only ooze? In 1952 M. Ewing suggested that on the steep slopes of the continental shelves, where the land suddenly drops away to the ocean floors 3 miles below, lie great deposits of mud and sand brought down by the world's rivers. These pile up higher and higher until an earthquake shakes their uneasy balance and sends them hurtling down the slopes in muddy turbidity currents that flow at express speeds far over the ocean floors. It has now been established that as these currents settle they deposit layers of sand that they have carried hundreds of miles from land. These great but rare rivers, or landslides, of mud flowing under the sea also explain the peculiar damage some earthquakes inflict on submarine cables. For years cable companies have puzzled over the fact that cables have not only snapped close to the site of an earthquake, but also sometimes three or four hours later and hundreds of miles away other cables have been broken, frayed, or buried in mud. Now they blame these engulfing slides of muddy water.

These vast slumps that cause turbidity currents also cause the disastrous seismic waves, or tsunamis, that accompany some large earthquakes. The last such earthquake in Chile, in May 1960, not only killed thousands of people and did vast damage on land in Chile, but also gave rise to a seismic wave that overwhelmed the coasts of Chile and travelled across the Pacific to drown a hundred and fifty people on the Japanese coasts when it reached there sixteen hours later. A great wall of mud, released by the earthquake, tumbled down the submarine coast of Chile to the deep sea floor, having the same effect on the Pacific Ocean as a large boulder sent crashing into a pond.

All during the IGY scientists continued coring—tracing the turbidity currents, sampling the floor of the sea, solving some riddles, propounding others. One of the intriguing questions raised concerns the origin of a layer of volcanic ash which J. L. Worzel of Columbia University traced at an average depth of about 50 feet below the bottom of the Pacific Ocean over a vast area off the coast of Mexico, Central America, and Peru. The presence of the bed was first noticed on seismic soundings, and then investigated by corers made of lengths of three-inch water-pipe dropped into the bottom. The ash, which is from four inches to a foot thick, seems all to be from the same layer. Worzel believes it to be due to a single volcanic eruption about eighty thousand years ago. This sounds straightforward enough until one realizes that the area covered is so large that the eruption which produced it must have been five thousand times larger than the great volcanic explosion of 1883 at Krakatoa in Indonesia. This seems improbable. No volcanic crater of such dimensions has been reported, and the ash-bed must remain an enigma until it can be investigated further.

Of great economic interest was the discovery that parts of the Pacific Ocean floor are strewn with nodules of manganese and other useful metals. Proposals have been made to dredge these commercially.

Another recently developed device measures the rate at which the earth loses heat. Compared with outer space, the earth is a warm body, but it is losing heat continuously. To measure this small loss, a thermal probe was developed by Sir Edward Bullard and during the IGY measurements of heat flow were made in about a hundred places in the deep oceans. In general, the heat loss is the same over oceans as over continents; but below the mid-ocean ridges the earth seems to be warmer than elsewhere, and it is losing heat faster there.

The development and application of devices for exploring the ocean floors did not attract much interest from government or industry until recently, and most of the credit for them goes to universities. Columbia, Cambridge, California, and Göteborg have all played important roles. Expeditions equipped with these new devices, as well as more conventional instruments, have been recently sent out from Denmark, Great Britain, the Soviet Union, Sweden, and the United States to continue the notable pre-war work of Holland and Germany. The discoveries which they have made have so revolutionized ideas about the ocean bottoms that individual governments and UNESCO are now becoming interested, realizing, as they do, the importance of the economic and military aspects of such surveys.

The vigorous program of international exploration of the sea instituted during the IGY has stirred great interest in the oceans, and a Special Committee on Oceanic Research has been established to co-ordinate the work. The Indian Ocean is the least known, and it is perhaps the most productive ocean biologically. Between 1959 and 1963 forty ships carrying scientists from twenty countries will be participating in the International Indian Ocean Expedition, at the end of which this may be the best known ocean.

The most remarkable of these recent discoveries is the evidence of the continuity of the mid-ocean ridge. It had long been known that remote islands were peaks on submarine ridges, but it was not realized that the ridges were continuous. In the Southern Ocean, during the IGY, American, West European, and Soviet ships filled many gaps in our knowledge and showed that the ridges are indeed joined. In the Arctic

Ocean, Russian and American soundings through the ice, and recent continuous profiles obtained by the submarines *Nautilus* and *Skate,* traced the northern extension past Spitsbergen across the Arctic basin to the Lena delta. The Indian Ocean branch was traced into the Gulf of Aden, the Red Sea, and the African rift valleys. The main ridge stretches for 40,000 miles, and with branches it may be 60,000 miles long. Like the course of the *Nautilus* of Jules Verne, the mid-ocean ridge extends 20,000 leagues under the sea, and it is by far the greatest mountain range on earth.

Not only is it the largest; it is the highest mountain system. At Mauna Loa and Mauna Kea, on Hawaii, the ridge rises to 33,000 feet from the ocean floor, and elsewhere it is rarely less than 10,000 feet high. It rises, steep and rugged, from the surrounding flat plain of the sea floor. Along most of its length there runs a central rift valley, or valleys, which like the rift valleys of Africa are shaken by earthquakes and are marked by magnetic disturbances. Earthquakes most frequently occur directly beneath these rifts. Active volcanoes rise along the ridge, and from time to time their growing cones break the surface of the sea as new islands. Perhaps the ridge is a crack opening as the earth expands and its crust is pulled apart. Lavas, gushing up from the earth's hot interior, fill the crack and overflow onto the surface. Slow viscous currents in the deep mantle, rising beneath the ridge, may account for the greater heat flow over the ridge. If P. A. M. Dirac is correct in his suggestion that the earth has slowly expanded during its long history, these ridges are the cicatrices that mark where the earth's surface has split under the pressure of its swelling. They have the properties that one would expect to find in such scars, and lend plausibility to Dirac's theory. But, then, by what mechanism were the continental mountains built? To date, mountains have been thought to result from contraction of the earth. The solution to this quandary eludes us still because, whether the earth is contracting or expanding, the rate is so slow that our instruments cannot detect any change.

Scientists also have been impressed by the possibility of yielding and flow within the earth, which could go on whether the earth is expanding or contracting or remains constant in volume.

During the IGY R. G. Mason and V. Vacquier carried out air-borne magnetic surveys of a branch of the mid-ocean ridge that reaches the coast of Lower California, and of some great cliffs, or scarps, associated with it which, it had been recently discovered by H. W. Menard, extend for 2,000 miles toward the Hawaiian Islands. By studying the displacement of magnetic anomalies, Mason and Vacquier concluded that there had been a horizontal movement of 800 miles along one fracture and lesser movements along others. The scarps do not appear to be actively moving now, but no one knows how old they are.

How to interpret these fascinating and unsuspected observations poses a great puzzle for earth scientists. Many answers have been proposed, but most of them cannot account for all the evidence. At the present time the idea that convection currents circulate in the mantle seems to be the most promising. H. H. Hess and R. S. Dietz have recently restated this old idea of F. A. Vening Meinesz of Holland and Arthur Holmes of Edinburgh. They suggest that rising currents lift the mid-ocean ridges and bring heat to the surface. There the currents part to form rifts and earthquakes along the central line of the mid-ocean ridges. Lava can then pour out to pile up volcanoes. The rate of movement in the enormously viscous rock (solid to all intents) is only about an inch a year. According to this view, the two sides of the Atlantic Ocean, once joined, have been moving steadily apart for the past 200,000,000 years. Rising currents lift up the mid-Atlantic ridge; and Iceland, the Azores, and Tristan da Cunha are the tops of volcanoes along the ridge. As the currents have moved apart, the Atlantic Ocean has been opened and new floors exposed. No sediments over 200,000,000 years old should be found there, a fact that it is hoped will be verified by drilling. On the westward-flowing current, the Americas have drifted steadily, borne like rafts upon the viscid mantle.

In the Pacific Ocean there are similar currents flowing out from the mid-ocean ridge. The eastward-flowing one reaches the west coast of the Americas and there both currents flow inwards again towards the centre of the earth like the convection currents in a pot of boiling water or like eddies in a stream. This action forms the great trenches off the coast of Chile, Peru, and Central America. In these trenches, where the mantle goes down, the sediments on the ocean floor are scraped off and piled up, like scum over a whirlpool, and added to the mighty Andes and the Cordillera. Near the surface the motion is not steady, but moves in jerks, jolting the earth with quakes from California to Chile.

We must now consider whether these currents have not always flowed in the mantle, pulling continents apart here, pushing them together there, and always turning over the ocean floors so as to scrape off the surface layers against the growing continents. A careful study of S. K. Runcorn's and P. M. S. Blackett's work on palaeomagnetism might enable us to trace the earlier positions and orientations of continents, but a complete re-examination of world geology is needed.

Once I liked the view of the earth propounded by the North American geologists and Jeffreys that the earth's interior is solid and crisp like the image in a photograph, but now I appreciate the greater scope and challenge offered by the swirling vision of convection currents that makes the earth look more like a painting by Van Gogh. The discoveries made on the ocean floors and in palaeomagnetism seem to demand this change in view to a picture of a more mobile earth.

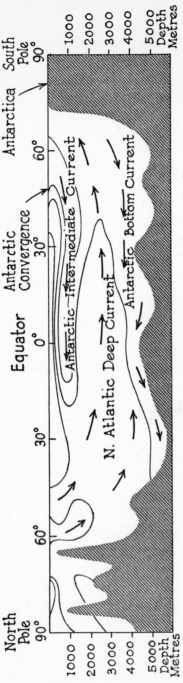

A vertical section through the Atlantic Ocean from pole to pole, showing in a greatly exaggerated vertical scale the shape of the sea bottom and the general circulation of the chief currents.

The seas, which fill the ocean basins, hiding their dark floors from view, themselves provide other mysteries no less challenging. As soon as ocean navigation began, sailors realized that currents flowed in the surface of the sea. The most famous of these, the Gulf Stream, was mapped by Benjamin Franklin. Recognition of the Humboldt Current off Chile and Peru, of the Kuroshio Current off Japan, and of the equatorial currents followed, until a picture of the regular movements of the surface currents of the oceans was completed. Many of the surface currents follow the direction of prevailing winds, but currents in general are formed and directed by four main factors: gravity, wind, the rotation of the earth, and the shape of the ocean basins.

The rotation of the earth and the prevailing winds cause the currents to be most intense close to the western sides of oceans. Thus, the Gulf Stream, moving at 3 to 5 knots off the coast of Florida, is much faster than any current off the opposite European shore. Investigation has also shown that whereas the western edge of the Gulf Stream is sharp enough, even if it snakes about rather unsteadily, the eastern edge is ill defined. Indeed, the whole Atlantic circulation is somewhat like the rotation of a large merry-go-round, with its centre in the Sargasso Sea.

The study of surface currents is comparatively simple, but deep currents are much more elusive and our knowledge of them is still far from complete. The methods developed for the plotting of air currents have not simplified our task here because, unfortunately, the problems are quite dissimilar. In the transparent and rapidly moving atmosphere the components are well mixed and constant, but the wind currents can easily be traced by releasing balloons and watching the direction and rate of their progress. The seas, however, are opaque, and until 1956 no means of observing their currents directly had been devised. But the components of the sea are not well mixed, and currents retain their separate identity for great distances, as anyone knows who has seen the waters of the Amazon, and other great rivers, staining the sea miles off the coast. The traditional method of tracking the path of an ocean current flowing far beneath the surface involved taking thousands of samples of ocean water by lowering bottles on long wire lines. By linking together the points from which identical samples had been drawn, the paths of deep currents were plotted. But this labour yielded no information on the rate at which the currents flowed.

The currents in the sea tend to form separate layers flowing in different directions, each layer denser than the one above it. Very cold water and very salty water constitute the heaviest layers. The very cold water generated off Antarctica could be traced along the bottom of the Atlantic Ocean as far north as the Bay of Biscay; at shallower depths warm tropical waters flowed south, toward Antarctica. If it were possible to devise a float so sensitive to pressure that it could maintain itself at a predetermined depth, it would be born along in one of these layers in the depths of the sea. In 1956 J. C. Swallow, of the British National Institute of Oceanography, succeeded in developing such a float. It was equipped with sound transmitters by which surface ships could track its course. During the IGY the American research vessel *Atlantis*, of Woods Hole Oceanographic Institution, and the *Discovery II*, from the British National Institute, on a cruise off the United States coast demonstrated by means of this device that a strong southwestward current flows at a depth of two miles below the Gulf Stream, in the opposite direction, at a rate of as much as a third of a knot. Another co-operative voyage by British, French, and Norwegian vessels some 400 miles off the west coast of Spain and Portugal revealed a current flowing at a rate of one or two miles a day, at a depth of about 4,000 feet,

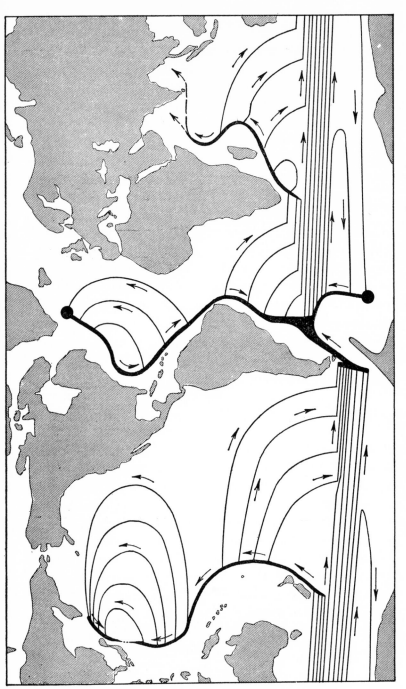

Diagram of deep circulation in the ocean basins. Water sinks to join the deep circulation in the north and south Atlantic only in the vicinity of the two large dots.

counter to the surface current. These floats have also shown that submarine currents do not flow smoothly but contain eddies which move much faster than the average flow and which may be the cause of sand ripples photographed on the ocean floor.

Exploration has recently revealed a very complex system of currents along the equator in the Pacific Ocean. In 1948 an American oceanographer, T. Cromwell, noticed that some deep-fishing lines were carried east against the westward flow of the surface current. Subsequently, the Cromwell Current has been found to lie at depths of between 100 and 800 feet, to be 250 miles wide, and to move eastward with velocities of up to 3.5 knots. It is located exactly along the equator and directly beneath the South Equatorial Current, which flows in the opposite direction. The Cromwell Current has a flow over a thousand times that of the Mississippi River. To date it has been traced for 3,500 miles from the Galapagos Islands to the International Date Line, but it may cross the whole Pacific Ocean and be 6,500 miles long.

Beneath the Cromwell Current flows another, weaker, westward current. Thus, there are three currents, one above the other, flowing in alternate directions. The full story is even more complex, for two more currents flow beside them. On the surface, beside the South Equatorial Current, lies the North Equatorial Current, which, as expected, flows in the opposite direction. Beneath it, in turn, a fifth current flows counter to it, as the Scripps Institution of Oceanography, using Swallow floats, has shown.

These currents follow the equator because of the rotation of the earth. Rotation, along with the difference in temperature between the equator and the poles, creates the trade winds, blowing from northeast and southeast toward the equator. These winds peel away the surface water at the equator, causing an upsurge of cooler, deep water. And these factors, in some indirect manner not yet fully understood, give rise to complex patterns of currents and counter-currents.

The rise of the deep water has another effect. The warm, sunlit surface waters of the tropical seas form a vast incubator for all sorts of marine life, which could not be supported were it not for the constant supply of phosphates and other nutrients welling up from the depths. Beneath this area, teeming with life, lies a submarine cemetery in the form of a low ridge of fossils. According to marine palaeontologists, these fossils form an equatorial ridge 900 feet high and 360 miles wide which extends right across the Pacific Ocean.

Finally, in the Southern Ocean there has long been known to exist a sharp dividing line between the bitterly cold waters that surround Antarctica and the somewhat warmer waters of the other oceans. It has generally been supposed that this line marks the place at which the cold Antarctic water sinks to the bottom before flowing north. The line is called the Antarctic Convergence. During the IGY the many ships navigating to Antarctica added greatly to our knowledge of the Convergence, which may be much more complex than had been thought. Here again investigation has only served to reveal the immensity of the problem.

Sailors and harbour masters long ago found that since tides are closely related to the phases of the moon, careful observation for a few months at any particular spot would enable them to predict tides there. A few harbours installed permanent tide-gauges, and over the years these have indicated that on the average sea level is slowly rising. Compared with tides, which are measured in feet or tens of feet, the long-range changes in sea level of a few inches a century are slight. There used to be so few tide-gauges that it was difficult to obtain accurate measurements, but during the IGY many maritime powers installed them. A good number of gauges are needed because any one of them may be rendered unreliable by changes in the pattern of the weather or by movements associated with earthquakes or the settling of the land. A particular effort was made to put gauges on remote islands where they would be subject to fewer disturbing influences. The nu-

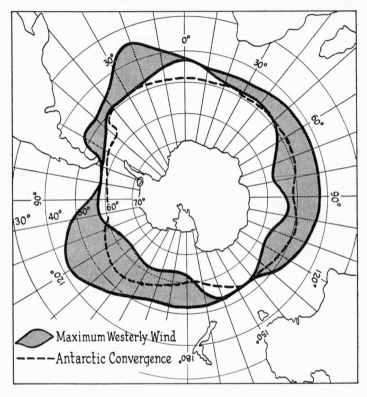

Position of the Antarctic Convergence, where the cold Antarctic waters appear to sink beneath warmer waters from the north. Notice its close relation to the zone of strongest westerly winds.

merous additional gauges installed during the IGY showed that in many places the average level of the sea was higher at some seasons than at others. For example, in July 1958 at Bermuda, sea level was observed to be 9 inches higher

than in August. Such changes seem to be largely due to the
transport of great masses of water about the earth by winds.
They may also be partly due to the heating and expansion
of sea water during summer. It should be possible to relate
such changes to minute alterations in the earth's rotation.
To obtain information with which to discriminate between
the effects of temperature and wind, some tidal stations during
the IGY recorded the temperatures of the sea water below the
gauges to depths of 1,000 feet. Such an installation on Pitcairn
Island was tended by a descendant of a mutineer from H.M.S.
Bounty.

During the last war the many landing operations on beaches
aroused a great interest in waves, and it was discovered that
several types could be distinguished. There are waves caused
by local winds; there are swells of longer wave-length which
have travelled thousands of miles from their origin in distant
storms; there are surges, long-period waves, like the seiches,
which cause rapid changes of a few feet in the level of the
water in the Great Lakes; and there are tsunami, or seismic
waves, caused by displacement of the ocean floor by submarine
flows triggered by earthquakes. At many places special gauges
were installed to record these phenomena.

In addition, the IGY saw many miscellaneous projects in
oceanography. Photographs were taken of the ocean floor.
New fish and invertebrates were discovered at great depths.
The carbon-dioxide content of deep ocean waters was studied,
for it is important to know whether it is increasing as a result
of the burning of coal and petroleum.

Samples of carbon-14, obtained from the depths, were used
to time the circulation of water in the oceans. California
oceanographers found that deep water from latitude 10° north
in the Pacific had not been at the surface for nineteen hundred years but that farther south, at latitude 45° south in
the same longitude, the deep water had been at the surface

thirteen hundred years ago. Since both these were, supposedly, samples from the current that sinks from the surface along the Antarctic Convergence and flows slowly northward, we can gauge the rate at which the waters flow. It would appear that the bottom current in the Pacific flows northward at a rate of about 8 miles a year.

The rate of flow and counter-flow of the oceans dictates the quantity of life in the sea. Without upwelling currents, the surface waters, in which light and warmth can support abundant life, would soon be eaten bare of their dissolved nutrients. Thus, the best fisheries are located where warm surface waters and cold rising currents mingle. In some areas, such as along the coast of Peru, under certain conditions of the winds the fertilizing currents fail. In those years the fisheries fail, the sea birds die, and there is famine in the sea.

CHAPTER 21

HAWAII
AND NEW ZEALAND

NOVEMBER 1958

On October 29, 1958, a month after returning from China, I left home again to join an inspection team from the United States National Academy of Sciences on board a military air-transport plane bound for a six weeks' tour of bases in Antarctica.

On the way there, and again coming back, our party stopped in Hawaii and inspected geophysical activities. On the island of Oahu at a point only a few miles' drive along the picturesque coast from Waikiki Beach and Diamond Head we visited a solar radio telescope run by physicists of the University of Hawaii, but the main IGY bases are on the largest islands, Maui and Hawaii. On Maui, in the great extinct crater of Haleakala there is a meteorological station and a large observatory for tracking satellites. While some of the party visited it, others flew the 200 miles to Hilo, on Hawaii, whence we drove nearly to the top of the great active volcano Mauna Loa.

Hawaii is really a multiple island made up of five separate volcanoes on an older part of the mid-ocean ridge. Mauna Loa and Mauna Kea, rising to 13,600 and 13,825 feet respectively, are the dominant peaks, the latter being the tallest mountain on earth if one measures its height from its base on the ocean floor 20,000 feet below sea level. Mauna Loa erupts at times, but Kilauea, one of the smaller peaks, has more numerous and spectacular eruptions, the last starting in December 1959 and continuing into 1960. There is a permanent volcano observatory there.

The road we followed climbed steadily for 40 miles. At first we passed fields of sugar and other crops by the edge of the road, then miles of tropical forests which gradually thinned out. Rocks showed through the moss. Over them sparse trees reached out their branches trying to close the open woodlands, but they seemed unable to maintain the effort and as we rose they grew more stunted and faded, till only bushes and tussocks of grass lined the hollows in the rock. Suddenly we passed on to a recent flow of lava and from there to the top the road ran over a lifeless slag-heap. There was nothing but crusts of lava, solidified in tortuous whorls, where the viscid, seething mass had frozen. The black, shiny surface was scarred to reddish dust and clinkers where the road had been roughly scraped over the martian landscape. We bumped and jolted up and over this wilderness while the air grew chilly and the sun overhead more and more blinding.

At 11,150 feet, the road stopped in front of three huts. We stepped out, surprised at the surrounding stillness. A mist so thin that it only accentuated the brilliance of the sun brought a flurry of snowflakes sweeping up the mountainside. A grey puff of cloud from the approaching squall whistled up the slope, carrying the circle of a perfect rainbow like a halo on its silver head.

From the tropical airport we had driven to the snowline.

It was windy and cold, and in spite of the desolate beauty of the scene, we were glad to enter one of the huts and be greeted by the isolated inhabitants—three American scientists.

This station, and much of the road leading to it, was built as part of a special program of weather studies initiated by the United States Weather Bureau. The research director of the Weather Bureau, Harry Wexler, was one of our team and he explained the program to us. The IGY had provided the opportunity to build several new meteorological stations in remote places, six in Antarctica, two on drifting stations on the Arctic sea ice, and this one at a great elevation and far from any mainland in the tropics. In addition to regular weather observations, these stations were making special studies of the radiation arriving from the sun and of the proportion of that radiation reflected back into space, of the amounts of ozone, of carbon dioxide, and of nuclear fall-out in the atmosphere. The results at these remote sites, uncontaminated by industrial pollution, provided calibration for comparison with regular stations nearer to industry and to nuclear-test sites, and gave some indications of the direction and rapidity of circulation and mixing in the atmosphere. For example, the quantity in the atmosphere of carbon dioxide produced by burning fuels varies from day to day, through a range of as much as 60 per cent in Europe, but at Mauna Loa the range is only 1 per cent, and at Little America only 0.3 per cent. The last two values provide a standard against which the variations in settled regions can be checked.

At Mauna Loa we were shown the chemical apparatus for measuring the quantities of different gases present in the atmosphere, and the optical instruments and balloons used for sampling them at great heights. We also saw the mechanical filters that sample the air for fall-out. Fans suck measured volumes of air through filters, trapping the radioactive dust blown into the air by nuclear explosions. By counting the radioactivity of the exposed filters, scientists are able to obtain a measure of the nuclear radiation, or fall-out, which is contaminating the air. Outside we inspected the radiometers and found that in spite of the cold we got more sunburned than the sun-bathers on the beaches below. Because we were above much of the atmosphere, we were unshielded and received more solar radiation than anyone on the beaches at sea level.

It is known that the radiant heat from the sun is trapped by the ozone, water vapour, and carbon dioxide in the earth's atmosphere. Careful measurements of these constituents and of the incoming and outgoing radiation at different localities will make it possible to determine the relative importance of these factors. When their roles are better understood and their variations have been charted, we can hope to understand the influence they have on changes in weather and climate and thus make better forecasts.

When we came out after lunch, the storm had cleared and we looked across the island of Hawaii to Mauna Kea, a giant among mountains, and a very broad one, for the lava of which it is built has flowed freely to give the slopes a gentle angle. Although the eruptions of the Hawaiian and other volcanoes on mid-ocean ridges are at times spectacular, hot basalt flows freely and does not give rise to terrible explosions like those that have killed tens of thousands of people around such andesite volcanoes as Krakatoa or Mont Pelée. Andesite, even when hot, is a more viscid lava than basalt. As a result, pressure builds up in these volcanoes and they are more likely to explode. Thus, the andesite volcanoes of the continental fracture system are more dangerous than the basalt volcanoes of the remote ocean islands. Awesome and terrible as volcanic eruptions may appear, neither kind is comparable in danger to humans to the insidious hazards that would arise from abundant radioactive fall-out.

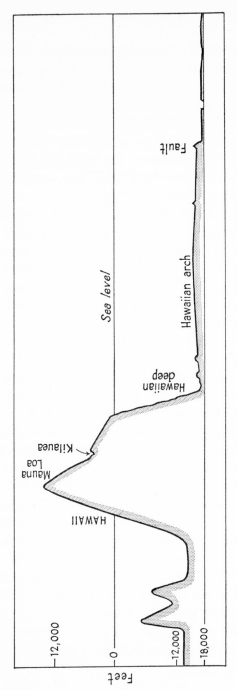

Cross-section, with great vertical exaggeration, of part of the Pacific Ocean. Note that the Hawaiian Islands are only peaks in a huge mid-ocean mountain range, most of which is below sea level.

From Hawaii we flew south to Canton Island on the equator. This island is a ring of limestone built of coral on the peak of an ancient volcano on the mid-ocean ridge, extinct and now slowly subsiding. On this lonely atoll an airstrip had been built during the war, and there we stopped to refuel. It is so small that one can walk from the strip to the coral beach and look amid the breakers for pieces of coral and the shells of giant clams, but in the black and breathless midnight of that visit good shells were hard to find.

It is difficult to imagine a greater contrast than that between Canton Island on the one hand and Hawaii, Fiji, and New Zealand on the other. Whereas the others are mountainous, lush, and tropical, Canton is a flat and lifeless desert without vegetation or any supplies of natural fresh water. On the equator the air currents rise straight up, and the moisture-bringing winds of most tropical islands do not reach there. Lying in the equatorial doldrums, Canton is like a misplaced fragment of the Sahara.

When we reached New Zealand, we paused. These islands are remote and their people welcomed the influx of American visitors en route to Antarctica. Very kindly the New Zealanders offered to drive us through much of their pleasant land so that we might visit universities and observatories and talk to the scientists there.

I like to think of New Zealand as the youngest and smallest of the continents. The thought that New Zealand is a continent in the first bloom of youth is a happy one. It is indeed a perfect miniature, compounded of the best and fairest scenery that the earth can offer. The only counterpart to which I can liken it would be Switzerland and Italy, if they were islands set in a remote ocean and inhabited by only two million unhurried and uncrowded people.

The history of New Zealand is well summarized in the inscription on a monument to the Maori people at Auckland,

New Zealand. "The first known Maori to visit these shores was Kupe, a Polynesian navigator, in the year 925. The first settlement under Toi took place in 1350, when the ancestors of the present Maori race arrived in the now historic canoes, Tainui, Aruva, Mata-atua, Aotea, Tahitumu, Horoute, Tohomaru, and others. In 1840 the Treaty of Waitangi was signed whereby the Maoris accepted the sovereignty of the British Crown and were thereby secure in all their rights and privileges as British Subjects."

It is only necessary to add that the first European to discover and explore the islands was Captain James Cook in 1775, and that the terms of the treaty have been observed.

North Island is the part like Italy. From semi-tropical plains and sand beaches around Auckland, one drives south through valleys of hot springs, past active volcanoes, and over upland pastures, to Wellington, the capital. There a ferry, which is a small ocean liner, takes one overnight to South Island. This is like Switzerland. Along its western coast are forests, beautiful fiords, and the snow-covered Southern Alps. From them, open plains sweep to the towns and beaches along the eastern shore. One of these towns, Christchurch, is the traditional point of departure for the Antarctic.

Nothing is very large in New Zealand, but the scenery is ever varying. The only constant feature is the sea, which laps the beaches and the cliff-foot at the end of every road.

In this idyllic setting live an easy-going, athletic people. To a truly remarkable degree their society is uniform and classless. No one appears to be wealthy, the hotels are few and not luxurious, the shops are not distinguished. One of our hosts said that there was only one really good restaurant in all New Zealand, but I found the hotel meals excellent. On the other hand, no one is illiterate and no one feels the pinch of poverty. The universities may be poorly housed and lack facilities for research, but their standards are high, their museums imaginative, and their libraries and bookstores both numerous and good.

There may be few mansions and few large cars, but everyone has a car, even if it is small and perhaps old. Everyone either lives in the country or goes to it for long week-ends. The New Zealanders are fully aware of the glory of their empty land, and they revel in the ease with which they can drive to the beaches for a swim, to the mountains for skiing and climbing, to the streams for fishing—or simply walk the open roads through unspoiled country. The price they pay for these pleasures is remoteness and strategic weakness, as was brought home to them in the last war. They are dependent for their livelihood on foreign trade, and as a result they are interested in the affairs of the world and have excellent news services. They rely largely on radio communication for knowledge of the rest of the world.

On these islands, earthquakes and volcanoes are commonplace. Wellington, like San Francisco, has through it an active fault on which there was a very large earthquake in 1855. Auckland and Christchurch are both surrounded by extinct craters. Their weather, blown from vast and empty oceans, is variable and difficult to predict. The International Geophysical Year was thus received by New Zealanders with immense interest, because it dealt with problems plain for them to see. New Zealand carried on a large and vigorous IGY program both on its home islands and on the nearest part of Antarctica. Since that part also happens to be the easiest gateway to the interior of the continent, many explorers—Scott, Shackleton, and the Americans since the first Byrd expedition—have used New Zealand as their jumping-off place. During the IGY the Antarctic operations of New Zealand and the United States were closely integrated on a most friendly and cordial basis.

By the time that I visited New Zealand, the IGY programs were in a general way familiar to me. In an observatory at

Wellington I was particularly interested to see a Danjon astrolabe, an instrument used for making measurements of changes in latitude and longitude. Designed by one of the leading French scientists of the IGY, it eliminates inaccuracies due to human judgement. Slight changes in latitude and longitude are attributed to a slight wobbling of the earth upon its axis, but we do not yet know whether the movements are progressive. If they are, observations carried on over a period of time should confirm this and show whether the poles of the earth are moving relative to the earth as a whole or whether there is in addition a relative motion between different parts of the earth.

Because New Zealand is an isolated island, it is an obvious place to look for evidence of continental drift. At the present time we not only are not sure about the existence or rate of these motions but we also do not know whether the continents are growing. The evidence, I believe, suggests that they are.

Continents, like humans, go through an infant stage, then youth, and in maturity, marriage and the union of several individuals into a family. The principal continents probably all started over two billion years ago as separate islands. Volcanoes on the margins of these islands fed them with lava from within the earth. The lava was eroded into sedimentary rocks, and these were piled up into mountains, which after long periods were levelled off. As the islands grew, they joined together, forming compound units. If this view is correct, the three centres from which North America developed were cemented into the heart of the continent and worn down to plains. These centres, which two billion years ago were three separate volcanic islands, now form the bed-rock of large areas lying north of Lake Superior, north of Great Slave Lake, and under the plains of Montana and Wyoming. The boundaries, and indeed the very existence of these continental nuclei, have only been ascertained in recent years by studies of the age of natural radioactive minerals, which act as clocks. After these centres had been joined, the Appalachian Mountains and, more recently, the Cordillera were added. At present the continent is active and growing along its entire west coast and along the Caribbean. Inexorably, but extremely slowly, the land is being built out unto the Pacific and towards South America. Like an egg that has cracked while being boiled so that gouts of white ooze out upon the shell, so has the earth cracked and exuded its continents. This opinion that the continents are growing is supported by evidence that the oceans and the atmosphere are also increasing through the addition of steam and gases from volcanoes. New Zealand may be a new continent in its first stage of growth.

This account may seem fanciful to some, for it is not what the old school taught, but the wider shores of knowledge of the universe which have been opened to our view through the windows of physics are forcing a complete reorientation in our ideas about the earth. In all, I think the simplest explanation of the origin of our surroundings is that the earth, in its youth, melted and then froze to a rather smooth surface, without any atmosphere or oceans. That surface is now buried. Everything above it—crust, air, and oceans—has been extruded from within the earth by slow volcanic action, such as we see today. The original surface may be the Mohorovičić discontinuity, or it may be some shallower level within the crust. Drilling the Mohole will help us to find out.

If the continents and the waters of the oceans are both growing, then one would expect the seas to flood and submerge the low plains of the continents. The fact that this has not happened, except to a minor extent, is an argument for the theory of an expanding earth. If the mid-ocean ridges are widening along their central cracks, the increase in the ocean basins can provide room for the waters flowing from within.

If the continents are growing, then the large islands that

fringe them, like the West Indies, Madagascar, Greenland, Indonesia, and the island chains along the Pacific shores of Asia, are all destined to become incorporated. Some of the islands, like Madagascar and Greenland, seem to have been born as small independent continents, but in the vast history of the earth they would appear to have no long future as separate entities. New Zealand, born a mere five hundred million years ago, made of the stuff of continents, growing by continental processes, far removed from other lands, is perhaps destined some day, a billion years after man's brief span, to join the race of giants—the continents. Other remote islands, like Hawaii and Canton in the Pacific, or Iceland, the Azores, and Ascension in the Atlantic, lie on the mid-ocean ridge and belong to a different race, not destined to grow. They are not infant Herculeses, but scions of a separate pygmy stock. The basalt lavas of the mid-ocean ridge are not poured out abundantly and hence do not constitute as rich a food on which to grow as is provided by the more numerous andesite volcanoes of the continents. If in future ages these basalt islands are carried into collision with continents, they will be overwhelmed, and New Zealand would be welded on as an addition. Thus, the ocean floors and their remote islands are all young and forever being renewed, but the continents are unsinkable and old and like froth floating forever down the river of time above the slowly churning eddies of the mantle.

This is the story of the origin of mountains, islands, and continents as I see it. It is still very uncertain. In the last decade so many new discoveries and new suggestions have been made that our old ideas have been thoroughly shaken, but new concepts have not yet crystallized. In science such periods of uncertainty mark the eras of greatest progress, for ideas in flux and contradictions waiting to be reconciled spur man to his mightiest efforts. From the present confusion we may confidently expect vast and enduring concepts to emerge.

CHAPTER 22

FALL-OUT

Nuclear Radiation was the name given to the IGY program that dealt with radiation caused by the decay of nuclear or atomic particles in air, water, or on land. The term was an unfortunate and confusing choice. Nuclear radiation refers to the radioactive isotopes of chemical elements produced in nuclear explosions and has nothing to do with the electromagnetic radiation that comes as waves of heat and light from the sun.

The radioactive isotopes included in the study of nuclear radiation are formed in four ways. Some were formed at the time of creation, along with the other elements; some are produced by cosmic-ray bombardment; some are made artificially in nuclear reactors; and some are generated in atomic explosions.

Let us consider first the radioactive elements formed at the time of creation. About a dozen isotopes of different elements in nature have been found to be feebly radioactive and to decay very slowly into isotopes which are stable. The continued existence of some of these radioactive isotopes in spite of the fact that they are constantly wasting away is only possible because they decay very slowly. Nevertheless, the implication is that they were formed at a not infinitely remote time. In fact, the rate of decay suggests that that time was about five billion years ago. This is now considered to be the probable date of the creation of all the elements in the solar system, although the elements in stars other than the sun and in other galaxies may have been formed at different, unknown, times. The solar system, including the earth, took shape out of these elements at a slightly later date, about four and a half billion years ago.

Of the dozen long-lived isotopes found in nature, five are quantitatively important: uranium-238, uranium-235, thorium-232, rubidium-87, and potassium-40. These isotopes are widely scattered in small concentrations and occur almost everywhere—in rocks, soil, water, and air, and even in human beings. None of these elements is dangerous to handle, and because the atmosphere very effectively shields us from most of the radiation emanating from outer space, over three quarters of all the radiation which affects us comes, and always has come, from these five isotopes. These isotopes are useful for determining the time when rocks were deposited, and they provide the chief clocks for our time scale of the earth.

One of them, potassium-40, is the source of most of the radiation that humans and other animals receive because it is a constituent of their bodies. Uranium and thorium do not occur in normal tissues in appreciable amounts, but radium, one of the elements formed by the decay of tissue, is found in small quantities in bones. Another, radon gas, can be detected in the air. At a conference in Utrecht in 1957, L. Machta pointed out that radon is constantly generated by rocks and that it has a half-life of only three and a half days. As a consequence, some air over land may have five hundred times as much radon as air that has spent a long time over the sea, where no radon is being generated. Since radon decays and is not renewed in air masses over the oceans, radon, he suggested, can be used to identify air masses and to trace their history. However, the proposal has not been widely put into practice.

The second kind of natural radiation is produced by the unstable isotopes produced by cosmic-ray bombardment. Cosmic rays are in themselves a form of radiation; in addition, they can knock other atoms about, creating radioactive isotopes which decay at a later time. The following are the isotopes so far discovered, with their average duration:

Beryllium-10	2,700,000 years
Carbon-14	5,600 years
Silicon-32	700 years
Hydrogen-3 (Tritium)	12.5 years
Sodium-22	2.6 years
Sulphur-35	87 days
Beryllium-7	53 days
Phosphorous-33	25 days
Phosphorous-32	14 days
Chlorine-39	1 hour

The most important of the isotopes produced by cosmic rays is carbon-14. According to J. R. Arnold and E. A. Martell, it causes only about one per cent of the feeble internal radioactivity present in humans, of which potassium-40 is the chief contributor. In the whole atmosphere and oceans and in living matter there are about 100 tons of this isotope, mostly in the form of carbon-dioxide gas dissolved in the oceans. There is about one ton in the atmosphere. Next in importance among the products of cosmic rays is tritium, as the highly radioactive isotope, hydrogen-3, is called. Before atomic bombs were exploded, there were only about 20 pounds of this on earth. The fact that such a small quantity could be detected even

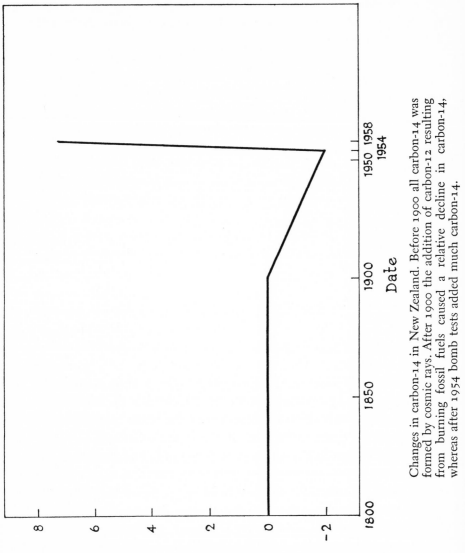

Changes in carbon-14 in New Zealand. Before 1900 all carbon-14 was formed by cosmic rays. After 1900 the addition of carbon-12 resulting from burning fossil fuels caused a relative decline in carbon-14, whereas after 1954 bomb tests added much carbon-14.

though it is thoroughly mixed with the atmosphere is an indication of the powerful nature of radioactive poisons.

Until 1932 all radioactivity was formed naturally, in one of these two ways. In that year Frédéric and Irene Joliot-Curie produced the first artificial radioisotopes, but they were not created in large numbers until the first nuclear explosion in 1945. The third kind of nuclear radiation, then, is that artificially created in controlled laboratory machines and in nuclear reactors. Many of the radioactive isotopes so formed, like cobalt-60, are useful for the treatment of disease and for industrial purposes. Some of them are suitable for release in the sea or air as markers and can be used like a dye to tag bodies of water or masses of air so that movements and rates of dispersion can be measured.

Had these three been the only kinds of nuclear radiation, their study might not have been included in the IGY, but there is a fourth kind—that resulting from explosion of nuclear bombs. The descent to earth of the abundant artificial radioactive isotopes created in atomic explosions is known as fall-out. The isotopes generally fall incorporated in clouds of very fine dust.

Although fall-out was already under investigation, much of the work was secret. During the IGY additional data were collected, and these were made available to the public. In spite of the political implications, no less than forty countries announced that they would participate in the program, and data from over half of them, including some results from Communist countries, had reached World Data Centre A in Washington by the end of 1959. The U.S.S.R. did not participate in this program.

The enormous controversy that has been associated with discussions of fall-out is of course a result of the potentially lethal effects of fall-out. But these can only be understood and guarded against if the physical phenomena with which fall-out is associated are understood. Fortunately, a study of fall-out has revealed information of value about atmospheric circulation.

After any nuclear explosion many tiny solid particles are carried up into the atmosphere. This fine dust is radioactive, for it contains about one hundred different radioactive isotopes created during the explosion as products of nuclear fission. Their relative abundance can tell much about the bomb that was their source. If the explosion takes place on the ground, the radioactive isotopes are more numerous than if it takes place high in the air or over water. If the explosion is large, such as that caused by a megaton H-bomb, a heavy fall-out occurs near the site during the first few hours, but a fireball carries the rest of the isotopes into the stratosphere, which begins at a height of from 30,000 to 55,000 feet. Once in the stratosphere, the particles are above the sources of rainfall. At one time it was thought that they would remain there as long as five years; this is now less certain. If, on the other hand, the explosion is smaller, such as from a kiloton A-bomb, then the fireball does not rise so high but remains in the lower atmosphere, or troposphere. In this case the radioactive dust is all brought down with rain and snow in a few months. Due to the nature of tropospheric circulation, little of this fall-out crosses the equator; most of it comes down in the hemisphere in which the explosion takes place. Stratospheric fall-out is the more important because, being generated by large explosions, it is more abundant, and because it may reach all parts of the world.

The IGY program concentrated on collecting data about the fall-out due to small solid particles in various parts of the world. This was done either by exposing sheets of gummed paper to the air and measuring their radioactivity, or by pumping measured volumes of air through suitable filters to trap the tiny particles. The apparatus we saw in operation on

Sr-90 in the stratosphere (microcuries per square mile)

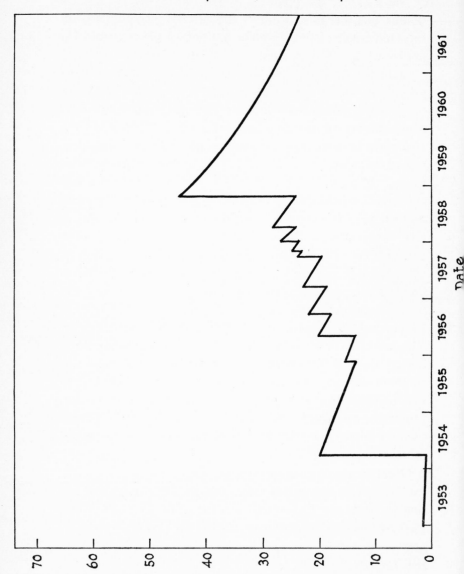

Theoretical estimate of strontium-90 in the stratosphere (above 40,000 feet) based upon the assumption that half of the strontium-90 will fall out in five years and that there will be no more nuclear tests.

Mauna Loa was an example of the latter procedure. One un-expected result of these studies has been a great increase in our knowledge of the circulation of the upper air.

At first it was supposed that the main fall-out from large explosions would settle down from the stratosphere very slowly and at a uniform rate all over the world. But the fall-out, it was discovered, settled much more rapidly than had been envisaged. In particular, large and small Soviet test explosions in mid-latitudes resulted in much heavier falls in the northern than in the southern hemisphere. On the other hand, the fall-out from large American and British explosions in the equa-torial regions came down from the stratosphere at a slower rate. It was then realized that in mid-latitudes mixing might occur between the troposphere and stratosphere in the vicinity of the strong currents known as jet-streams. Such mixing in mid-latitudes would explain the faster rate of fall-out from Soviet explosions in Siberia, and the absence of mixing over the equator would account for the slower rate of fall-out there. The matter was explored further in experiments conducted during the last American tests. The metals tungsten and rhodium were incorporated into the bombs to produce unu-sual radioisotopes, and the particles tagged in this way con-firmed the earlier theories. In this way bomb tests have been used to improve our knowledge of circulation in the upper atmosphere.

Other measurements have shown that as a result of nuclear explosions the amount of carbon-14 in the atmosphere has doubled from one to two tons and the amount of tritium has increased from 20 to 100 pounds. But the effects of these in-creases are not yet serious; the total radiation so produced is still far less than the radioactivity of natural uranium, tho-rium, and potassium.

It is of interest to mention the possible effects of fall-out on human beings. The particular danger of fall-out is that of

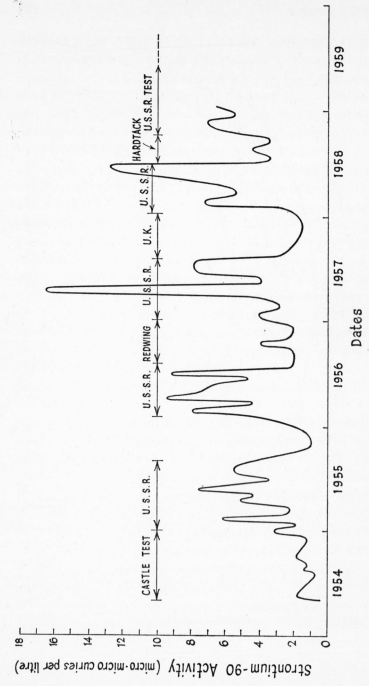

Strontium-90 activity for rainfall in north temperate latitudes, with dominant test sources indicated.

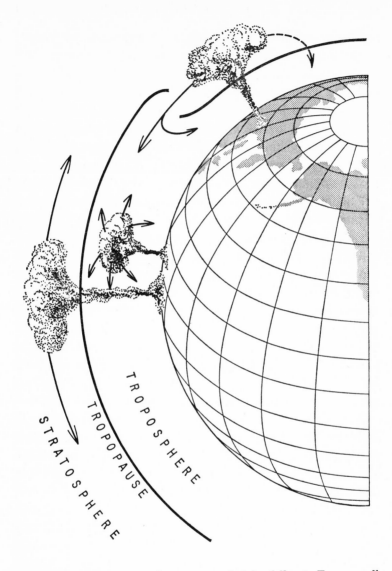

Structure of upper atmosphere as revealed by fall-out. From small explosions it drops locally and quickly. However, in high latitudes fall-out from large explosions leaks down in the same hemisphere more quickly than fall-out in equatorial regions.

about a hundred products of fission, four tend to be trapped in the human body. Hence, they can easily become concentrated in sufficient amounts to produce dangerous radioactive radiation within humans. Two of these radioactive isotopes, iodine-131 and barium-140, have short lives and can only be dangerous for a few weeks or months after an explosion. Strontium-90 and cesium-137, however, collect in bones and flesh respectively and remain dangerous for periods comparable with the span of human life.

Fall-out is not entirely new; it is an addition to a natural phenomenon that has always existed. We have to consider separately the dangers to existing creatures and to future generations. We must also distinguish between the dangers of the present situation, which is not generally regarded as serious, and the dangers that may arise if nuclear explosions and atomic waste are allowed to continue to contaminate the air and water. Natural radioactivity is not dangerous, but exposure to massive doses of radiation, such as have been released in a few accidents in nuclear physics laboratories, is quickly lethal. Between these extremes is a very wide range, and we have not yet had enough experience to fix the safety limits.

Natural radiation causes genetic changes by occasionally damaging the very complex molecules through which characteristics are transmitted. Most genetic changes, or mutations, are harmful, and we know that natural radiation already creates some imperfect offspring. But no one knows the extent to which these effects would be increased by increases in radioactivity. If a certain increase in radioactivity would produce congenital defects in one birth in a million, or cancer in one person in a million, then, some have argued, this is not very important and the necessity of testing weapons for defence purposes justifies the increased suffering. Others emphasize that there are 2,500 million people in the world and that to cause 2,500 more children to be deformed or 2,500 more people to suffer from cancer is intolerable.

Biologists are now hard at work on these problems, for it is certain that we need additional information not only in the event of other nuclear explosions, but also in order to be able to control the hazards produced by natural radioactivity and by the operation of nuclear reactors for peaceful uses.

In July 1959 a study by the New York Operations Office of the United States Atomic Energy Commission was published, comparing the effects of the existing level of fall-out with natural radioactivity. The report states that "the maximum foreseeable dose from strontium-90 in the New York area is thereby estimated to be about 5 per cent of the dose due to natural radioactivity." This does not sound like a very serious increase, until one realizes that the distribution is not uniform. J. L. Kulp has made extensive studies of the variations and concludes that whereas many children will be subject to less than the average increase of 5 per cent, some will be exposed to more, and a few to much more, as much as double, or 200 per cent of the natural amount. According to Kulp, even if no more atomic bombs are exploded, the dose in most children will continue to increase until 1966, as they absorb more and more of the strontium-90 already formed. After that time, the natural decay of strontium-90 will exceed the amount eaten and absorbed. The present situation, it would seem, is not alarming, but additional explosions would be certain to increase the hazard, unless they were confined below ground.

CHAPTER 23

ANTARCTICA

NOVEMBER 1958

The last outbound stage in my travels was from New Zealand to Antarctica. It is a journey which only a few thousand men and a dozen women have ever made. All of them must have been impressed, for as the fields and gardens, the forests and the towns of New Zealand fade behind, one leaves the land of familiar things to enter scenes of icy splendour, of grandeur and desolation, and of human endeavours unmatched on earth.

Antarctica is unlike any other continent. Uninhabited and virtually without life, it is still entirely in the ice age. Separated from other lands by thousands of miles of sea and storm, it is isolated and alone. It is the land of the absolute. No one comes here casually. Every action must be planned; nothing can be left to chance. It is a continent of extremes and of contrasts where there is no middle way.

On November 6 we got up at dawn, had breakfast, and drove through silent streets bathed in the golden misty light of spring sunrise, to the airfield at Christchurch. Every house was shut and dark, but in the wonderful New Zealand gardens the walls and fences overflowed with roses and wistaria. In the low orange light the grass glistened, but in the shadows it was white with drops of dew. At the airfield we clambered up the steps to the plane, feeling clumsy, self-conscious, and hot in mukluks and padded trousers, unbuttoned woollen shirts and underwear, and carrying bags full of parkas and mittens, sun glasses and scarves, which seemed so unnecessary at Christchurch but which would be vital at our destination. At the moment they served to remind us how long our journey would be and how far removed from the ordinary world was the polar continent.

Strapped in our seats and facing backwards in the United States Navy's Super Constellation, sixty-five of us—scientists, Navy men, and newspaper correspondents—saw the green coasts and distant hills of South Island slip away in the sunlight as we plunged into the decks of cloud that swirl over the Southern Ocean. For many hours little was to be seen but grey clouds, and through them glimpses of the dark and churning ocean whose waves broke into plumes of flying foam before and swathes of breaking surf behind. By radio we learned that the weather ship at the halfway point was rolling up to 55 degrees in 18-foot waves.

Then we saw the ice. At first I was not sure whether the white patches might not be just the crests of breaking waves, but soon bigger pieces of a blue-white colour were unmistakable. At the next break in the clouds, the whole sea was covered with pans of ice rocking slowly up and down as a steady swell rolled past them. Finally the motion died away, and the sea below was covered with an apparently motionless but broken pack of ice, frozen last winter and now gradually thawing and breaking up under the continuous play of summer sun and southern winds. From this thin skin upon the ocean protruded a few much higher icebergs that had last year broken off the Antarctic ice cliffs and glaciers and had drifted this far to the north before being frozen in the pack.

Each winter the sea around Antarctica freezes for a distance
of hundreds of miles, and each spring the ice breaks up; some
of it drifts north and melts, but it never all thaws before being
caught and frozen again. Ships venturing to Antarctica must
always force their way through it.

As we approached the continent some seven hours and 2,000
miles after leaving New Zealand, the sky cleared. The sun's
reflection from the ice dazzled us, until we put on dark glasses.
Then we saw it in the distance—the land of Antarctica—as
white and brilliant as the sea ice, but standing up bold and
formidable in mighty cliffs and mountains. Our first sight-
ing was not of the mainland but of the inaccessible Balleny
Islands, mile-high volcanoes scintillating in the sun. We estimated that they were between 30 and 50 miles away, but such
is the magnitude and clarity of the polar scene that, as we
later learned from the radar operator, our nearest approach
was 102 miles. They are outposts off Antarctica on the mid-
ocean ridge.

Soon afterwards we passed over Capes Adare and Hallet,
headlands of the coast, whose bold cliffs mark the corner
where the Ross Sea joins the Southern Ocean and whose black
rocks stem the flood of inland ice.

The whole continent is covered with a smooth sheet of ice
which floods and pours off the margins like too much soft
icing from a cake. The mountains holding it back rise in magnificent dark cliffs, worn and sculptured into jagged peaks, as
much as 13,000 feet from the sea. The great wall of mountains
along which we were then flying extends far into the continent. It is indeed one of the greatest breaks, or fractures,
known on earth and may extend right across the continent between the Ross and Weddell Seas from New Zealand to South
America, dividing Antarctica into two parts. The part, lying
on the side of the fracture towards the Pacific Ocean, forms
a group of islands. The other part, facing the Indian Ocean,

forms a true continent. By the time we arrived, investigations had already shown that the larger continental part forming eastern Antarctica is indeed a continent covered with a mile or two of ice, but the exact nature of the rest of Antarctica had not then been revealed. During our visit we were to await anxiously the daily reports from travelling parties who were measuring the thickness of the ice. Slowly they disclosed one great depth of ice after another, thus confirming the separation of Antarctica into two parts.

The importance of this great fracture was brilliantly impressed upon our minds as we approached our destination—McMurdo Sound—an arm of the sea which lies over the rift, with the imposing wall of the Royal Society Mountains lifted up on one side and the majestic cone of Mount Erebus, a smoking, ice-sheathed volcano rising 13,350 feet straight from the sea, on the other. There is little doubt that this great peak is fed from the same fracture and that inactive volcanoes along our route have been so fed in past times.

We descended into McMurdo Sound and landed on the thick bay ice, where Navy men and scientists milled about eager to greet their replacements, to collect mail, and to assist in the unloading of our huge plane. Instead of the misty hayfields of the morning, our airfield was the frozen ocean. Then we were glad of our warm clothes, as we thrust our hands into the great mitts which hung on strings about our shoulders. It was zero Fahrenheit, and a steady breeze off the ice wrapped our thick clothing about our leaning bodies and swept away the steaming exhaust fumes of the waiting orange vehicles. Here indeed was not only excitement and activity but colour. After the dazzling emptiness of splendid scenery seen from aloft, we were now surrounded by welcoming men, by tractors, and by other planes that were here to bring supplies to parties on the inland ice. We were shut in and awed by the surrounding mountains and especially by the volcano Erebus, whose blue-white sides and dusty purple smoke were now touched and gilded by the evening sun. It did not set, but for hours each night it coloured the bleak hills and limitless ice, until the unfulfilled promise of sunset passed at midnight into the recurring memory of a sunrise now two months old.

The slanting light, the cold, the vapour of men's breaths, the tracked snow vehicles, the ice-blue mountains, and the vast solitude drove home the thought that we had reached the seventh continent, an ultima Thule, more remote than any visited or imagined by the Greeks.

Phil Smith, the cheerful liason between the Navy and the scientists, took us in his ancient weasel, a wartime tracked vehicle, across the ice to the Navy base, Williams Naval Air Facility, located on a beach of volcanic debris at the foot of Mount Erebus.

Here sixty shacks and huts, painted bright orange, straggled up the hillside. Around them, scattered about the heaps of black volcanic ash that enclosed this sheltered hollow, were large gasoline tanks, a wealth of vehicles, a thin forest of radio towers, and a tangle of pipelines and crates, all the apparent confusion of the main base which supplied and supported most of the American work in Antarctica. Although it was still cold, the brilliant sun of early summer was already evaporating the drifts in which the camp had been buried during the Antarctic night. Bulldozers were clearing the last of them out, to prevent the camp from becoming a quagmire in the short melting season ahead. We were glad to enter the hut which served the Navy as mess deck, and to be given a hot meal.

As we ate, Lloyd Berkner, the chief of our party, had a decision to make. If we stayed at McMurdo, we could fly the next day over the pole in one of the three globemasters that had come to drop 450 tons of supplies by parachute, in 10-ton lots, at the south pole. It was tempting for Dr. Berkner, who had been in Antarctica in 1929, to wait and fly over the pole; but a plane was also leaving in a few hours for Little America and Byrd stations, both of which are built upon the ice sheet itself. Since our party could accomplish no scientific work by looking at the pole and we hoped to land there and visit it later, it was obvious that we should take this chance to go to Byrd station on the interior of the ice cap far to the southeast.

While we waited for the plane, Dr. Berkner, an enthusiastic student of the Antarctic, led us half a mile to Hut Point. There Scott had established his first base, and there still stands the hut he built in 1901, the second building to be erected in all Antarctica. Such is the preserving effect of the frigid climate that apart from being partly buried in drifts, it is much as Scott left it. A bronze tablet has been added, but the hut has never been tidied up. Sleds and clothing, tins of food, and skis are still lying about. Protruding from the snow are even some sides of frozen mutton from the forty-five sheep Scott brought south on the deck of the *Discovery*. From curiosity, I tentatively sampled some biscuits from opened tins and found that I preferred the taste of the mellowed dog biscuits to the rather grey ship's biscuits for the men.

A hundred yards away at the top of the point is a memorial cross to Vince, the first man to be killed in an accident in the Antarctic. He had been with Shackleton on the first ascent of Mount Erebus, which reared its smoking top so far above us, and on the return he had fallen down a cliff in a blizzard. Nearby a small United States Navy tanker was locked in the ice against the beach and appeared to be breaking up; she had been deliberately beached for use as a convenient fuel storage until more permanent tanks were erected on land. Directly across the camp a mile or so away rose Observation Hill, which Dr. Edward Wilson, Scott's doctor, artist, and final companion, had climbed every fine day, a habit we found pleasant

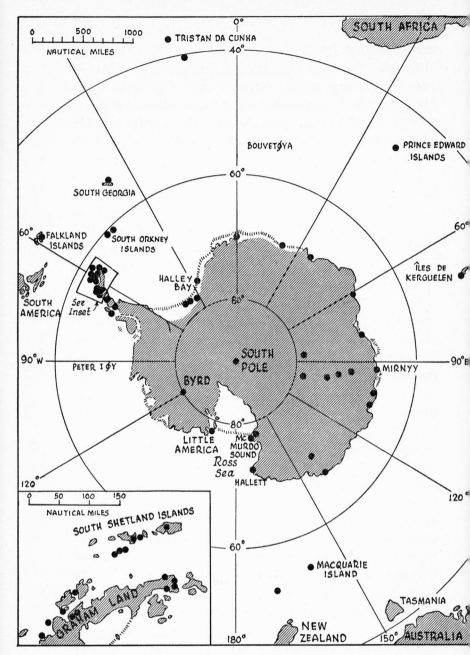

Map of Antarctica showing the location of International Geophysical Year stations.

to imitate. From the top there is an unbroken view to the south of the great Ross ice shelf and the route to the pole. There in 1912 not far from sight Captain Robert Falcon Scott, R.N., Dr. Edward Wilson, and their three companions had perished on their return journey from the south pole. On the summit, a great oak cross bears their names and the inscription: "To strive, to seek, to find and not to yield."

In the century and more since Captain James Clark Ross first penetrated these ice-bound waters, naming the great volcanoes Erebus and Terror after his wooden sailing ships, no place in the Antarctic has witnessed more activity or stored more memories. For cold and pitiless beauty, no place on earth can match McMurdo Sound, nor better suggest the majesty of the universe and the insignificance of man.

By the time we returned to base, the plane was ready, and we embarked to fly 400 miles across the flat and brilliant white plain of the Ross ice shelf to Little America. It was three o'clock in the morning when we reached Little America and tumbled into our bunks to sleep, before pushing on to Byrd station. In Antarctica the weather is so changeable and so frequently bad that no opportunity is lost to travel when one can, and we took off again early next morning.

There are three types of stations in the Antarctic: coastal stations established by ships; inland bases supplied by air; and mobile tractor trains. All earlier stations and most of those of the IGY were coastal bases. From these bases much exploration and many hard and brave journeys had been made in summer. These included the famous poleward dashes of Amundsen, Scott, and Shackleton, the flights of Byrd and Hollick-Kenyon, and the tractor crossing of Antarctica by Fuchs supported by Hillary. But if men were to stay on the ice cap in winter to learn its full secrets, more stations were needed.

The south pole station and Byrd station are examples of

the second kind. At the former everything—huts, vehicles, supplies—was dropped by parachute or landed by plane, but Byrd station was built from supplies delivered both by airplane and tractor-drawn sleds. The planes were found to be more efficient and were used exclusively after the first season, in spite of the problems. The pole station is at 9,200 feet above sea level and has a normal summer temperature of about 15° to 20° below zero Fahrenheit. The highest ever recorded is 5° F above. The wind blows constantly and furrows the frozen snow into drifts as much as 4 feet high. These make landings rough and dangerous but do not prevent parachutes from dragging supplies great distances if the ground crews fail to halt them. A motor and a generator dropped at Byrd station were dragged 96 miles before the crew of a snowmobile tracked and recovered them.

Byrd station is not as cold because its elevation is only 5,000 feet, but the heavy falls of wind-driven snow also present difficulties.

The Soviet coast base at Mirny is supplied by ship, and the inland stations by great tractor-trains. Russian mobile laboratories and living quarters on sleds have travelled far over the eastern Antarctic to the centre, where the ice reaches heights of 13,000 feet above the sea. There the most formidable conditions yet encountered by men have been recorded. On August 24, 1960, in the depth of winter, the coldest recorded surface temperature, 158° F below zero, was reached. Under such conditions of cold, thin air, driving wind, and months of darkness, men can only venture out for twenty minutes at a time to make measurements, and they must be entirely encased in special suits, with masks and breathing tubes. Electrically heated suits have been tried, but rather unsuccessfully. The bond existing among explorers and scientists of the IGY, the common urge to discover the unknown, was extended in the

Antarctic to a common courage in facing the extremes of nature.

The inside of the freight plane in which we travelled from Little America to Byrd station looked like a small and rather drab warehouse. Along each side were benches of a most awkward and uncomfortable design, made of canvas and webbing stretched on a metal frame. Upon them sat two rows of khaki-padded figures. Our plump and cheerful meteorologist was swathed in an extra tent-like outer parka and resembled nothing so much as one of his own meteorological balloons blown up and gathered into the cloth shroud used for launching it. Overflowing aft and forward were piles of crates and baggage, topped with engine covers, repair kits, and 1,000 pounds of emergency gear. A sled for hauling men was strapped to the roof, along with a couple of extra bunks for the crew, and beside the 650-gallon extra gas tanks twenty sleeping bags and a tent were stuffed. There was little room to move about. Up forward in the grey interior was the space for the non-commissioned member of the regular crew, ironically called the crew chief, who perpetually brewed coffee for the pilots, little of which except the smell reached the passengers farther aft. If one managed to swivel around in one's canvas seat and look out of the small, low windows, and if one was so fortunate as not to be over the wing, there was likely to be little below except the drift pattern of driven snow on the ice sheet, or the broken pack of sea ice separated by irregular leads of black sea water.

After flying for four hours, our ski-equipped DC-3 circled and bumped to a rough landing on the frozen, wind-swept snow at Byrd station. It is the most isolated of all the bases in the Antarctic; even the south pole is closer to other bases, Sovietskaya and Beardmore support station. We tumbled out, glad of our bulky clothes, for although it was brilliantly bright the sun gave little heat. It was 20° below and windy. In every direction for 500 miles stretched the unbroken surface of the ice sheet. We were indeed in the heart of a modern ice age, and it was strange to reflect that until eleven thousand years ago most of Canada, northern United States, Europe, and Siberia, was also covered with ice a mile or two thick.

The camp afforded the only break in the scene, but there was not much of it to be seen. The place was covered by a great mound of drifted snow from which protruded two observation towers, a few radio masts and chimneys, and some guide poles with fluttering red flags, half buried piles of gas barrels and a snow-encrusted orange tractor. I walked up a low slope towards the camp and stood examining the desolate scene. Slowly I realized that I was standing higher than the roofs of the buried camp. It dawned on me that Byrd station was not built on a hill, as it seemed, but that the hill was a vast snow drift built on top of Byrd station. The camp had been built on a level plain, but great snow drifts had buried all of it during the first winter; and each winter since then more snow has piled on top, so that the old and sagging camp is to be replaced by an entirely new one. A figure suddenly popped out of the camp like a rabbit emerging from its burrow, calling: "Dr. Berkner! Dr. Berkner! Washington wants you on the phone!" A long-distance call relayed by a radio amateur had tracked us down. By the time I had followed Berkner into the station and got my heavy clothes off, someone said: "Washington's on the line. Is there anyone near there you would like to speak to?" I asked to be connected by long-distance phone to Toronto.

It was three o'clock on the morning of the ninth when my wife was wakened by the telephone with a polite enquiry as to whether she would accept a collect call from me in Washington. She bleakly imagined that I had been shipped out of Antarctica in disgrace and was stranded in Washington. Through a fog of sleep and the complications of ham radio, we established my whereabouts and embarked on a conversation. But even a general question about the time of day presented a problem: it was only 11 p.m. at Byrd on the eighth; yet we had recently left Little America at 2 p.m. the following afternoon. Such are the peculiar effects of flying east or west close to the pole and across the international date line.

Inside the vast snow drift that had buried the camp, Byrd station was a complex of buildings clustered about a gloomy, unheated storage hall, a passageway improvised out of piled-up crates and fuel drums that kept the snow out and enabled men to pass easily and safely between the principal buildings. Six of these were like large industrial refrigerators, even to the massive insulated doors, except that the heat was inside and the cold outside. Each was a rectangular box made of neatly joined slabs of insulating material enclosed in sheet metal. One building served as a warm and steamy mess deck and kitchen, two served as sleeping quarters, and two as laboratories. The sixth contained washrooms and laundry, complete with automatic washing machines and driers. The other two buildings consisted of a great shed used as a garage and workshop and heated only by the electrical generator it contained, and a smaller shed used for recreation.

In this camp twenty-four men lived alone and cut off from the rest of the world except for radio. Half were Navy men who ran the camp, and half were scientists. It is unusual to give a medical officer a command, but Lieutenant Peter Ruseski, M.D., officer in charge, had fulfilled the expectations placed in him. So had Steve Barnes, the senior scientist. After nine months of isolation, everyone's morale was high.

What did these men at Byrd station do and think about? In the first place, they were extremely busy and had little time for anything but work. Not only had they a scientific program to carry out, but due to the heavy snowfall and the breakdown of their tractor, they had unexpectedly had to do an enormous

amount of snow-shovelling every day in the cold and darkness
to keep their doorways and instruments clear.

They had got into a routine and were not as excited by the
arrival of our plane as I would have expected, knowing that
ours was one of the three or four which would land that year
and that each brought replacements for some of the men. They
appeared to be much more interested in the Husky puppies
which they showed us in an unheated corridor. These were,
I suppose, their only touch with family life except for the
ham radio. We were shown the recreation room to which the
men could retire and relax. In it were 600 books, 400 records,
and 50 reels of movies which they had seen so often that they
sometimes ran them backwards, chanting from memory the
dialogue appropriate to each scene. They also had a snack bar
at which anyone could cook himself a meal if he wanted a
change, but the men agreed that they had the best cook in the
Navy and steak four times a week.

We were taken around the laboratories and shown the records. Alan Shapley, a member of our team from the National
Bureau of Standards, was asked the significance of the peculiar
magnetograms and ionosphere records. Such readings had
never before been taken in a place so close to the south magnetic pole, so he, too, was often puzzled.

Byrd station is in the maximum auroral zone, and the auroral observer was very excited. From his unheated plastic dome
he had watched, photographed, and taken spectrograms of
magnificent displays lasting for days on end in the winter darkness. From the same vantage point he had kept a watch for
safety's sake on the journeys of the expert on snow and ice. We
have already mentioned the need for more reliable figures on
the rate of accumulation of snow in Antarctica. Blizzards
and drifting make this rate hard to estimate accurately. The
best method devised to obtain data involves thin bamboo
sticks stuck in the snow at intervals far enough removed from

the disturbances created by camps. Every few days the glaciologist set out to ski around a 10-mile route to measure snowfall
against these stakes. If the weather was good, it was safe to do
this down to 70° below zero, but as a precaution the skier carried a flashlight and signalled to the auroral observer every so
often—a yellow spark below the gleaming southern stars and
the bands of aurora.

I climbed down a pit 30 feet deep which the glaciologist had
dug to examine the snow layers. Then I went outside to watch
our plane take off on a visit to a tractor party 100 miles away
which was exploring and measuring the thickness of the ice
sheet. The runway was marked by up-ended gasoline barrels
and bamboo poles with fluttering flags. Some attempt had
been made to smooth the worst drifts by shovelling, but the
ancient R4D8 (a DC-3 to all but the Navy), loaded to 40,000
pounds with gasoline and supplies for the tractors, heaved and
bumped down the runway. The commercial limit for these
planes is 34,000 pounds, but airlines don't use jet-assisted
take-offs. When the JATO bottles fired, there was a flash of
flame, a great cloud of smoke, a rattle like din incarnate, and
the plane leaped forward and staggered into the air. Like 250-
pound bombs, the empty bottles fell away, their mission completed. The plane reminded me of an old warrior taking a last
swig and throwing away the bottle before a battle; nevertheless, the DC-3's proved to be the real work horses of the Antarctic.

After the plane had disappeared to the south and the smoke
from the jet bottles had drifted away, I was alone on the ice
cap. In every direction lay the plain, the greatest and most
truly lifeless desert on earth. A white nothing, you say? No,
rather a scene of infinite variety in soft and ever-changing
pastel tones. When the sun was at its highest, its cold brilliance imparted a lustre to the snow, which was broken only
by the drifting shadows of the clouds. Later, when the sun

dropped lower during the night hours, the shadows lengthened and their deep blue contrasted richly with the yellow tones of the sun in the south. The clouds wore haloes and brooded darkly against the northern sky.

When we think of snow, we think of a soft blanket falling in a silent winter night, of crystal stars on gloves, of shadowy flakes around street lamps, of shovelling the soft and feathery whiteness off the path in the morning. Snow in the Antarctic is not like that. It is the foundation of everything. From one's feet to the horizon there is a flat but furrowed plain of white, so hard that one can walk anywhere on its wind-blown surface, so rough and corrugated that one trips on its jagged crests and stumbles into its deep hollows and around the obstructions. Across it whips the undying wind and wisps of driven snow grains are ever running past on their way over the great ice, like the ghosts of all the mice that ever were, parting around one's boots or leaping into the air behind a lifeless tractor.

In a storm, and they were frequent, the colours fled, greys filled the sky, and the world became dead white and ceased to glisten. Racing snow filled the air, hiding the ground until only the brave flags and radio masts stood out above the cloud of blizzard. Whipped across the plains by a strengthening wind, it often rose higher, shrouding one in a blast of cold, white streaks, and cutting off the view of everything except one's feet.

When the sky became completely overcast, the resulting white-out deprived one of all judgment of direction and distance, of all orientation. This peculiar effect arises when the ground is entirely covered by snow and the sky by cloud. Sunlight diffused through the cloud is reflected back and forth between ground and clouds, so that shadows and horizons are lost, and everything is pure white. If there are no familiar objects to relieve the blankness and provide a scale, white-out can occur even when it is not snowing.

Blizzards and white-out conditions make travel on the ground dangerous and difficult, but pilots can continue flying to reach more favourable conditions for landing. When blizzards struck, outdoor work stopped at camps, although white-out conditions were less of a hindrance there than on the trail because the many familiar objects around a camp enable a man to judge his position and keep properly oriented. In either case, it was good to go below, to pat the four Husky puppies in the hallway as one entered, to square away to the cook's steaks, and to flake out in an upper bunk and sleep to the hum of generators, heaters, and ventilators. At other times, we listened to the scientists tell of breakdowns and ingenious repairs, of unexpected phenomena, and of the accounts they had by radio of other parties in Antarctica. They followed the progress of Russian parties or Belgian experiments with keen interest and were more interested in these than in the activities of the outside world, with which they had lost all contact except for family ties. As one of them remarked to me, "what we need is a broadcasting station for Antarctica. After all, we are on a separate continent, and the activities of the other parties interest us more than the crazy things nations do in the rest of the world."

When our plane had replenished the supplies of the tractor party, it returned, and several men whose replacements had arrived on our plane joined us for the flight back to Little America. My seat was far enough behind the wing so that by squirming around and diligently scraping away frost, I could get a good view of the pale desert below. It was touched with an infinite variety of changing colours and mottled with shadows of shifting clouds. At times, when there was no wind, we could see the damask pattern of the drifts, rough and irregular in detail on the ground, uniform and parallel from the air. Elsewhere the wind whipped up the snow and the pattern became lost in a blizzard of snow flowing over the surface. At still other times, we passed between clouds and became lost in white-out. Thus we flew over the ice, hour after hour, for Antarctica is nearly comparable in size to North America and distances are great. Only once when gazing out of the window did I see any trace of life or civilization. That was one black oil drum, a relic of the tractor trail. Most of the time the effort to turn around and look out of the window was too great, and we slept or read, sitting bundled in layers of soft warm clothes and facing inwards to the pile of cargo and baggage. Sometimes the heater worked and enabled us to read or write in comfort, but often the cabin was cold. Then we pulled on hoods and heavy gloves and dozed, cold-nosed but peaceful.

Little America, to which we returned, is not one place but five, for each of the five times the place has been occupied a new camp has been built at a slightly different site. The ice on which the Little Americas have been built is the Ross ice shelf, a bay 400 miles long and wide, filled with an enormous unbroken sheet of floating ice, 1,000 feet thick, with another 1,000 or more feet of black and airless water beneath it. This shelf is fed at the back by some of the greatest glaciers in the world, which cascade through the mountains off the polar plateau. The advantage of using the Ross Sea for a base is that it is a great bay penetrating farther towards the south pole than any other part of the coast. But for the whole 400 miles across the bay, the front of the shelf stands up in vertical cliffs 100 feet high. It is impossible to scale these vertical ice walls to reach the flat surface at the top. The cliffs are renewed by the calving of bergs, which form ice islands like T-3 in the Arctic. Occasionally these islands reach dimensions as vast as 100 by 30 miles; when they break off, they drift northwards and melt in the southern seas. The secret of McMurdo Sound and of Little America is that they lie at either end of the Ross shelf, where rocky islands break up the ice cliffs, so that it is possible to land and get to the top of the shelf. At McMurdo Sound the foot of Mount Erebus provides the route; at Little America the broken ice in the Bay of Whales does. These being the coastal bases closest to the pole, some inconvenience must be expected and accepted.

At Little America the rock island does not show through the ice, which merely cracks and rides over it, so that it is necessary to build the bases on the ice itself. This practice is satisfactory for a brief expedition but constitutes a great disadvantage in a permanent base. Any camp built on the ice is each year buried deeper under snowdrifts and at the same time flows with the ice towards its edge. Amundsen's camp, Maudheim, and Little America IV have already broken away. Little Americas II and III are going now, and only I and V are left, V because it is new and I because it was built so far inland. In company with Dr. Berkner, we visited the site of Little America I and we could only find showing above the snow the top of a radio mast that he had erected in 1929. The mast was originally 70 feet high, but 65 feet of snow had piled on it since, and on his second visit Dr. Berkner had no trouble sitting on the top.

The situation at Little America disturbed the American scientists, for it was hopeless as a permanent base. McMurdo Sound would be all right, but the New Zealanders, who claim that part of Antarctica, had already built a scientific station which the Americans were loath to duplicate. They had only a supply base and were looking about for a permanent site that would meet the requirements of airfield and ship harbour on bed-rock clear of snow and permit access inland. Eventually the signing of the Antarctic Treaty in 1959 solved their problems. This treaty, which has been agreed to by each of the dozen countries with parties in Antarctica, in effect maintains Antarctica as an international scientific region open to all nations. As a result of the treaty, all territorial claims remain frozen and everyone is free to work wherever he wishes. The treaty makes Antarctica the first truly international territory.

Little America V was a much larger station than Byrd, but, being on the coast, was much more subject to melting. By January 1956 twenty big buildings had been erected and joined by a corridor. Now, three years later, all were buried in a mound of snow. Each hut had melted out around it a hollow space, into which some of the huts had settled at odd angles. Walking on top of the camp was hazardous, because one might fall through, and we avoided this except when necessary to shovel out the fire doors after each storm. The corridors especially had suffered, and in the dim light they sloped and tilted in a queer way, like the deck of a ship.

Power for the camp was provided by large diesel generators whose throbbing beat provided a monotonous background to life in Little America. The air brought in from outside and used in the radiators circulated into the corridor and in spring was warm enough to cause melting. The roof dripped and built up ice masses on the floor. In a deserted store-room, ice had grown under persistent drips until it looked like rows of white bottles on the floor. In the passage the Navy maintenance crews attacked the ice each morning, but they could never get rid of it all, so that the passage was cold, misty, and slippery, like the open levels of a frozen mine. It reminded me of the candle-lit passages of the Imperial Hotel in Tokyo during typhoon Ida.

Inside, however, the huts were bright and warm. Each had an oil stove, a fan, and electric lights, and our cubicles resembled the cabins in a ship. This was appropriate because it was the Navy who ran the camp, and it seemed natural to hear the orders from the squawk boxes beginning, "Now hear this. Now hear this. Outgoing mail will close at 0600 hours," or to read on the notice boards the "plan of the day," which the Army would have called "orders of the day." To refer to instructions as a "plan" instead of an order had an appropriate nautical touch of deference to the elements.

At Little America one building was devoted to the IGY Antarctic Weather Central Office. Four times a day reports from all Antarctica came in by radio, and were plotted and used for weather forecasts. We had a good scientific meeting there, with each of the forecasters—American, Argentine, Australian, French, and Russian—giving a paper on his research. They had discovered that storms are able to break across Antarctica in winter and bring heat as well as snow and wind onto the plateau. As a result, there was a temperature range of as much as 70° F each month at Little America. These ameliorating winds saved the situation at the south pole. As darkness closed in during the early part of the first winter, the party there had recorded an average drop of about a degree a day for two months. When in May 1957 the temperature reached 100.4°F below, everyone began to worry in earnest. What if the temperature continued to drop at this same rate until spring came in September? Could the party survive? At such temperatures it was certain that no planes could fly in and rescue them. Then the weather broke. A storm at a mere 60° to 70° below zero crossed Antarctica, bringing comparative warmth again. It was succeeded by others, so that no temperatures more severe than 110° below have been recorded at the south pole. The Russians later had even lower temperatures at Sovetskaya and Vostok, because they are 4,000 feet higher and even farther from the coast.

After returning to McMurdo Sound, we flew out to visit an exploring party in snowmobiles under the charge of Dr. A. F. Crary, chief scientist of the American wintering-over parties. We landed on skis beside their vehicles, saw how they used them as mobile homes and offices, and watched their work. Every few miles the party would stop, with an auger cut a hole 30 feet deep to sample the ice, fire explosives in the hole to get an echo from the rock below, and read ice temperatures, gravity, and the strength of the earth's magnetic field before

moving on. In the bright sunshine of a calm day, the work
looked pleasant and easy, but the boom with a crevasse detector on it, in front of the lead vehicle, reminded us that they
were constantly in danger of at least partly dropping into an

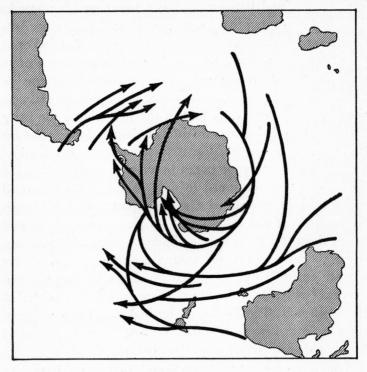

Map of Antarctica showing the tracks of storms crossing or
entering the continent in 1958.

unsuspected crack. At other times they had to hole up until a
blizzard passed. On a later occasion Sir Vivian Fuchs told me
that in his "summer" crossing of Antarctica, the worst conditions were 68° below zero with a 45 m.p.h. wind. Poor weather
in which to be out driving!

We had a splendid flight over the dry valleys near Mc-

Murdo. These huge areas are cut off from the inland ice by mountains and have so little snowfall that they have become deglaciated. Now they were empty except for a few glacier tongues. What had been ice-filled valleys were now cold deserts. Geologists were studying them, while engineers looked for a good site for a permanent airbase. Clearly, over the past several thousand years the ice level on Antarctica has fallen, for connected with the dry valleys we saw the channels by which the ice had once overflowed and entered from a higher level.

We flew also to Cape Hallett, a station run jointly by New Zealanders and Americans, who got along very well, but whose presence was resented by the original inhabitants, an estimated quarter of a million Adelie penguins. These amusing and bold birds, about the size of a goose, spend the winters at sea on the southern pack ice but every spring return to this and other sheltered beaches to breed and lay their two eggs in ridiculous-looking nests built of pebbles. Elsewhere around the coasts other penguins and also seals have their young on the shore, while big skuas prey on them. These noisy gull-like birds fly down from Japan each summer. In winter Antarctica is deserted save for the Emperor penguins, which lay and hatch their eggs in winter so that the chicks can have the summer in which to grow and mature.

I was sorry to think that I might not see Antarctica again, but we had an excellent send-off. We flew back on the same plane that carried Rear Admiral George Dufek away from his command for the last time. A veteran of much polar work, he had been called out of retirement to lead the Navy's arm of the American IGY program. After a splendid achievement, this distinguished and popular officer was leaving. All hands turned out, and a colourful parade of dog teams, snowmobiles, tractors, and helicopters saw him off, with flags flying and cheers ringing over the lonely ice.

CHAPTER 24

THE WEATHER

Everyone is familiar with the general properties of air, but most people do not realize how much air there is. It has been estimated that there are two million tons for each inhabitant of the earth, and that if the atmosphere could be compressed into a layer as dense as water it would be 30 feet thick. This suggests why it is such an excellent shelter for us from the blasts of outer space.

The two major constituents of air are oxygen and nitrogen. Among its several minor ones, water vapour and carbon dioxide are of special importance. Unlike the other gases, they vary in amount. Whereas most of the constituents maintain a constant ratio in all parts of the earth and up to great heights, moisture and carbon dioxide vary with both time and place.

The air absorbs moisture from the oceans and transports it to the land to drop it as rain and snow. The capacity of the air to transport water is, of course, greater than the flow of all the rivers of the world, and dwarfs all the pumps and canals of men. One can appreciate this by reflecting for a moment on the rainfall on Japan during typhoon Ida or on the vaster and gen-

tler storms that bring rain to all the temperate regions of the
world every few days.

The atmosphere is as effective in distributing heat and in
dissipating cold as it is in bringing moisture, and its circulation
makes the land habitable. Without the rain which it transports, the land would be a desert. Only fish would have developed, and the extremes between the equator and the poles
would be even greater than they are.

The other variable constituent is carbon dioxide, which can
be absorbed by water and which over the polar seas is slightly
less abundant and much less variable than elsewhere. It may
be effecting a change in our climate. The atmosphere now
contains about 2.4 million million tons of carbon dioxide.
Since the beginning of the century this amount has been observed to increase by more than 10 per cent. It is tempting to
believe that the increase is due to the combustion of fuels,
both coal and petroleum. G. E. Hutchinson, however, claims
that the excess carbon dioxide could have been absorbed by
the oceans, and that it has increased in the air because the
clearing of forests has reduced the rate of its absorption on
land. The precise quantities involved are unknown, but carbon
dioxide is definitely increasing, and it has the property of retaining heat on the earth's surface. Adding extra carbon dioxide to the air is like putting thicker glass into a greenhouse
roof. The addition is often cited as the reason that the earth's
climate has been warming recently, and its effects may be
cumulative.

The burning of fuel is certainly not the only factor causing
a warming of the climate. The melting of the northern ice
sheets occurred 11,000 years ago, when there were no fires of
any consequence.

At any rate, if the climate continues to get warmer and drier,
regions such as the Mediterranean, California, and Australia
may be seriously affected, but drought in those regions could

be offset by engineering measures and the losses might be compensated for by improved conditions in places that are now
wet and cold. On the other hand, although the climate has
been improving for over two centuries, there is recent evidence
that the amelioration has slowed in the last decade or so, and
some scientists think that it is now becoming colder again.

These, then, are some of the properties of the atmosphere.
It shields us from harmful radiation. It transports moisture
and heat about the earth. It permits the sun's light and heat to
enter and warm the earth's surface, and it prevents the escape
of the longer heat waves that are radiated by the earth's surface. In so doing, it maintains more equitable temperatures at
night and in the winter than would otherwise be the case. To
understand how the atmosphere exercises these functions, we
must remember that the earth receives most heat from the sun
in the tropics and that it loses heat to outer space in the polar
and temperate regions. These differences in temperature are
the cause of a steady circulation in the atmosphere.

The IGY made a vast contribution to meteorology; I shall
mention just two developments. For the first time instruments
were placed above the atmosphere, in satellites, to scan both
the earth and outer space continuously and thus measure both
the radiation arriving from the sun and the radiation reflected
back from the earth into space. It became possible to prepare
a balance-sheet for the heat budget of the earth and to decide
more exactly during which seasons and in which places the
earth gains heat, and when and where it loses heat. Climatolo-
gists were also able to try to relate the net gain in heat with
the rate of melting of ice sheets and with the warming of the
oceans and the climate.

Another significant achievement of the IGY concerned the
installation of many more weather-observing stations around
the earth. From watching weather-prediction programs on
television we are accustomed to following the flow of air

masses and of the weather across North America, and we
know that weather maps are prepared from observations made
at hundreds of weather stations. But North America comprises
only 15 per cent of the earth's surface; before the IGY there
were immense regions from which no observations were available.
To realize the extent of our ignorance, take a small globe,
turn it upside down, and trace out the vast area lying from the
equator through the whole southern Indian Ocean across Antarctica
and back to the equator again in the Pacific Ocean. A
few years ago there were scarcely any weather stations in that
part of the world. If you then turn the globe right way up
again, you can see that this area is roughly equal in size to
North America, the Arctic basin, Europe, and Asia put together.
Other large gaps in our knowledge of weather were the
north Pacific, the south Atlantic, and many deserts and jungles.
During the IGY some of the worst gaps were filled, and
for the first time it was possible to prepare maps of the world's
weather as a whole. For example, no less than fifty-five stations
were established in Antarctica and its vicinity. Although many
of these new stations had to be closed at the end of the IGC
1959, a permanent advance was made with the launching of
weather satellites, particularly Tiros I and II. These can view
large areas of the earth and transmit pictures of the cloud patterns
back to earth.

Local weather is not an isolated phenomenon; it is part of a
world-wide pattern. Clearly the first step in making accurate
forecasts is to determine how weather is behaving now. Before
the IGY only about one fifth of the atmosphere was being
probed daily by surface readings and by the observations of
upper-air balloons. Today the chief gap left in the observing
network is the vast expanse of the south Pacific Ocean between
Antarctica, New Zealand, Pitcairn, and Easter Islands,
and Chile. No one has offered to place a single weather ship in
this unfrequented and desolate region. Satellites supplement

surface observations when they are aloft, but they have not yet been developed to the point that they can replace ground stations.

The significance of the lack of data from this region was brought home to us in the under-snow huts of Antarctica Weather Central in Little America. Each day the forecaster on duty collected the teletyped radio messages from the southern hemisphere and plotted the storms and fronts moving west from the Indian Ocean across Antarctica and New Zealand. Each day some of these features disappeared into the great blank spaces of the Pacific. Unexpectedly, other weather phenomena would emerge from this watery void and materialize on the coast of Chile and Antarctica—making forecasting in Chile and along the Pacific coast of Antarctica extremely uncertain.

Not only are the oceans the most difficult places from which to obtain weather information; the ocean waters, like the air, are themselves part of the climatic transportation system and a tremendous reservoir of heat and cold. We can understand this if we think of the balance between the radiation which comes into the earth and that which goes out of it. During the IGY radiation was measured by satellites and by ground instruments. The results, when compiled and calculated, will tell us the net loss or gain in the earth's heat during any period of observation. On the average the earth absorbs 175,000 calories on each square centimeter each year, and it radiates about the same amount. Suppose measurements indicate that during 1958 the earth retained an additional 1 per cent of the heat it received and that it was warmed thereby. H. Wexler has pointed out that if all that energy were concentrated on warming the oceans, their temperature would rise by one hundredth of a degree Fahrenheit, which would be undetectable. If the energy were absorbed by the world's glaciers, an average of 9 metres of ice would be melted from their surfaces. This could

only be detected on mountain glaciers that had been subject to
the most detailed investigations. On the other hand, if all the
heat were absorbed by the atmosphere, the temperature would
rise by 12° F everywhere, and the world's climate would be
profoundly affected. This extreme example illustrates the great
volume and enormous heat capacity of the oceans. Because of
these qualities, ocean currents are as important in the control
of climate as are the prevailing winds. We know that the cli-

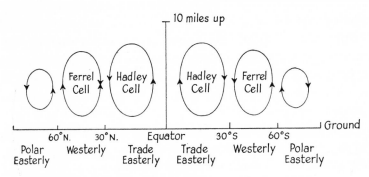

Idealized diagram of atmospheric circulation along any
meridian of longitude. The surface winds are named
below.

mate of northern Europe is warmed by the broad circulatory
current in the north Atlantic, of which the Gulf Stream forms
the border, while the coast of Peru is cooled to a similar extent
by the Humboldt Current from the south. Even the slow creep
of cold Pacific bottom water northward at the rate of 8 miles
a year is important, for the eventual rise of this vast volume of
cold water in equatorial regions moderates the tropical climate.

In spite of these moderating influences, it has long been obvious that the tropical regions (between 38° N and 38° S) receive more heat than they radiate, and that the polar regions
radiate more than they receive. This discrepancy is the chief
cause of the movement of air in the atmosphere and one of
the major factors influencing the flow of ocean currents.

It might be supposed that the heated air rising in the tropics would flow upwards and outwards to the polar regions, where it would settle and flow back along the surface towards the equator; but the facts are a little more complicated. The trop-

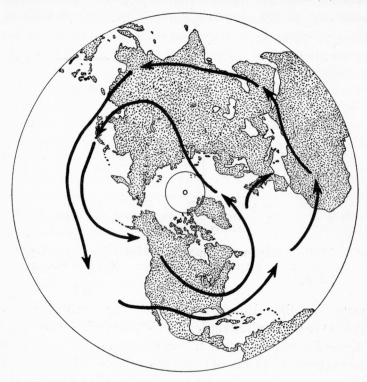

Distribution of jet-streams in the northern hemisphere on a typical day—December 19, 1953.

osphere, as the lower part of the atmosphere is called, breaks up into not one but three convection cells in each hemisphere. The air is constantly circulating about the earth in these six currents, or vortices, which are arranged about the earth like six flattened doughnuts or like the tires around the man in the Michelin tire advertisements in Europe. The boundaries be-

tween these rotating cells are called fronts, and the four which
lie in temperate and sub-tropical latitudes wobble about. For
this reason, those of us who live in Canada, Europe, or the
United States are sometimes within a northern polar cell, a
mass of cold air moving generally southward and easterly, and
sometimes within an intermediate Ferrel cell, a mass of

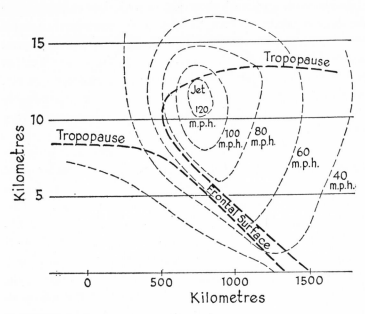

Typical cross-section through a front and jet-stream at the
junction of two cells in the atmosphere.

warmer air moving generally northwards and westerly. When a
front or boundary between these two systems passes near us,
the weather changes abruptly and violently from warm to cool,
or vice versa. Each system tends to produce stable weather, but
the boundaries between systems are stormy.

This has been known in broad outline since the 1920's, and
in part much longer, but the details are only now being established. For example, jet-streams, a peculiar feature of the

fronts, have only been studied extensively in the past decade. These are narrow streams of air flowing east much faster than the general circulation, at speeds of between 100 and 200 miles an hour. Since they form at altitudes of about 30,000 feet, they have become of great importance to jet airplane travel.

In the southern hemisphere not enough data existed before the IGY to enable us even to attempt to draw weather maps. We have already indicated our ignorance about Antarctic weather by describing the surprise which the winter weather there occasioned when the first camp was established in 1957. At first the temperature dropped much more precipitously than had been expected, and then storms blew in from the Southern Ocean, bringing in life-giving warmth.

Another example of the balance in radiation is provided by measurements made at the south pole. The loss of heat through radiation is enough to have cooled the top 30 feet of snow by 160° F a year, but temperature measurements to that depth show no appreciable change from year to year. It is evident, therefore that the heat annually carried towards the pole by storms is sufficient to compensate for the heat radiated out.

Perhaps the chief advance made in meteorology during the IGY was the calculation of the behaviour of the whole atmosphere made possible by the relatively complete collection of data from all parts of the world. It is clear that the atmosphere contains a fixed amount of air, which gains heat in some places and loses it in others, and that a balance is maintained by the general circulation of the air. Using these controls, scientists can frame equations for its behaviour. If enough data are available to describe the situation in every part of the earth at a particular time, these equations can be used to calculate the future possible behaviour of the air. The mathematics are done quickly by electronic computers. Such mathematical forecasting is being introduced as an alternative to the older system of drawing maps and then estimating changes by human judgment. If the equations are accurate, the observational data sufficient, and the computers fast enough, this method of forecasting may prove considerably more accurate. It may also be possible to provide the computers with the history of the development of previous weather situations, thus supplementing the other data. Such is the speed and accuracy of the instruments used that they may be able to make better use of past experience than even the best human minds.

CHAPTER 25

THE YEAR'S HARVEST

I returned from Antarctica in time to dance out the year of the new moons with my wife. But when January 1, 1959, dawned, the IGY was by no means dead. Mountains of data awaited reduction and publication by returning scientists. New bases and promises of fresh discoveries beckoned. By its success the IGY had made an enduring imprint, and three trips during the next year and a half brought home to me what its chief achievements had been.

In my opinion they were three: a vast increase in international co-operation in science; the transformation of earth science into planetary science; an example of how international relations can be amiably and fruitfully conducted.

My first trip in the summer of 1959 was to wind up the affairs of the IGY at a meeting of the International Council of Scientific Unions in The Hague. Many investigations of great importance had been started which required continuing international co-operation. Accordingly, when CSAGI, the special committee of the ICSU for the IGY, was disbanded, amid thanks and congratulations of all, four new committees were established to continue its work. SCOR, SCAR, and

COSPAR were the special committees for oceanographic, antarctic, and space research, respectively. In addition, the International Geophysical Co-operation of 1959 (IGC 1959) was organized to oversee a tapering-off program for other IGY programs. All four are functioning well today, the last with the new name of Committee on International Geophysics (CIG).

SCOR has arranged for ships from twenty countries and oceanographers from forty to participate in the exploration of the Indian Ocean, whose monsoons and fisheries are of such importance to the surrounding lands. SCAR co-ordinates the work of a dozen nations in the Antarctic, where, since the signing of the Antarctic Treaty, any country is free to conduct scientific work without affecting territorial claims or political rivalries. COSPAR's role of arranging co-operation in the realm of space is more difficult, but at least representatives of all the countries concerned with launching and tracking satellites and rockets meet regularly. CIG has gone on to organize new programs, including a World Magnetic Survey to correct navigational charts; an International Quiet Sun Year to study solar-terrestrial relations during the sun-spot minimum of 1965; and an Upper Mantle Project to investigate the earth's interior, where earthquakes, volcanic lavas, and mineral ores all originate.

An important consequence of these deliberations, and one reason for not merely extending the IGY, was the desire of scientists in other fields to participate. The marine biologists, for example, are as much interested in oceanography and promise to be as active in the International Indian Ocean Expedition as the geophysicists.

My second trip, to South America in the spring of 1960, impressed me with the change in direction and emphasis in the earth sciences. When I had been to Peru eight years before, my ideas about earth science and those of my hosts were centred on mining. On this trip I was shown the great variety and increase in studies of the earth and its surroundings, including a moon-camera in Brazil, an oceanographic research establishment in Argentina, a weather forecasting centre in Paraguay, an earthquake research institute in Chile, a satellite-tracking station in Ecuador, cosmic-ray and glacialogical work in Bolivia, and ionospheric sounders in Colombia. This diversification in the earth sciences was not wholly due to the IGY, but the IGY did assist in obtaining increased support, greater public interest, many more stations, and the linking together of isolated workers.

This last point, the desire to foster international relations, was indeed the reason that prompted me to visit South America while I was still connected with the IUGG. Because South American scientists are so far from the chief centres of scientific work, they have found it difficult to join in international meetings and scientific affairs as fully as their excellent work warrants. I wanted to call on the national committees there as a gesture of appreciation. To do so, I travelled through the length and breadth of that continent, visiting ten republics, from Colombia in the north to the farthest tip of Chile in the south, where Punta Arenas slopes down a hillside to the Straits of Magellan, its back to the wind and its face towards Tierra del Fuego.

I was unprepared for the European-like diversity of South America. Chilenos are as different from Argentinos as the Germans are from the French, and Bolivianos have little in common with either. The countryside is as varied as the people. Overnight I traveled from the equatorial heat of a desert station at sea level, up 17,550 feet above the snow-line of the Andes to the highest inhabited laboratory in the world at Chacaltaya, outside La Paz, Bolivia.

Anyone who has not been to La Paz can be forgiven for questioning the sanity of building a capital at an elevation of

12,000 feet, but the visitor is immediately captivated by the
city, which clings to the sides of a mountain chasm as though
the houses had been scattered haphazardly down the slope by a
giant's hand. Around it in alpine glory rise encircling peaks;
and from the Chaco far below, the winds carry the warm,
sweet scent of tropical forests. On Sunday morning the young
townspeople parade along the main boulevard in the latest
finery, country women in bowler hats and gay shawls sit on
the kerb selling oranges, and the bells ring out in the mountain
air.

The richness and beauty of nature in this continent made a
lasting impression on me. It is not surprising that the great
naturalists Humboldt and Darwin found their inspiration
there. Whether in the Andes or on the Amazon, whether in
the Atacama desert or flying over Tierra del Fuego, I felt
surrounded by overpowering forces. Faced with such magnificence, one can understand the South American's willingness
to accept the good things of life as he finds them. With a
civilization twice the age of ours, these people have tended
to excuse their own poverty by thinking of Norte Americanos
as grasping and uncultured newcomers, but the winds of
change are blowing, and many are no longer satisfied with
this rationalization. As a thoughtful Ecuadorian said to me:
"Most of my youth I spent in Europe, especially in Paris,
where I was educated. But this was not good for our country,
and it was not good for me. We need a modern state. My sons
are going to be engineers in Ecuador. One is at M.I.T. now.
His elder brother has already graduated, and I hope you will
meet him tomorrow, for he is associate director of the satellite-
tracking station you are going to visit."

The prestige and excitement which, since the time of the
Conquistadors and El Dorado, had been associated with seeking new lands and prospecting for new mines has passed in
the eyes of the public to the exploration of space. During the

IGY the science of the solid earth was absorbed into the broader framework of a new planetary science. For centuries exploration of the uttermost parts of the earth has provided an outlet for the energy and dreams of young men and excited the admiration and interest of those who stayed behind. Today, with the continents all mapped and within easy reach by plane, explorers search the ocean depths, voyagers girdle the earth in a hundred minutes, and plans are made for flights to the moon and other planets. By organizing the exploration of the seas, of Antarctica, of the earth's interior, and especially by launching the first artificial satellites, the IGY vastly enlarged the scope of man's activities and gave him a new vision of his place in the universe. Contemplating the vast scope of space exploration, man cannot but feel an increased sense of humility, a heightened feeling of brotherhood with his fellow earthlings.

My third journey was to chair the meetings of the IUGG in Helsinki in July 1960, and it brought my official connection with the IUGG and the IGY to a close. In the three years since the meetings at Toronto, most of the world's geophysicists had come to know, to like, and to trust their colleagues in other countries, so that sustained by Finnish hospitality, we had a most harmonious and stimulating time. As befitted those who had carried a great international endeavour to a successful conclusion, the affairs of the Union were settled in what seemed to us a fair and equitable way. It was resolved to hold the next meeting in California under a Russian president, Professor V. V. Beloussov, who had guided his country's efforts in the IGY. The scientists of East and West Germany joined as a single delegation; China and Taiwan were both admitted in principle, but neither cared to join under our condition that any national committee represent only the area in which it controls scientific work.

Most of the discussion of the two thousand geophysicists

gathered for two weeks concerned the results of the IGY. It is easy to adopt one of two extreme views: that of the pessimists who say that the success of the IGY has little significance for international affairs because the IGY dealt with subjects that did not involve difficult problems and thus did not show how to solve such problems; or that of the extreme optimists who claim that if everyone else were as sensible as the scientists, all arguments between nations could be resolved.

I feel that I have been much too closely associated with the IGY to try to assess at what point between these two false extremes the balance lies, so I shall merely list some of the ways in which the IGY may have influenced the conduct of international affairs and leave the reader to judge its importance for himself.

In the first place, the IGY brought many men together under conditions that tended to create harmony and sympathy between them. It is an unfortunate characteristic of men that they are suspicious and often prepared to think the worst of one another. The dangerous tensions that can so easily be thus generated between nations can best be resolved by friendly communication, and this is most easily achieved in those few subjects, including the arts, athletics, and science, for which standards of excellence are universally accepted and applicable across national barriers.

In the second place, the friendliness created by scientific exchanges was cemented by the need for co-operation. Many examples have been cited of the interlocking of international plans in ways that forced scientists from East and West to agree on procedures and to exchange information.

Third, as we have already mentioned, a start was made in the exploration of space, and this engendered a sense of humility and brotherhood. It is awesome and salutary to realize how small and isolated is the habitable film on the earth's surface and how hostile to man is the immense vacuum, the absolute cold, and the occasional stellar furnace that constitute the universe.

Fourth, this promising, if still feeble, feeling of unity was made more secure by the release of nationalist pressures affected by the IGY. To the extent that men's combative instincts and nations' industrial potentials are employed in conquering space, so are those dangerous capacities less likely to be employed in waging war. The great surge of activity generated by the IGY with the object of starting lunar exploration has probably been a real safety-valve for mankind. The manufacture of spaceships is as economically rewarding as the manufacture of armaments, and a great achievement in the exploration of space provides as much national satisfaction as winning a battle—and without bloodshed.

Fifth, the IGY provided an example of how international agreements can be made to work smoothly. If the same principles could be adopted, agreements on trade or disarmament could be made as easily as those on geophysics. The IGY was operated successfully because the scientists began by reaching a precise agreement upon what was to be done. This was not a general platitudinous statement, but a detailed inventory. They then adopted a plan of execution which was both politically and financially practicable. Essentially, it consisted of dividing the task into sixty-seven national parts and of letting each nation carry out its own part in whatever way it liked; but it also involved having a central committee that wrote the rule books, called meetings, and settled problems.

The senior scientists trusted one another and expected, in turn, to be trusted. Generally speaking, this faith was justified and generated confidence. Finally, the participants were alive to human frailty and to the reality of political influences, so they did not expect perfection. They complained as little as possible of the shortcomings of others, and they acclaimed the large measure of co-operation they did obtain. If the Soviets made propaganda out of the Sputniks, and the Americans were secretive about atomic blasts, the reasons were understood and such weaknesses were not allowed to interfere with the progress of the program.

To apply these principles to other human endeavours, we must begin by defining what it is that we propose to accomplish; we must devise the international organization suitable for the promotion of these ends; and we must generate sufficient trust to enable the plans to be executed.

The sixth point, and perhaps one in which the IGY played a minor part, is the securing of a proper relation between the sciences and the humanities. The humanities and the social sciences are concerned with the conduct and study of society. Recently some humanists, frightened by the rapid development and application of science and the fact that scientific projects have been obtaining more and more monetary backing, have seemed fearful that scientists will usurp their jobs. This is nonsense. Scientists are concerned not with the conduct of society but with the study and control of nature. Far from undermining the humanities, scientists, by helping increased populations to survive and making society ever more complex, have made the role of the humanist and the social scientist more difficult but also more important than ever before. Indeed, the task of organizing society is becoming so difficult that the social scientist is increasingly in need of help from (but not substitution by) the natural scientist. The ideal man should be something of each.

It is perhaps not unreasonable to maintain that the greatest achievement of the IGY lay not in its remarkable technical advances, but in the demonstration that scientists are good humanists, for they successfully organized a small but complex segment of society which worked. This is where the sciences and the humanities meet, in the realization that each needs the other, that both are integral parts of our complex international society and our highly developed culture.

To the extent that the IGY showed that scientists could play a fruitful role in international negotiations and could strengthen international organizations such as ICSU and its parent body UNESCO, so it may have helped achieve a better balance between humanism and science.

It is imperative to consider the role of science in international affairs. Because of its discoveries, mankind faces a choice that can lead to greater good or to disaster. On the one hand lies good health, well-being, the fufillment of man's creative instincts in the arts, the play of his social urges in the better organization of his affairs, and the exercising of his mind in the exploration of the universe and in the study of himself and of nature. On the other hand lies death by atomic obliteration or by slow starvation on an overcrowded earth.

In order to avoid either of the latter alternatives, we must foster increased international co-operation. Already in technical matters it has enabled the nations of the world, working together, to speed the mails, forecast the weather, allocate radio frequencies, guide airliners, and control plagues. Now these joint efforts must be extended to include the control of nuclear fission and the problem of an increasing population; or we are lost.

In the clamor over passing political storms, we tend to lose sight of the fact that the people of the world are already agreed on one prime objective: to lead as useful and as comfortable a life as possible. In our crowded world only the application of science can make possible the attainment of this goal, which involves having adequate food and shelter for all, and the leisure to develop government and codes of ethics.

No one desires material progress more than the political leaders of the Communist countries; in their drive toward it

U. S. Army engineers are shown drilling
through the Antarctic ice cap to a depth of
1,000 feet.

Three members of the first U. S. Navy unit to spend a winter in
the Antarctic explore ice formations in an Antarctic ice cave
filled with stalactite-like icicles.

Hummocky sea ice, formed by pressure of winds and ocean currents in the Antarctic.

Little America V at the time of construction in March 1957.

The Little America station after it had been
buried in snow. U. S. Naval personnel are
shown digging their way out.

Annual layers in ice cliffs near Lewis Island, Davis Bay, Antarctica.

Sno-Cats of the Ellsworth Station traverse party halted in front of peaks of the Dufek Massif, Pensacola Mountains, Antarctica. This was the first exploration on the ground of these peaks. Notice the crevasse detector in front of the second vehicle.

A Soviet tractor train which served as both transportation and a base in the interior of the Antarctic.

Professor Maurice Ewing, launching a coring tube from the side of the *S.S. Vema*. The tube is designed to penetrate the ocean floor and recover a sample of sediments from the bottom.

Lowering a Nansen bottle on a line from the *S.S. Crawford*. These devices collect samples of sea water at predetermined depths.

A Soviet oceanographer recovering a double coring tube on board the S.S. *Vityaz*.

The *Vityaz*, one of the twelve oceanographic research ships of the Soviet Union.

they have trained large numbers of engineers and scientists to implement a technological revolution. It may be that minds trained to seek truth in science will seek it in other fields also, and that in their increasing numbers may lie hope for the international co-operation essential to our future. During the IGY scientists the world over worked together for common ends and in so doing realized that they held in their hands, besides the keys to the nature of the earth, the keys to the future of mankind.

TABLES

REFERENCES FOR
FURTHER READING

INDEX

1

Countries Which Participated in the IGY

Argentina	Italy
Australia	Japan
Austria	Jugoslavia
Belgium	Korea (Democratic People's Re-
Bolivia	public)
Brazil	Malaya
Bulgaria	Mexico
Burma	Mongolian People's Republic
Canada	Morocco
Ceylon	Netherlands
Chile	New Zealand
Colombia	Norway
Cuba	Pakistan
Czechoslovakia	Panama
Denmark	Peru
Dominican Republic	Philippines
East Africa	Poland
Ecuador	Portugal
Egypt	Rhodesia and Nyasaland
Ethiopia	Romania
Finland	Spain
France	Sweden
German Democratic Republic	Switzerland
German Federal Republic	Taiwan (Academia Sinica)
Ghana	Thailand
Greece	Tunisia
Guatemala	Union of South Africa
Hungary	Union of Soviet Socialist Republics
Iceland	United Kingdom
India	United States of America
Indonesia	Uruguay
Iran	Venezuela
Ireland	Viet-Nam (Democratic Republic)
Israel	Viet-Nam (Republic)

NOTE: A committee formed by the People's Republic of China in September 1955 withdrew in June 1957.

2

Bureau of the Comité Spécial de l'Année Géophysique Internationale 1957–1958 (CSAGI) with Dates of Appointment and Bodies Represented

S. Chapman   (U.K.),   President, 1953, ICSU
L. V. Berkner   (U.S.A.),   Vice-President, 1952, ICSU
M. Nicolet   (Belgium),   Secretary-General, 1952, ICSU
V. V. Beloussov   (U.S.S.R.),   Member, 1955, IUGG
J. Coulomb   (France),   Member, 1952, IUGG

3

IGY Subjects: Their Reporters, with Dates of Appointment and Bodies They Represented

I	World Days—A. H. Shapley (U.S.A.), 1956, URSI
II	Meteorology—J. Van Meighem (Belgium), 1953, WMO
III	Geomagnetism—V. Laursen (Denmark), 1952, IUGG
IV	Aurora and Air Glow—S. Chapman (U.K.), 1953, ICSU
V	Ionosphere—W. J. G. Beynon (U.K.), 1952, URSI
VI	Solar Activity—H. Spencer Jones (U.K.), 1953–6, IAU
	—Y. Ohman (Sweden), 1956–8, IAU
	—M. A. Ellison (U.K.), 1958, IAU
VII	Cosmic Rays—J. A. Simpson (U.S.A.), 1954, IUPAP
VIII	Longitude and Latitude—A. Danjon (France), 1953, IAU
IX	Glaciology—J. M. Wordie (U.K.), 1952, IGU
X	Oceanography—G. Laclavère (France), 1953, IUGG
XI	Rockets and Satellites—L. V. Berkner (U.S.A.), 1952, ICSU
XII	Seismology—V. V. Beloussov (U.S.S.R.), 1955, IUGG
XIII	Gravimetry—P. Tardi (France), 1953–6, IUGG
	—P. Lejay (France), 1956–8, IUGG
XIV	Nuclear Radiation—M. Nicolet (Belgium), 1952, ICSU

4

*Members of CSAGI, with Dates of Appointment
and Bodies They Represented*

Bureau Members (see Table 2)
Reporters (see Table 3)
M. Boelle (Italy), 1953, URSI
A. F. Bruun (Denmark), 1955, IUBS (Biological Sciences)
E. Herbays (Belgium), 1952, ICSU
J. van der Mark (Netherlands), 1956, CCIR (Radio Communications)
B. van der Pol (Netherlands), 1956, CCIR
H. Pushkov (U.S.S.R.) 1955, IUGG
T. E. W. Schumann (South Africa), 1953, WMO
S. Vallarta (Mexico), 1954, IUPAP

5

*Record of Artificial Satellites
and Space Probes Launched in 1957–8*
(INTERNATIONAL GEOPHYSICAL YEAR)

NAME	DATE OF LAUNCH	DATE OF FALL	APOGEE (MILES)	PERIGEE (MILES)	NO. OF PARTS
Sputnik I	Oct. 4	Jan. 4, 1958	588	96	3
Sputnik II	Nov. 3	Apr. 14, 1958	1,038	103	2
Explorer I	Jan. 31	About 1962?	1,573	114	1
Vanguard I	March 17	After 2150?	2,453	409	2
Explorer III	March 26	June 27, 1958	1,746	115	1
Sputnik III	May 15	April 6, 1960	1,167	106	5
Explorer IV	July 26	Oct. 23, 1959	1,380	110	1
Pioneer I (Space Probe)	Oct. 11	Oct. 11, 1958	Went 75,000 miles		1
Pioneer III (Space Probe)	Dec. 6	Dec. 6, 1958	Went 65,000 miles		1
Score	Dec. 18	Jan. 21, 1959	920	101	1

6

Record of Artificial Satellites and Planets Launched in 1959
(INTERNATIONAL GEOPHYSICAL CO-OPERATION, 1959)

NAME	DATE OF LAUNCH	DATE OF FALL	APOGEE (MILES)	PERIGEE (MILES)	NO. OF PARTS
Lunik I (Art. Planet 1)	Jan. 2		123,100,000	91,200,000	2
Vanguard II	Feb. 17	About 1970?	2,064	341	2
Discoverer I	Feb. 28	March 5, 1959	605	99	1
Pioneer IV (Art. Planet 2)	March 3		106,100,000	91,700,000	1
Discoverer II	April 13	April 26, 1959	220	142	1
Explorer VI	Aug. 7	About 1961?	26,380	157	2
Discoverer V	Aug. 13	Sept. 28, 1959	450	136	1
Discoverer VI	Aug. 19	Oct. 20, 1959			1
Lunik (Moon Probe 1)	Sept. 12	Hit moon on Sept. 13			
Vanguard III	Sept. 18	After 2000?	2,330	318	2
Lunik III	Oct. 4	April 1960	300,000	29,000	2
Explorer VII	Oct. 13	After 1964?	678	344	2
Discoverer VII	Nov. 7	Nov. 26, 1959	515	100	1
Discoverer VIII	Nov. 20	March 8, 1960	1,040	117	1

7

Record of Artificial Satellites Placed in Orbit
January 1, 1960, to April 12, 1961

NAME	DATE OF LAUNCH 1960	NAME	DATE OF LAUNCH 1961
*Pioneer V	March 11 *	*Samos II	Jan. 31 *
*Tiros I	April 1 *	Sputnik VII	Feb. 4
*Transit I-B	April 13 *	Venus Probe	Feb. 12
Discoverer XI	April 15	Sputnik VIII	Feb. 12
*Sputnik IV	May 15 *	*Explorer IX	Feb. 16 *
*Midas II	May 24 *	*Discoverer XX	Feb. 17 *
*Transit II-A	June 22 *	*Discoverer XXI	Feb. 18 *
*Transit Piggyback	June 22 *	*Transit III-B Lofti	Feb. 21 *
Discoverer XIII	Aug. 10	Sputnik IX	March 9
*Echo I	Aug. 12 *	*Explorer X	March 25 *
Discoverer XIV	Aug. 18	Sputnik X	March 25
Sputnik V	Aug. 19	*Discoverer XXIII	April 8 *
Discoverer XV	Sept. 13	Vostok (Yuri Gagarin)	April 12
*Courier I-B	Oct. 4 *		
*Explorer VIII	Nov. 3 *		
Discoverer XVII	Nov. 12		
*Tiros II	Nov. 23 *		
Sputnik VI	Dec. 1		
Discoverer XVIII	Dec. 7		
Discoverer XIX	Dec. 20		

* Still in orbit on April 12, 1961

NOTE: The Sputniks and Yuri Gagarin's Vostok were launched by the U.S.S.R., the others by the U.S.A.

8

Features of Sputnik Satellites

NAME	WEIGHT (LBS.)	RADIO LIFETIME	EXPERIMENTS	SPONSOR	VEHICLE
Sputnik I	184	23 days	Internal temperature and pressure Geodetic	Soviets	Modified IRBM?
Sputnik II	1,120	7 days	Physiology of dog Cosmic rays Solar ultra-violet and X-rays Temperatures and pressures	Soviets	Modified IRBM?
Sputnik III	2,925	Indefinitely	Pressure and composition of atmosphere Concentration of positive ions Electric potential of satellite Geomagnetic field Intensity of solar radiation Composition of cosmic rays Micrometeorites Temperatures	Soviets	Modified ICBM?

NOTE: All Sputniks are believed to have been launched from Kaspin Yar near Stalingrad, at an angle of inclination of 65° to the equator. Soviet scientists reported that there were no failures in this series.

9

Features of Vanguard Satellites

NAME	WEIGHT (LBS.)	RADIO LIFETIME	EXPERIMENTS	SPONSOR	VEHICLE
Vanguard I	3.5	Indefinite	Temperatures Geodetic	U.S. Navy	Vanguard
Vanguard II	20.7	1 month	Earth's cloud cover (but wobble made interpretation impossible	U.S. Navy	Vanguard
Vanguard III	100	3 months?	Earth's magnetism Solar X-rays Micrometeorites (with 4 detectors	N.A.S.A.	Vanguard

NOTE: Vanguards were launched from Cape Canaveral at an inclination of about 33° to the equator. Other Vanguards failed to orbit when launched on Dec. 6, 1957; Feb. 5, April 28, May 27, June 26, and Sept. 26, 1958; and on April 13 and June 22, 1959.

10

Features of Explorer and Score Satellites

NAME	WEIGHT (LBS.)	RADIO LIFETIME	EXPERIMENTS	SPONSOR	VEHICLE
Explorer I	30.8	4 months	Cosmic rays Micrometeorites Temperatures	U.S. Army	Jupiter C
Explorer III	31	3 months	As above (with tape recorder	U.S. Army	Jupiter C
Explorer IV	38.4	2½ months	Cosmic rays (with 4 counters) Temperatures	U.S. Army	Jupiter C
Score-Atlas	8,750	12 days	Radio communications First speech transmission	U.S. Air Force	Atlas
Explorer VI	142	2 months	Ionosphere Geomagnetic field Micrometeorites Cloud cover Equipment checks	U.S. Air Force N.A.S.A.	Thor-Able
Explorer VII	91.5	1 year ?	Earth's radiation balance Cosmic rays Solar ultra-violet and X-rays Micrometeorites Lifetime of solar cell Temperatures	U.S. Army N.A.S.A.	Juno II

NOTE: All were launched from Cape Canaveral at an angle of inclination to the equator of about 33° for I, III, and Score, and 50° for the others. Explorer II (March 5, 1958), Explorer V (Aug. 24, 1958), Explorer (July 16, 1959), two Beacons (Oct. 23, 1958, and Aug. 15, 1959), and Transit I (Sept. 17, 1959) all failed to orbit.

11

Features of Pioneer Space Probes and Planet

NAME	WEIGHT (LBS.)	RADIO LIFETIME	EXPERIMENTS	SPONSORS	VEHICLES
Pioneer I	84.4	Throughout flight	Radiation in space	U.S. Air Force	Thor-Able
Pioneer III	12.95	Throughout flight	Radiation in space	U.S. Army	Juno II
Pioneer IV	13.4	82 hours	Radiation in space Test of moon camera	U.S. Army	Juno II

NOTE: I and III were space probes which fell back to earth; IV was placed in orbit as an artificial planet around the sun. The first moon probe and Pioneer II failed on Aug. 17 and Nov. 8, 1959.

12

Features of Discoverer Satellites

NAME	WEIGHT (LBS.)	RADIO LIFETIME	EXPERIMENTS	SPONSOR	VEHICLE
Discoverer I	1,300	Not disclosed	First polar-orbit tests of propulsion, guidance, and communications	U.S. Air Force	Thor-Hustler
Discoverer II	1,610	Not disclosed	195-lb. capsule, carrying cosmic-ray pack, ejected but not recovered	U.S. Air Force	Thor-Hustler
Discoverer V		Not disclosed		U.S. Air Force	Thor-Hustler
Discoverer VI		Not disclosed		U.S. Air Force	Thor-Hustler
Discoverer VII	1,700	2 weeks	(Capsule did not separate)	U.S. Air Force	Thor-Hustler
Discoverer VIII	1,700	Not disclosed	(Capsule ejected but not recovered)	U.S. Air Force	Thor-Hustler

NOTE: All Discoverers were launched in a north-south orbit and were designed to test and develop the technique of recovery of a capsule after a space flight. Discoverers III and IV launched on June 3 and June 25, 1959, failed to orbit.

13

Features of Lunik Space Probes and Satellites

NAME	WEIGHT (LBS.)	EXPERIMENTS	SPONSOR	VEHICLE
Mechta (Lunik I)	3,245 (800-lb. instrument package)	Temperatures Magnetic fields of earth and moon Composition of interplanetary matter, radiation from sun, and cosmic rays Micrometeorites Sodium vapour cloud	Soviets	ICBM
Lunik II		Moon hit	Soviets	ICBM
Lunik III		Photographing far side of moon and televising picture to earth	Soviets	ICBM

14

Times and Places of Argus Experiments

EXPERIMENT	TIME	DATE	LOCATION
1	0230 UT	Aug. 27, 1958	38°S 12°W
2	0320 UT	Aug. 30, 1958	50°S 8°W
3	2210 UT	Sept. 6, 1958	50°S 10°W

NOTE: The above times were released by the United States as approximate times. Dr. Valeria Troitskaya of the Soviet IGY Committee reported recording Argus 3 within one second of 22h.12m.34s. at four stations in the U.S.S.R.

15

Radioactive Isotopes Created by Cosmic-Ray Bombardment
of the Atmosphere

ISOTOPE	PARENT ISOTOPE	HALF-LIFE
Beryllium-10	2.7 million years	Nitrogen-14, Oxygen-16
Carbon-14	5,600 years	Nitrogen-14
Silicon-32	700 years	Argon-40
Hydrogen-3	12.5 years	Nitrogen-14, Oxygen-16
Sodium-22	2.6 years	Argon-40
Sulphur-35	87 days	Argon-40
Beryllium-7	53 days	Nitrogen-14, Oxygen-16
Phosphorus-33	25 days	Argon-40
Phosphorus-32	14 days	Argon-40
Chlorine-39	1 hour	Argon-40

16

True Direction of Magnetic Compass at London

YEAR	1600	1650	1700	1750	1800	1850	1900	1950
Declination	8°E	1°E	7°W	18°W	24°W	22°W	16°W	8°W

17

Changes in the Strength of the Earth's Magnetic Field

DATE	OBSERVER	STRENGTH AT THE EQUATOR (IN GAUSS)
1830	Gauss	0.331
1845	Adams	0.328
1880	Adams	0.324
1880	Newmayer	0.323
1885	Schmidt	0.324
1885	Fritsche	0.322
1922	Dyson and Furner	0.316

18

IGY Stations in the Antarctic and the Sub-Antarctic Islands

COUNTRY	ON CONTINENT OR ICE SHELVES	ON ISLANDS	TOTAL
Argentina	3	5	8
Australia	2	1	3
Belgium	1	0	1
Chile	2	2	4
France	2	1	3
Japan	1	0	1
New Zealand	1	1	2½*
Norway	1	0	1
South Africa	0	3	3
United Kingdom	9	6	15
United States	6	0	6½*
U.S.A./N.Z.	1*	0	—
U.S.S.R.	7	0	7
	36	19	55

* Joint United States–New Zealand project.

19

Some of the World's Record Cold Temperatures

DATE	PLACE	ALTITUDE	TEMPERATURE (*below zero*)
—	Verkhoyansk, Siberia		85°F
Feb. 1937	Oimekon, Siberia		90°F
May 11, 1957	South Pole, Antarctica	9200′	100.4°F
Sept. 17, 1957	South Pole, Antarctica	9200′	102.1°F
Sept. 13, 1959	South Pole, Antarctica	9200′	110.0°F
Aug. 25, 1958	Vostok, Antarctica	12,000′	125.3°F
Aug. 24, 1960	Vostok, Antarctica	12,000′	158°F
Feb. 1947	Snag Airport, Yukon *		81.4°F
Feb. 1950	Icecap, Greenland *		86.8°F

* North American records.

REFERENCES FOR
FURTHER READING

Those works intended for the general reader are marked with an asterisk

ABOUT THE IGY

* Bates, D. R.: *The Planet Earth*. London: Pergamon Press; 1957.
* Chapman, Sydney: *IGY: Year of Discovery*. Ann Arbor, Michigan: The University of Michigan Press; 1959.
* Fraser, Ronald: *Once Around the Sun: The Story of the International Geophysical Year 1957–8*. London: Hodder & Stoughton; 1957.
* Life, Editors of: "New Portrait of Our Planet: What IGY Taught Us." *Life*, Vol. 49, Nos. 19–22 (November 7–28, 1960).
* Marshack, Alexander: *The World in Space: The Story of the International Geophysical Year*. New York: Thomas Nelson & Sons; 1958.
* Sullivan, Walter: *Assault on the Unknown: The International Geophysical Year*. New York: McGraw-Hill Book Company; 1961.

GEOPHYSICS

Bartels, Julius (editor): "Geophysics." *Encyclopedia of Physics*, Vols. 47–9. Berlin: Springer-Verlag; 1956.

Howell, B. F., Jr.: *Introduction to Geophysics*. New York: McGraw-Hill Book Company; 1959.

Jacobs, J. A., Russell, R. D., and Wilson, J. Tuzo: *Physics and Geology*. New York: McGraw-Hill Book Company; 1959.

Jeffreys, Harold: *The Earth*. Fourth edition. Cambridge: Cambridge University Press; 1959.

* Massey, H. S. W.: *The New Age in Physics*. New York: Harper & Brothers; 1960.

* Moore, Ruth: *The Earth We Live On: The Story of Geological Discovery.* New York: Alfred A. Knopf; 1956.

REFERENCES TO SPECIFIC PROGRAMS

Solar Activity

* Newton, H. W.: *The Face of the Sun.* London: Penguin Books; 1958.

Satellites

Berkner, L. V., and Odishaw, Hugh (editors): *Science in Space.* New York: McGraw-Hill Book Company; 1961.

Kallmann, Hilde (editor): *Space Research: Proceedings of First International Space Science Symposium,* Nice, France, 1960. Amsterdam: North Holland Publishing Co.; 1960.

* Melin, Marshall: "Observing the Satellites." *Sky and Telescope,* Vols. XVII–XXI. Cambridge, Mass.: Sky Publishing Corp.; 1957–61.

Cosmic Radiation

Fluegger, S. (editor): "Cosmic Rays." *Encyclopedia of Physics,* Vol. 46. Berlin: Springer-Verlag; 1961.

Peters, B.: "Progress in Cosmic Ray Research Since 1947." *Journal of Geophysical Research,* Vol. 64, No. 2 (February 1959), pp. 155–73.

Geomagnetism

Blackett, P. M. S., Clegg, J. A., and Stubbs, P. H. S.: "An Analysis of Rock Magnetic Data." *Proceedings of the Royal Society of London,* Vol. 256 (1960), pp. 291–322.

Chapman, Sydney: *The Earth's Magnetism.* Second edition. London: Methuen & Co.; 1951.

Hide, Raymond: "The Origin of the Main Geomagnetic Field." *Physics and Chemistry of the Earth,* Vol. 4 (1961), pp. 27–98.

Ionosphere

* Massey, H. S. W., and Boyd, R. L. F.: *The Upper Atmosphere.* London: Hutchinson & Co.; 1958.

Aurora and Air Glow

Armstrong, E. B., and Dalgarno, A. D. (editors): *The Airglow and the Aurorae.* London: Pergamon Press; 1955.

Störmer, C.: *The Polar Aurora.* Oxford: Clarendon Press; 1955.

Glacialogy and Antarctica

* Dufek, G. J.: *Operation Deepfreeze.* New York: Harcourt, Brace & Company, 1957.
* Fuchs, Vivian, and Hillary, Edmund: *The Crossing of Antarctica: The Commonwealth Trans-Antarctic Expedition, 1955–8.* London: Cassell & Co.; 1958.
* Schulthess, Emil: *Antarctica.* New York: Simon and Schuster; 1960.
* Sharp, Robert: *Glaciers.* Seattle: University of Oregon Press; 1960.
* Siple, Paul: *90° South: The Story of the American South Pole Conquest.* New York: Putnam & Co.; 1959.
* Sullivan, Walter: *Quest for a Continent.* New York: McGraw-Hill Book Company; 1957.

Gravimetry

Heiskanen, W. A., and Vening Meinesz, F. A.: *The Earth and Its Gravity Field.* New York: McGraw-Hill Book Company; 1958.

Seismology

Richter, C. F.: *Elementary Seismology.* San Francisco: W. H. Freeman & Company; 1958.

Oceanography

* Carson, Rachel L.: *The Sea Around Us.* New York: Oxford University Press; 1951.

Heezen, Bruce: *The Floors of the Ocean: I. The North Atlantic.* New York: Geological Society of America, Special Paper 65; 1959.

Fall-out or Nuclear Radiation

Glasstone, S. (editor): *The Effects of Nuclear Weapons.* Washington: U.S. Atomic Energy Commission; 1957.

Pirie, A.: *Fallout.* London: MacGibbon and Kee; 1958.

Meteorology

* Löbsack, Theo: *The Earth's Envelope.* London: William Collins Sons and Co.; 1959.

* Sutton, O. Graham: *Understanding the Weather*. London: Penguin
  Books; 1960.

JOURNALS CONTAINING NUMEROUS ARTICLES ON GEOPHYSICS
(There is no single consolidated report on the whole IGY.)

Advances in Geophysics. New York: Academic Press.

Annals of the International Geophysical Year. London: Pergamon
Press.

* *Discovery*. Norwich: Jarrold & Sons.

Geophysical Journal. London: Royal Astronomical Society.

* *ICSU Review*. Amsterdam: Elsevier Publishing Company (for the
International Council of Scientific Unions).

IGY Bulletin. Washington: National Academy of Sciences.

Journal of Geophysical Research. Washington: American Geophysical Union.

Journal of Glaciology. Cambridge: Scott Polar Research Institute.

Nature. London: Macmillan & Co.

* *The New Scientist*. London: The New Scientist.

Planetary and Space Science. London: Pergamon Press.

Physics and Chemistry of the Earth. London: Pergamon Press.

Quarterly Journal, Royal Meteorological Society. London.

Reports of World Data Center A. Washington: National Academy
of Sciences.

Science. Washington: American Association for the Advancement
of Science.

* *Scientific American*. New York: Scientific American.

Transactions of the American Geophysical Union. Washington:
American Geophysical Union.

INDEX

Academia Sinica, Peking, xii, 228, 230, 234
Academia Sinica, Taipeh, xii, 228, 235
Academy of Sciences of the U.S.S.R., xii, 62, 178
Academy of Sciences of the U.S., see National Academy of Sciences of the U.S.
Addis Ababa Geophysical Observatory, 117–18
Advanced Research Projects Agency, 71
air glow, 138–9
Alfvén, H., 81
All-Union Geological Institute, 211
American Astronomical Society, 60, 75
American Space Science Committee, 61
American tracking systems, 63, 236
andesite, 219, 223, 267
Andreasen, O., 146
Ångström, A. J., 134
anomaly, 184, 254
Antarctic Convergence, 256, 261–3
Antarctic Treaty, 305, 321
Antarctic Weather Central, 307, 314
Antarctica, 10–12, 152, 162–7, 216, 272, 288–309
Appleton, Edward, 121, 123

Arctic, 78, 103, 106, 154; archipelago, 105; Institute of the U.S.S.R., 211
Argus Experiment, 81–3, 142–3
Argus shells, 78, 82; radiation in, 81–2
Argus III, 82
Arlberg-Orient Express, 41
Arnold, J. R., 278
Artificial Planet II, 71
artificial satellites, see satellites
Ashby, Eric, quoted, 237
Astronomical Observatory (Smithsonian Institution), 59
Atlantis (ship), 258
Atlas ICBM, 71
Atlas-Score satellite, 71
atmosphere, 20, 26–7, 32–3, 65–7, 79, 83–4, 92–3, 101–2, 115–16, 120–1, 124, 129, 137–8, 143–4, 257, 273–4, 277–8, 281, 282, 311–14, 318; lower, 65; radioactivity of, 102; upper, see upper atmosphere
aurora, 7–8, 31, 77–8, 80, 82, 85, 109, 118, 128, 131–44, 301; australis, 131, 134; borealis, 7, 131–2; polaris, 131
Australian Antarctic expedition, 164

Baby Doe Tabor, see Tabor, Baby Doe
Bader, H., 155
Bardin, Ivan, 178

Barnes, S., 299
Bartels, J., 8
basalt, 223, 268
bathymetrical chart, 246
Beloussov, V. V., xii, 62, 172–3, 324
Bennett, J. G., 149
Bering Strait, proposal to dam, 150
Berkner, L. V., vii–iii, 9, 62, 292–3, 298, 305
billion electron volts (Bev.), 92
Blanchett, P. M. S., 255
Bouguer, P., 180
Boyd, R. L., 100
British Antarctic expedition, 164
British National Institute of Oceanography, 258
Brussels, 170–2
Bucharest, 45–50; Observatory, 48; School of Mines, 48; University of, 48
Bullard, E., 251
Byrd Station, 293–5, 297–300, 306

Cambridge, University of, 180
Canada, Government of, viii, 103, 217
Canadian Broadcasting Corporation, 62
Canadian Clubs, Association of, xii
Canadian Committee of the IGY, xii
Canadian rocket program, 76
carbon-14, 101–2, 263, 278–9, 283
Carnegie (ship), 113
Carnegie Institution of Washington, 99, 217, 249
Carrington, R., 31
Central Geophysical Observatory of China, 232
Chacaltaya Observatory, 115, 322
Challenger (ship), 246

Chao, Chin-chan, 231
Chapman, S., 7, 9, 137
Chen, Tsung-chi, 231
Cherwell, Lord, 137
China, 227–35, 324
Chow, Kai, 233
Christofilos, N. C., 81
chromosphere, 27–8
Chung, C.-T., 233
climate, 311–12
Climax high-altitude solar observatory, 17, 21, 26, 31, 33, 127–8
Colorado, 14–8; University of, xii, 17, 34
Comité Spécial de l'Année Géophysique Internationale (CSAGI), viii, 9–10, 12, 320
Committee on International Geophysics (CIG), 12, 321
Constantinescu, Dr., 45
continental drift, 224, 273
continental fracture system, 219–23
continental shelves, 245, 250
convection currents, 224, 254–5
Cook, Captain James, 270
core, 110–12, 116, 249
corona, 27–8, 32, 139
corpuscular radiation, 88
cosmic-ray counters, 96
cosmic rays, 32, 69, 70, 75, 77, 88–102, 116, 125, 143, 232, 277–9, 322; age of, 100; primary, 93, 95; secondary, 95
Crab nebula, 97, 101
Crary, A. F., 307
Crimea Observatory, 127
Cromwell Current, 260
Cromwell, T., 260
crust, 112, 216–18, 223–6, 253
Curie, see Joliot-Curie

Danjon astrolabe, 186, 273
Davidchev, M., 193

de Alzate Ramírez, Father J. A., 166
Defence Research Board of Canada, xii
De Long, George, 148–9
de Mairan, M., 134
Demetrescu, A., 45
Deminitskaya, Mme, 212
Dicke, R. H., 190, 225
Dietz, R. S., 254
Diplan, P., 45
Dirac, P. A. M., 189, 253
Discoverer program, 58, 71–2
Discovery II (ship), 258, 293
Dominion Observatory, 107
Doppler effect, 135
dry valleys, 168
Dufek, G., 309

earth: contraction of, 254; expansion of, 189–90, 253–4, 274; gravity of, 71, 307; interior of, 110–11, 183–5, 190, 219, 253, 321; magnetic field of, 31–2, 66, 72, 79, 81–2, 97–9, 107, 109, 110–18, 133, 136–8, 307; rotation of, 123, 263; wobble of axis, 35, 187, 273
Earthquake Research Institute, Tokyo, 242
earthquake waves, 111
earthquakes, 35, 111, 204, 214–26, 262–3, 272, 321
echo-sounding, 246, 248
eclipse, total, 188
Eisenhower, Dwight D., 70–1
electro-magnetic waves, 23–4, 88
Ellesmere Island, 147, 151, 155, 160, 164
Ewing, M., 218, 220, 248, 250
exchange of data, 61
Expéditions Polaires Françaises, 162
Explorer program, 58, 68–70
Explorer I, 58, 60, 68, 81, 83; II, 69; III, 60, 69; IV, 81; VI, 61,

Explorer I (continued)
69–70, 80, 85, 144; VII, 70, 80, 85, 144

faculae, 29
fall-out, 268, 276–87
faults, 214, 219, 269
Fedynski, V., 193
Fermi, Enrico, 97, 100
Ferraro, V. C. A., 137
Fielder, G., 73
First International Polar Year, 6–8, 29, 133, 152
Forbush, S. E., 99
Fotheringham, J. K., 187
fractures, 290
Fram (ship), 149–50, 246
Franklin, Benjamin, 257
Franklin, J., 107, 148
French Antarctic expedition, 164
Fritz, H., 133
Frobisher Bay, 103–4
Fu, Cheng-yi, 231
Fuchs, V., 164, 308

Gagarin, Yuri, 55, 66
galaxy, 99–100; magnetic field of, 97, 100
Gartlein, C. W., 134
Gauss, C. F., 133
geodesy, 184–5
geodetic data, headquarters for, 35
geodetic surveys, 184, 186
Geological Survey of Russia, 211
geomagnetic data, study of, 137
geomagnetism, 35, 118, 128, 136, 224
Georgia, U.S.S.R., 201–7
Georgian Academy of Sciences, 204
Gilbert, W., 107, 112
glaciers, 145–7, 153, 155, 159–61, 164–7, 289, 301, 304, 309, 314–15, 322

Goddard, R., 56
Gordienko, P. A., 211
Goudin, Urey, 178, 194–5
Graf instrument, 181
gravimeters, 180–3
gravity, 179–90, 307; reduction in, 190
green flash, 33
Greenland, 154–69, 275
Gulf Stream, 245, 257, 315

Hagen, J. P., 66
Hakkel, Ya. Ya., 211
Hale, G. E., 31
Halley, E., 133
Hart, P. J., xii
Hattersley-Smith, G., xii
Hawaii, 265–70; University of, 265
Heard, J. F., xii
heat flow, 251–3
heat loss, 251
Heezen, B. C., 190, 220, 225
Hertz, H. R., 121
Hess, H. H., 254
Hess, V. F., 88–9
Hines, C. O., xii
Holmes, A., 254
Humboldt Current, 257, 315, 323
Hutchinson, G. E., 311

ice, 154–69, 306–7, 309; cap, 160, 162; land, 145, 290–1; melting of, 160, 167–8; sea, 145, 290; sheet, 159, 162–9, 312
icebergs, 161
ice-rivers, 161
Imperial Hotel, 242, 306
infra-red waves, 26, 120
Institute of Geological Prospecting, Peking, 233
Institute of Geophysics and Meteorology of the Academia Sinica, Peking, 231
Intermediate Range Ballistic Missile, 68

International Astronomical Union, viii, 8
International Council of Scientific Unions, viii, 9, 320, 329
International Geographical Union, viii, 9
International Geophysical Co-operation, 10, 12–13, 321
International Indian Ocean Expedition, 252, 321
International Meteorological Congress, 6
International Quiet Sun Year, 321
International Union of Geodesy and Geophysics, vii, xii, 7–8, 12, 34, 36, 62, 172, 228, 322, 324
IUGG XIth General Assembly, 36
International Union of Pure and Applied Physics, 9
Intourist guides, 173, 175–77, 201–2
ionosphere, 116, 118–19, 121–3, 125–30, 236, 300
ionospheric sounders, 122, 125
ionospheric winds, 126
Iowa, State University of, 77, 80

Jacchia, L., 84, 143
Japan, 241–243
Japanese Broadcasting Corporation, xii
Jason project, 143
Jastrow, R., 84–5, 144
Jeannette (ship), 148–9
Jeffreys, H., 222, 255
jet-streams, 316–7
Jodrell Bank, 60, 73
Johansen, F. H., 149
Joliot-Curie, Frédéric and Irene, 280
Jones, T., xii
Jupiter C rocket, 68

Kaplan, J., 134
Khimish, G., 227
King Carol, 47–8
King-Hele, D. G., 84, 142
Kullenberg, B., 249
Kulp, J. L., 287
Kuroshio Current, 257
Kyoto, University of, 242

Laclavère, G., xii, 12
la Cour, D., 8
Lanchow, 230–4
Lee, Shan-pang, 231
Lejay, Father P., S.J., 232
Lenin (icebreaker), 151
Leningrad, 207–12
Lindemann, F. A., *see* Lord
    Cherwell
Lister, H., 167
Little Americas, 293–5, 297,
    303–7
Loewe, F., 167
Lomonosov ridge, 151
Longitudes and Latitudes
    program, 186
Longley, Professor W., 16
Lorenzo, J. L., 166
lunar tides, 116
Lunik program, 58, 66, 69, 72–5
Lunik I, 72, 143; II, 73; III, 73–5
Lyman alpha line, 27

MacDowall, J., 216
Machta, L., 277
MacRae, D. A., xii
magnetic field, 30, 82, 87, 91,
    97–8, 101, 126
magnetic storms, 7, 31, 80, 96,
    117–18, 127–30, 133,
    136–7
magnetic surveys, 113
magnetism, 8, 114
magnetograms, 300
Manning, T., 105
mantle, 111, 217–20, 223–6,
    254–5, 275

Marconi, G., 121
Markham, C., 148
Markowitz moon camera, 186
Martell, F. A., 278
Masevich, Mrs. A., 60
Mason, R. G., 254
Massey, H. S. W., 100
Maury, M. F., 245
maximum auroral belt, 82, 126,
    128
Maxwell, J. C., 121
McLennan, J. C., 134
McMurdo Sound, 291, 294–5,
    304–9
Meinel, A. B., 135
Menard, H. W., 254
meteorites, 83, 112
meteorology, 8, 297, 310–19
Mexican expeditions, 166
Microlock interrogate satellites,
    59
micrometeorites, 64, 69–70, 83
microseisms, 216–17
mid-ocean fracture system, 220–3
mid-ocean ridge, 220–2, 225, 247,
    252–5, 265, 268–70, 274
Millman, P. M., xii
Milne, J., 218
Ministry of Geology of the
    U.S.S.R., xii
Minitrack stations, 59, 63
Minnaert, M., 33
Mirny base, 294–5
Mohole project, 226, 249, 274
Mohorovičić discontinuity, 223,
    226, 274
moon, magnetic field of, 72; pho-
    tograph of far side, 55, 74
moon-camera, 322
Moonwatch scheme, 59, 63, 236
Moos, N. F., 133
Moscow, 170–8; University of,
    173
Moscow Seismological Station,
    231

mountain building, 50, 52, 189, 222, 225, 253
Mtskheta, Georgia, 206
Munk, W. A., 187
mutations, 286

Nansen, F., 147, 149–50, 160
National Academy of Sciences of the U.S., viii, xii
National Aeronautics and Space Administration, 71
National Bureau of Standards, see U.S. National Bureau of Standards
National Research Council of Canada, xii
National Taiwan University, 236
nearby space, 12, 21, 32
Nescherskii, 56
New York Operations Office, U.S. AEC, 287
The New York Times, 62
New Zealand, 270–5, 279, 288–90, 294
New Zealand Department of Scientific and Industrial Research, xii
Newbrook meteor station, 63
Newmayer, G., 6
Newton, Sir Isaac, 20, 222
Nikolski, G. M., 211
Nordenskjold, Baron, 148
Norris, C., 15
North Equatorial Current, 260
north magnetic pole, 98, 103–9, 110, 113–114, 133
north pole, 85, 180, 187
Norwegian-British-Swedish expedition, 163–4
nuclear radiation, 276–87

Ob (ship), 211
Obayashi, T., 241
Oberth, H., 56
Obreztsov, S. V., 175
Obsérvatoire de Meudon, 127

ocean currents, 250, 257–60, 315
ocean floor, 217–18, 246, 248–52; 255, 260, 263, 275, 278; geology of, 190, 211–12, 256
oceans, 12, 16, 168, 182, 244–64, 273–4, 291, 310, 312, 314, 322; age and origin of, 250
O'Connell, Father D. J. K., 33
Odishaw, H., xii
O'Keefe, J. A., xii, 85–6, 184
One Chinese Moon, viii
Ontario, Province of, 38
Operation Deepfreeze, 164
Orichenko, V., 193
orogenesis, see mountain building
outer space, 89, 121
ozone layer, 119

paleomagnetism, 255
Paris Observatory, 20
Pavelescu, C., 45
Pei, Li-shan, 230
penguins, 309
Permanent Services, 35
Peter the Great, 147, 208–10
photosphere, 27, 29
Piccard, A., 248
Piccard, J., 248
Piggott, C. S., 249
Pioneer program, 69–71
Pioneer I, 71; II, 71, 81; III, 71–2, 143; IV, 71–2, 82, 143
plages, 29
polar regions, 10, 79, 81, 98, 126
poles, mobility of, 225
Polish Antarctic expedition, 166
Popvici, Dr., 45
Pratt, G., 164
Press, F., xii
Prince Michael, 48
Princeton University, 20

radiation, 21, 28, 64, 66, 69–70, 73, 77–8, 80–1, 83, 88–9, 101, 116, 119, 124, 126, 129, 277, 280, 283, 286, 312, 314, 318

radio astronomy, 101
radio blackouts, 80
radio noise, 101, 127
radio telescopes, 17
radio transmission, 31, 109, 126
radio waves, 20, 23, 25–6, 120–1,
    124–5, 129
radioactive elements, 276
radioactive isotopes, 277, 280–1,
    286
radon, 277
rain-gauges, 229
Redstone ballistic rocket, 68
Resolute airfield, 108–9
Rockefeller Foundation, 8
rocket astronomy, 20
rockets, 20, 26–7, 55–88, 93, 126,
    321; meteorological, 76
rockoon, 75, 80
Romania, 40–53
Romanian Geological Survey, 48
Romanian Institute of Cultural
    Relations with Foreign Coun-
    tries, xii, 46
Romanian National Committee
    on Geodesy and Geophysics,
    45
Roosevelt (ship), 246
Rose, D. C., xii
Ross, James C., 107, 110, 245
Ross ice shelf, 295, 304
Rossi, B., 100
Rowley, G., 105
Royal Canadian Air Force, 104
Royal Ontario Museum, 38
Runcorn, S. K., 255
Ruseski, P., 299

Sacramento Peak Observatory,
    127
Sargasso Sea, 257
satellites, 20–1, 26–7, 54–88, 92–
    4, 121, 126–44, 184, 191, 312,
    314, 321, 323; ground observa-
    tion of, 84–5; results of
    programs, 77–87

Scheidegger, A. E., 222
Schwabe, H., 30, 133
Scott, R. F., 293, 295
Scripps Institution of Ocean-
    ography, 260
sea level, 168–9, 269
sea water, analysis of variations
    in, 35
Second International Polar Year,
    6–9, 29, 133
Sedov, L. I., 71, 75
seismic waves, 214–26
seismograph, 215–16, 218
seismological stations, network of,
    218, 232
seismology, 214–26
Sergeant rocket, 68, 70
Serson, P. H., xii, 110
Shapley, A. H., xii, 300
Shu, L.-H., 233
Sian, 230
Siberia, 228
Sigma Xi, Society of, xii
sills, 245
Singer, S. P., 55
Smith, P., 292
Smithsonian Astrophysical
    Observatory, 84, 143
solar corpuscles, 77, 136, 138
solar eclipses, 10, 18
solar flares, 17, 26–7, 29–33, 70,
    84, 88, 96, 127–8, 136–7, 141,
    143
solar outbursts, 122–3, 142
solar prominences, 27, 29, 33
solar shock waves, 32
solar tides, 116
"solar wind," 21, 79, 99, 116,
    125, 128, 137, 143
solar-flare patrol telescope, 232
South Equatorial Current, 260
south magnetic pole, 7, 98, 133
south pole, 85, 164, 187; station,
    33, 294, 296–9, 318
Southern Ocean, 7, 289, 318
Soviet Union, 10, 191–213

space, 21, 119, 121
Special Committee for Antarctic Research (SCAR), 320–1
Special Committee for Oceanographic Research (SCOR), 252, 320–1
Special Committee for Space Research (COSPAR), 321
spectrograph, 31
spectroscopy, 26
spicules, 29
Sputnik program, 62–6, 71, 171, 191, 193, 327
Sputnik I, 53–4, 58, 63–4, 68, 73; II, 58, 64–5, 69; III, 65, 69, 84, 101, 143
Stanescu, S., 45
Star of Bethlehem, 97, 101
Stefansson, V., 146
stellar blasts, 88, 97
Storkerson, S., 146
Störmer, Carl, 81, 133
stratosphere, 20, 281–3, 285
strontium-90, 282, 284, 287
submarine ridges, 220, 245, 252
Sullivan, Walter, 62
sun, 19–33, 84, 88, 96–7, 99, 114, 116, 121, 123–4, 126–7, 137, 139, 142–3, 268, 312; magnetic field of, 99, 112, 115; rotation of, 96
sun-spot activity, 7, 115, 141; maximum, 10, 30, 99, 131; minimum, 8, 321
sun-spot cycle, 30, 84, 99, 114, 133
sun-spots, 27, 29, 30–2, 112, 114–15, 118, 127, 136–7
super-novae, 97, 100–1
surges, 263
Swallow, J. C., 258, 260
Swedish-Finnish-Swiss expedition, 165

Tabor, Baby Doe, 76
Taipeh, 235–41

Taiwan, 235–41
Teepee scheme, 60
Thule airbase, 155, 157
tide-gauge, 109, 168, 261–2
Tien, Yu-san, 233–5
Tiflis (Tbilisi), 201–3, 205
Tokyo, University of, xii, 241–2
Toronto, 34–40; University of, viii, xii, 37, 60
Trans-Siberian Railway, 193, 212, 227
trenches, ocean, 248
Trieste (bathysphere), 248
Troitskaya, Mme V. A., xii, 62
troposphere, 281, 283, 285
Tsaidam depression, 234
Tsiolkovskii, 56
Tsuboi, C., 241
tsunamis, 250, 263
Tuimasi oil fields, 193–4, 217
Tully, J. P., xii
turbidity currents, 250
Tuve, M., 121

ultra-violet rays, 19, 25–8, 32, 70, 116, 120, 123, 125–6
UNESCO, 252, 328
l'Union Radio Scientifique Internationale (URSI), viii, 8
U.S.S.R. Academy of Sciences, see Academy of Sciences of the U.S.S.R.
U.S.S.R. Antarctic expedition, 164
United Kingdom rocket program, 76
United Nations, 34
United States Air Force (U.S.A.F.), 70–1
U.S.A.F. Thor-Able IRBM rocket, 70
U.S. Antarctic expedition, 164, 309
U.S. Army, 68, 70
U.S. Coast Guard, 80
U.S. Government, 152

U.S. National Academy of Sciences, 265
U.S. National Bureau of Standards, 17, 123, 236, 300
U.S. National Science Foundation, 249
U.S. Navy, 55, 288, 292–3, 299, 306
U.S. rocket program, 76
U.S. Weather Bureau, 265
U.S.S. *Albermarle* (ship), 82
U.S.S. *Nautilus* (ship), 147, 151, 253
U.S.S. *Norton Sound* (ship), 81
U.S.S. *Point Defiance* (ship), 28
U.S.S. *Skate* (ship), 147, 253
upper atmosphere, 66, 78, 84–5, 109, 116, 119–30, 135–7, 141
Upper Mantle Project, 321

V2's, 21, 56
Vacquier, V., 254
Van Allen belts, 9, 55, 66, 69, 71, 77–87, 114, 119, 124–8, 136, 142
Van Allen, J. A., 9, 69, 77
Vanguard satellites, 55, 66–8
Vanguard I, 60, 63, 67, 84–5, 143; II, 67; III, 68
Vanguard Computing Centre, 59
Vatican City Observatory, 33
Vegard, L., 133–4
Vening Meinesz, F. A., 181, 224, 254
Vernov, S. N., 143
Vestine, E. H., 133
Victory (ship), 108

Vityaz (ship), 248
volcanoes, 268, 270, 272, 275, 291

Walker, L., 16
Walsh, D., 248
water, circulation of, 263
weather, 70, 272, 307–8, 310–19
Wegener, A., 224
Wexler, H., xii, 267, 314
Weyprecht, Carl, 6
white-out conditions, 302–3
Wiggins, J., 148
Wild, H., 6
Wilson, E., 293, 295
Wilson, J. Tuzo, vii–ix, 194
Woods Hole Oceanographic Institution, 258
World Data Centre A., xii, 12, 127, 139, 216, 280
World Data Centre B, xii, 12, 127, 139, 205, 216
World Data Centre C, xii, 12, 127, 139, 216
"world days," 12
World Health Organization, 34
World Magnetic Survey, 321
World Meteorological Organization, 34
World's Fair, Brussels, 170
Worzel, J. L., 181, 251

X-rays, 25–8, 68, 70, 94, 120, 123, 126

Young Communist Pioneers, 206
Yuan, F.-L., 233

Zarya (ship), 113

A NOTE ABOUT THE AUTHOR

J. Tuzo Wilson *was born in Ottawa in 1908. He earned a* B.A. *from Trinity College of the University of Toronto, a* B.A. *and* SC.D. *from the University of Cambridge, and a* PH.D. *from Princeton. Now Professor of Geophysics at the University of Toronto, Professor Wilson is widely regarded as one of the extraordinary men of science in North America. He combines great physical vigor (he has been an explorer and mountain climber) with a remarkably brilliant mind (his contributions to the theory of mountain-building and continent formation are many and notable). During the International Geophysical Year, he was president of the International Union of Geodesy and Geophysics, one of the founding organizations of the IGY. He is the author of many scientific articles and books, and one previous book for the layman:* One Chinese Moon, *the story of his travels in Communist China, which was published in 1959.*

July 1961

A NOTE ON THE TYPE

This book *is set in* Electra, *a Linotype face designed by the late W. A. Dwiggins (1880–1956). This face cannot be classified as either modern or old-style. It is not based on any historical model, nor does it echo any particular period or style.*

*Composed, printed, and bound by
Kingsport Press, Inc., Kingsport, Tennessee.
Paper manufactured by
P. H. Glatfelter Company, Spring Grove, Pa.
Typography and binding design by
VINCENT TORRE*